MW00837038

Continence and Incontinence: Psychological Approaches to Development and Treatment

CONTINENCE and INCONTINENCE

Psychological Approaches to
Development and Treatment

PAUL S. SMITH M.A., M.Sc., Ph.D.
Clinical Psychologist, Northumberland Health Authority,
District Psychology Service, Northgate Hospital,
Morpeth, Northumberland NE61 3BP   UK

LINDA J. SMITH M.A., M.Sc.
formerly Clinical Psychologist, Northumberland Health Authority

CROOM HELM
London & Sydney

© 1987 Paul S. Smith & Linda J. Smith
Croom Helm Ltd, Provident House, Burrell Row,
Beckenham, Kent BR3 1AT

Croom Helm Australia, 44–50 Waterloo Road,
North Ryde, 2113, New South Wales

British Library Cataloguing in Publication Data

Smith, Paul S.
  Continence and incontinence: psychological
  approaches to development and treatment.
  1. Faeces — Incontinence 2. Urine —
  Incontinence
  I. Title   II. Smith, Linda J.
  616.6'3   RC921.15

  ISBN 0-7099-3386-X

Distributed exclusively in the USA by Sheridan House Inc.
145 Palisade Street, Dobbs Ferry, N.Y. 10522

Filmset by Mayhew Typesetting, Bristol, England

Printed and bound in Great Britain by
Biddles Ltd, Guildford and King's Lynn

Contents

To Fiona and Jessica

Acknowledgements

We wish to acknowledge the advice, help and support of colleagues, too numerous to mention by name, throughout a period of over ten years of our involvement in work in the field of continence promotion and the treatment of incontinence. The range of disciplines and agencies, including psychologists, nurses and doctors in different specialties, medical physicists and others in the Health Service, together with workers in education, social services and voluntary agencies, reflects the multidisciplinary nature of the field. We also wish to acknowledge the contribution that incontinent people and their families have often made to our views on many issues. Finally, special thanks must go to Mrs Margaret Turner for her contribution, which went far beyond that normally expected from a good secretary.

1

Introduction

I know that the wiser sort of men will consider, and
I wish the ignorant sort would learne; how it is not
the baseness or homelinesse, either of words or matters,
that make them foule and obsceneous, but their base
minds . . . that handle them.

Sir John Harington 1596[1]

The topic dealt with in the book presented here broadly concerns the
development of daytime urinary continence. The purpose of this
chapter is to explain the overall approach taken — what this book
is about and what it is not about.

Incontinence is a major human problem, yet one that is little
talked about and about which relatively little is known. It presents
as a problem in many health fields in work with the elderly, mentally
ill, mentally handicapped and the physically handicapped, following
surgery and in the fields of paediatrics and gynaecology. Yet it is
still largely a taboo subject.

Medically, incontinence is a symptom and not a disease. The
approach taken here is to view incontinence as a behaviour or set of
behaviours. The purpose of this is not to deny the importance of
physical factors but to shed light on what psychological approaches
can contribute to understanding and treatment of the problem. But
of greater importance, one of the major thrusts of this book is to turn
the issue round and to look at *continence* and the development of
continence as a process or a set of behaviours. The view taken here
is that more light may be shed on the failure to acquire continence
or the breakdown of continence if more is understood about the functions, acquisition and maintenance of continence at a behavioural
level. A clearer understanding of the fundamental underlying normal
behavioural mechanisms is important if we are to seek to remedy any
abnormality occurring in the process. Thus, this book starts by
reviewing what is known about continence and finishes by focusing

---

[1] Part of the supporting argument that Sir John Harington prepared in 1596
to justify his publication of the details of the first flushing toilet.

more heavily on incontinence. There is not a simple split into two parts, as that is impossible, nor is it wholly desirable to maintain. However, there is a progression from continence to incontinence. Although incontinence is the issue that practitioners are interested in initially, the approach outlined here is a reflection and extension of current trends in practice: this approach is one of *continence promotion* as opposed to the treatment of incontinence.

The acquisition of continence is a major milestone in child development, yet it has not received the attention that it merits from developmental psychologists. The research literature is scant compared with that on other important areas such as language or cognition. Similarly, the research and professional training literature on incontinence is under-represented in view of the size of the problem (King's Fund 1983). Until relatively recently, continence problems have been viewed as largely intractable, and direct carers, including nurses and families, have been left to cope as best they can with little help from other professionals. Attitudes towards toileting, determined by our Western European culture and the unattractiveness of the topic, are no doubt two of the factors that have contributed to the lack of interest researchers have shown. If even a very small proportion of the research expertise and ingenuity that is invested in other areas of health care or psychology were devoted to the study of continence processes, then considerable progress would be made in this area.

It should be clear by now that this book does not aim to be a comprehensive textbook on incontinence. Much of the book is concerned with daytime bladder control. There is some consideration of nocturnal continence, of bowel control and of incontinence in the elderly, as they are important issues. There are chapters on training of continence and treatments of incontinence and also on treatment of a variety of continence-related problems that do not necessarily involve incontinence. There is a strong focus on work from the field of mental handicap. This is because in recent years relatively more has emerged from this field on the training of continence behaviours that potentially has wide application and is little known to workers in other fields. As in other areas, there is much to be gained by cross-fertilisation between specialties, and continence promotion generally has become a multidisciplinary, multi-modal endeavour. Focusing on psychological approaches is not seen as being incompatible with either appropriate physical treatments or the appropriate use of continence aids and appliances.

It may be noticeable that the term 'habit training' is little referred to in this book. Despite the fact that it is widely used in the nursing and medical literature, the use of the term should ideally be discouraged as it is not at all clear what it means or how it is achieved. By contrast, as will become apparent in later sections of this book, it is possible to specify in considerable detail the key features in organising, implementing and maintaining continence-training programmes using a behavioural approach.

The meaning of the term 'psychological approaches' also needs to be elaborated on. It does not mean the psychoanalytic approach. Rather it refers to objective, measurable, empirical approaches to studying human behaviour at different levels and in different ways. This differs from its use in some other articles on the psychology of incontinence, such as those provided by Sutherland (1976) and Wells (1984). Presentations such as that provided by Wells (1984) are important in helping professionals to develop sympathetic and empathic approaches to people with continence problems, but they are rooted within an untestable, psychodynamic neo-Freudian framework. The use of the term 'psychological' here has more in common with 'behavioural' psychology as in Whitehead, Burgio and Engel's (1984) contribution.

Three major psychological theoretical views of human development have involved the psychodynamic theories, Piagetian cognitive developmental theories, and the learning theories. The discussion in this book will be limited as far as possible to consideration of fairly hard evidence. Few psychodynamic theorists have been noted for an acceptable empirical approach to human development and behaviour. The work inspired by Piaget has been instrumental in promoting consideration of behaviour from a developmental viewpoint and in raising questions such as whether development of a particular behaviour is smooth and continuous, or stage-like. Although extremely important for understanding normal development, developmental theories have not thus far provided a springboard for the design of treatment or training programmes for problems in the acquisition of normal developmental skills or abilities. Many of the training approaches discussed later in this book have their origins in the various learning theories, and in operant conditioning in particular. The main theoretical framework implicit in much of the content of this book is based on a combination of developmental and operant views. This is not because all human behaviour is viewed as operant — far from it — but simply that, as will become clearer, this approach thus far has had most to offer the understanding of continence and the treatment of continence problems.

3

The ethological approach has influenced the organisation of the first chapters of this book, providing as it does a structure for integrating the available information and for pointing to what is not yet known. This approach is expressed most succinctly by Tinbergen (1951). Tinbergen describes six types of enquiry necessary to understand and explain any behaviour. These concern the following:

1. Causality. We must know what stimuli (whether internal or external) give rise to the events.
2. Mechanisms. We must know what mechanisms at the conceptual level (theoretical models), or preferably at the physiological or biochemical levels, underlie the behaviour.
3. Ontogeny. We must know how the behaviour develops in the life history of the individual, involving the interaction of genetic processes with the environment in both maturation and learning.
4. Genetics. We must know the genetic background itself.
5. Function. We must know what the behaviour is for and how it contributes to the survival of the species.
6. Phylogeny. We must know how it evolved.

These areas of enquiry — the bare bones of psychological enquiry — can be seen underlying the early chapters of this book following the setting of the social, cultural and historical scene of current attitudes towards continence and incontinence.

THE EFFECTS OF LOSS OF CONTINENCE ON THE SUFFERERS AND THEIR FAMILIES

Clearly, the only people who really know what it is like to lose control of their continence processes are incontinence sufferers themselves. Sadly, many mentally handicapped people who have never developed continence and many elderly people suffering from severe dementia and whose general functioning has deteriorated, are unable to articulate and describe the experience. Much of what has been written in the past by professionals about this experience has been psychodynamic, pseudo-scientific theorising about the supposed overwhelming impact of toilet-training experiences in early years. Recently, however, a few personal accounts of the experience, and even surveys of the views and experiences of incontinent people have begun to emerge. It is true that sexuality looms large, but largely from the practical point of view. But it is a range of other practical matters in coping with incontinence in a continent society and with the behaviour and attitudes of others that are of greater importance to incontinent people. Borthwick (1985) and Masham (1985) appear to have adjusted to coping with life in a wheelchair and total loss of continence for 17 and 28 years respectively. Borthwick describes as a frightening and embarrassing prospect the initial trauma of not just paraplegia and incontinence but of leaving the hospital where toileting needs were cared for. From both accounts it is clear that a high degree of competence and practice in the use of continence aids is necessary, as is strong motivation, a sense of humour and a firm routine. All this is necessary to deal with what most of us take for granted. Gartley and her colleagues (Balson, Gartley and Humpal 1985) and Gartley and Humpal (1984) give qualitative descriptions from tape-recorded, open-ended interviews with a range of people who are incontinent. Feelings of anger, shame, depression, isolation, fear of accidents and changes in feelings about sexuality were highly salient, recurring themes. Wheelchair users are reported to rate the re-establishment of control over continence processes more highly than regaining control over their legs! Gartley and Humpal describe coming to terms with incontinence as a progression through a series of stages moving from depression to anger to sharing the problem with another trusted person to a final philosophical and tolerant view of their own incontinence and others' responses to it and them.

One of the best studies of which aspects of patients lives are affected by incontinence has been carried out by Norton (1981, 1982), who surveyed 44 female sufferers (of mean age 50 years) who had been incontinent for an average of five years. Fifty-one per cent rated their leakage of urine as a small amount, 37 per cent as moderate and 12 per cent as a large amount, and 76 per cent of the women wore pads. The questions, based on earlier work, covered physical and mental health, ability to do a job or housework, social life, family relationships and restriction of activities. The women rated the effects of incontinence on individual areas using a four point rating scale ranging from 'not at all' to 'a great deal'. The results showed that one-third of the women concerned felt moderately or severely affected in nearly all the areas questioned. Least affected were reported to be family relationships and work, whereas most affected were ratings of social life and feelings of mental well-being. About half felt that their activities were significantly restricted by fear or embarrassment. The most common examples given concerned fear of smell, social embarrassment and sexual restriction.

Interestingly, there was no simple age effect. Using a cut-off of 50 years, there was no significant difference between ratings of effect between younger and older women. When asked what the worst effect was, 16 per cent said odour, but for the rest, no strong common themes emerged. It appears that the personal effects of incontinence in this group are idiosyncratic. There is a need for more studies of this type to help understand the psychological effects of incontinence in order to gear professionals, families, communities and support services to meet those needs.

A survey of satisfaction with the management of their incontinence was carried out by Thomas, Karran and Meade (1981), on 50 patients suffering from multiple sclerosis. Only seven of them appeared to be satisfied. When asked questions about which aspect of their bladder problem was most difficult to cope with, the replies varied. Eight considered catheter leakage to be the worst problem, 15 felt that physically transferring from wheelchair to toilet or commode was the worst problem, and ten reported embarrassment to be their main problem in daily life. Overall, 23 patients regarded embarrassment and/or restriction of activities as a serious problem for them.

COST

Detailed studies of the costs of incontinence to the families of handicapped children in particular have been carried out by Bradshaw (1978), Parker (1983), Townsend *et al.* (1981) and Thomas (1986). Bradshaw was among the first to itemise the extra expenditure incurred for launderette charges or for the purchase of washing machines, running costs for these machines, their earlier replacement because of constant use, soap powders, bleaches, fabric softeners and so on. Extracts from transcripts of interviews with mothers of incontinent multiply handicapped children are appended to Bradshaw's (1978) report. These emphasise another aspect of incontinence, that of the economic cost and the workload posed by the additional laundry entailed.

Townsend *et al.* add the costs of disinfectants, talcum powder or cream, additional pairs of pants, plastic pants, rubber sheets etc., as well as estimating from a study of 75 families with a handicapped incontinent child that an average of ten and a half hours per week was spent on additional incontinence-related tasks. In economic terms, this is time when the carer, usually the mother, has to forgo the possibility of alternative paid employment and hence income. Even within the British Welfare State, the true costs of incontinence to families are not met, and Parker (1983) has reported that level of provision of services and take up of services varies between families and across different geographic areas. Studies such as these, too, are extremely important not only in understanding the impact of incontinence, but in designing the services to meet the needs.

DEFINITIONS

The concept of 'incontinence' includes the notion of lack of constraint or control over bodily secretions that are normally voluntarily controlled. Thus, it is possible to be incontinent not only of urine or faeces, but of tears, milk, sperm and mucus. Here we shall consider, for the large part, urinary incontinence.

Superficially it seems easier to start to define incontinence than to define continence. Incontinence looks an excellent topic for empirical study: one can see it, feel it, smell it, count it, measure it — it is an objectively observable phenomenon. Yet it has been noted (Arie, Clarke and Slattery 1976) that definitions are often absent or vague. Incontinence is not a simple all-or-nothing phenomenon. It is not normally distributed throughout the population whereby an arbitrary cut-off point can be determined. It is a complex, multi-factorial process and a complete definition would have to include a number of features.

Thomas (1986), who has provided the most extensive studies of prevalence of incontinence, includes in her simple working definition 'two or more "accidents" per month or continuous leakage . . .'

One attractive example of a simple definition of incontinence is provided by Yeates (1976) who defines urinary incontinence as 'the passing of urine in an undesirable place'. Although simple, this is in fact a very broad definition, as will be seen when contrasted with the International Continence Society's (1984) definition, which echoes the earlier definition of Stanton (1977), of incontinence as 'a condition in which involuntary loss of urine is a social or hygiene problem and is objectively demonstrable'. According to this definition, incontinence has three main features and we will consider each briefly in turn.

Involuntary loss

Incontinence as involuntary loss clearly excludes instances where socially inappropriate voiding may not be outside voluntary control but may have some other purpose or function. Obvious examples include deliberate faecal smearing and copraphagia. These are clearly continence-related problem behaviours but may not be considered as incontinence according to this definition. It is not argued that this is right or wrong, simply that it is necessary to be clear about it. One possible disadvantage in considering the voluntariness of the action is that one is often making inferences about whether the incontinent act was voluntary or not. In some instances this is likely to lead to inter-observer disagreement. A further disadvantage of this definition is that if one focuses on the 'loss' aspect, this would exclude from the definition individuals who are dependent on others for their toileting needs: some mentally handicapped, elderly or other handicapped people may possibly remain dry so long as their carers toilet them reliably and help them to achieve the highest level of continence possible. Again, this is not to imply that this definition is in some sense wrong, merely that it is necessary to be clear that continence and incontinence are not necessarily corollaries. Such a person may not be incontinent but nor can they be considered to be fully continent in the full human adult sense.

Social or hygiene problems

Incontinence as a social or hygiene problem is an important aspect, as effective disposal of body wastes in our culture or in any society beyond a hunter-gatherer economy, is extremely important. Here too it is important to understand to whom or for what a social or hygiene problem presents. For example, babies and young children, before they achieve full control, will not see their lack of continence as potentially presenting a hygiene problem to others. It may not be statistically abnormal to be incontinent at that stage and it will not therefore be included in prevalence rates of incontinence, but it is still incontinence according to this definition.

An objective phenomenon

The concept of incontinence as being objectively measurable, as defined by Stanton and the ICS, is a very important one. Subjective judgements are inherently unreliable. In one study, discussed later in this book, in a mental handicap hospital there was a correlation of about 0.5 for inter-rater reliability for agreement between nurses on opposite shifts for a simple rating of frequency of incontinence for 100 hospital residents (Smith 1979b). It should be possible to quantify and record basic data for features such as frequency, volume and time and for more sophisticated urological measures. Until relatively recently such aspects have been largely neglected. The development of the Urilos system for measuring volume of urine through capacitance in a pad worn by the incontinent patient has been problematic but has stimulated much further work and debate (Niblett 1984; Vereecken, Jacquemyn and Cornelissen 1983; Kiernan *et al.* 1983; Klarskov and Hald 1983; Wood *et al.* 1983). Indeed, Walsh and Mills (1981), in a novel study of increase in pad weights following pads being worn by continent volunteers for two hours, have suggested that an increase of pad weight in excess of 1 g should be regarded as incontinence.

The importance of clear definition of incontinence comes to the fore when trying to compare studies of treatment outcome. This will be apparent later in this book and is discussed further with respect to specific types of incontinence, for example nocturnal enuresis. It should also be apparent from the foregoing discussion that there are many problem toilet behaviours that are not easily included under any precise definition of incontinence, but which are nonetheless important problems: for example messy toileting in adult males who stand to urinate but who spray urine round the toilet area as well as into it presents a social and hygiene problem, but of course cannot be regarded as incontinence. Many of these too will be discussed later in this book.

Let us now turn briefly to the issue of definition from the other side — continence. Again the word has the same root as the verb to contain and this is illustrated in the earlier, wider use of the word. For example, the following 17th century (obviously male) proverb states that 'no woman has much continence in her tongue'. If there are problems in defining urinary incontinence, then there are problems in defining urinary continence too. No neat, concise definition will be offered here, as it is argued in this book that the mechanism, development and functions are as yet incompletely

9

understood. What is known and what is not known about it will be considered in some of the following chapters.

PREVALENCE OF INCONTINENCE

More detailed discussion of prevalence rates for daytime incontinence in mental handicap and nocturnal enuresis in non-handicapped children will occur at appropriate points. At present, we will give a brief general overview of continence and incontinence prevalence rates for the whole population. This is now possible due to the outstanding work of Thomas and her colleagues (Thomas *et al.* 1980, 1984; Thomas 1986). Prior to Thomas' studies, the issue of overall prevalence of incontinence was impossible to estimate with any degree of accuracy. Various studies of varying quality had been carried out by using a variety of definitions on separate populations such as elderly people, mentally handicapped people, women and so on. Thomas' work now makes rational planning feasible for comprehensive community and hospital continence promotion services.

Thomas *et al.* have reported the prevalence of urinary incontinence and of faecal and double incontinence separately (Thomas *et al.* 1980, 1984, respectively), using the same approach. The definition used throughout was 'involuntary excretion or leakage of urine and/or faeces in inappropriate places or at inappropriate times and producing two or more "accidents" a month or continuous leakage . . .'. They make an extremely important distinction between recognised incontinence and unrecognised incontinence. To estimate the prevalence of recognised incontinence, they exhaustively surveyed incontinent patients known to health, social service, education and voluntary agencies in two geographic areas of Greater London with a total population of over 350,000. To estimate the prevalence of unrecognised incontinence, they conducted an exhaustive postal survey of over 22,000 people registered with two general medical practitioners. The response rate was high (89 per cent), reflecting the careful organisation and the two reminders sent out at three-week intervals. Not only is the size of the study impressive, but the weight that can be placed on it is enhanced by the general standard of checking and follow through. Among other things, Thomas *et al.* checked the reliability of those replies recording 'unrecognised' incontinence by home visits to a sample of these respondents. They specify in their reports how many

Table 1.1: An estimate of patients with recognised and unrecognised urinary incontinence in a United Kingdom health district of population 250,000. This does not include children of school age with nocturnal enuresis and account has been taken of people receiving more than one service

Patients	Male	Female
Long-stay geriatric patients	50	175
Long-stay psychiatric patients	40	110
Mental handicap hospitals	25	35
Old people's homes	45	175
District nurse patients	55	95
Other community services — pad service, laundry service	40	90
Handicapped children (5–14 years)	50	35
Others (including acute geriatric wards, day centres, outpatient)	65	150
Those living at home with urinary incontinence causing some restriction in activity but who are not in touch with medical services		
Age 15–64	400	1050
Age 65+	Few	200
Those living at home with urinary incontinence which does not restrict their activities who are not in touch with services		
Age 15–64	650	4900
Age 65+	750	1700
Total	2170	8715

Source: Thomas and Meade 1982

Table 1.2: Community prevalence of urinary incontinence by age

Age (years)	Never incontinent (%)		Occasionally incontinent (%)		Regularly incontinent (%)		Uncertain (%)	
	M	F	M	F	M	F	M	F
5–14	81	82	11	11	7	8	1	1
15–24	95	82	2	12	1	4	1	2
25–35	95	72	3	20	1	6	2	2
35–44	94	67	2	21	1	10	2	3
45–54	93	64	4	22	2	12	1	2
55–64	89	67	6	19	3	12	3	3
65–74	81	73	8	15	6	9	5	3
75–84	75	63	10	14	8	16	7	7
85+	69	61	3	16	15	16	13	7
Total	89	72	6	17	3	9	2	2

Source: Adapted from Thomas (1986)

11

replies gave unclear or uncertain answers and they conducted a one-year follow-up visit to 158 incontinent adults. That incontinence is a remarkably common symptom or behaviour is evident from Tables 1.1 and 1.2: the prevalence is far higher than most would have thought. Even in a country with well-developed health and social services, it is remarkable how many people are attempting to cope with the problem unknown to the services. Clearly, as our population continues to age, the absolute numbers incontinent in the different age ranges will change. Women who have never had children are less likely to report regular incontinence and women who have had four or more children are even more likely to suffer regular urinary incontinence. Possible mechanisms for this have recently been proposed by Snooks *et al*. (1984). An interesting ethnic difference in Britain has been reported by Thomas (1986). After allowances are made for age, Asian women are relatively less likely to suffer urinary incontinence and Afro-Caribbean men are relatively more likely to suffer urinary incontinence.

Results of surveys of incontinence, however, have been found to be affected by the way in which questions are asked. Milne (1976) cites the results of earlier work that asked women the question 'does urine ever come away unexpectedly and without your being able to stop it, and you get wet', followed by supplementary questions, and resulted in a prevalence rate for stress incontinence of 12 per cent in the population surveyed. By contrast, changing the order of questions, beginning with those about urgency and following those with questions about stress incontinence, gave a prevalence of 31 per cent for stress incontinence in a similar population. As Milne comments, possibly it is easier to admit to stress incontinence than to say 'yes' to a question that simply covers all forms of incontinence.

THE LITERATURE ON INCONTINENCE

It has been stressed that this is not a book primarily about incontinence. However, many of those who use this book will do so as a result of a clinical or service interest in one of the many health and social service areas in which incontinence presents as a problem. At this point, therefore, it is worth cataloguing a sample of the key works available. These will provide more detailed consideration in their specific areas together usually with guidelines for treatment, practical help, and, of great importance, a lead into other relevant literature.

Mandelstam (1986a) has written a general textbook covering a wide range of aspects of incontinence. Norton (1986) has recently also produced a comprehensive textbook for nurses. Feneley and Blannin (1984) have produced a handbook for patients and Gartley (1985) has edited, through the eyes of an incontinence sufferer, a guide to living with loss of bladder control. A general incontinence bibliography listing 1200 publications over a six-year period is also a useful work (Mandelstam and Lane 1981). Other worthwhile leads into the general literature include the King's Fund report 'Action on Incontinence' (1983) and the volumes of conference proceedings produced by the International Continence Society over recent years. The International Continence Society (1984) has also produced a definitive description of the terminology used to describe lower urinary tract function.

Details of where to obtain and the specifications of a wide range of continence aids, including catheters, clothing, drainage bags, odour-control products, incontinence pads, toilet aids and so on are listed by the Association of Continence Advisors (1986). A range of bathroom aids and adaptations for people with physical disabilities and handicaps is described by Wilshere (1985). The Disabled Living Foundation's (1985) notes on incontinence and incontinence aids are revised regularly and up-to-date printouts covering both recently marketed toilet aids and on-going projects to develop aids can be provided by B.A.R.D. (British Database on Research into Aids for the Disabled). The practical management of faecal incontinence and of stoma care is described by Leacock (1984) and Cochrane and Leacock (1984).

There are few comprehensive works on the psychological treatment of encopresis but general reviews are provided by Schaeffer (1979) and Gabel (1981). The use of biofeedback in the retraining of bowel control is outlined by Whitehead, Burgio and Engel (1985). The treatment of nocturnal enuresis has an extensive literature, but useful works include Doleys (1977), Doleys, Schwartz and Ciminero (1981), Kolvin, McKeith and Meadow (1973), Schaeffer (1979) and Morgan (1981). The training of daytime continence in mental handicap is described in manuals by Bettison (1982) and Foxx and Azrin (1973). The use of alarms in continence training is discussed by Smith (1977) and Yonovitz and Michaels (1977). Manuals for parents toilet-training normal children are also available (e.g. Azrin and Foxx 1974; Griffiths, undated). Particularly helpful to parents are picture story books about toilet training for reading to toddlers, for example Macdonald (1980) and Selzer (1971).

Stanton's (1977) textbook is solely devoted to female urinary incontinence, and the growing interest in incontinence in the elderly population is reflected in the basic texts by Brocklehurst (1984a), Willington (1976a) and in several chapters in Mandelstam (1986a). Following surgery, the regaining of bladder control through exercises, physiotherapy and biofeedback is outlined by Montgomery (1983) and Whitehead *et al.* (1984). The Multiple Sclerosis Society (1984) provides a useful information sheet for people with physical handicaps on managing and coping with incontinence.

2

History of Continence and Incontinence

To keep your houses sweete,
cleanse privie vaults,
To keep your soules as sweete,
mend privie faults.
Sir John Harington 1596[1]

THE HISTORY OF CONTINENCE BEHAVIOUR AND EXCRETA DISPOSAL

This chapter provides the framework by which an understanding may be reached of the low regard with which professionals and academics hold continence processes and problems. It also helps to provide an understanding of the physical/design and psychological/attitudinal constraints on this topic in Western society. Although this is an obscure branch of history, serious students of the topic have a rare treat in store for them. There are a number of little-known but splendid and enjoyable books that contribute significantly in different ways.

THE LITERATURE

First, there is Sir John Harington's epoch-making book *The Metamorphosis of Ajax* (1596). Sir John Harington (1560–1612), as all good students of continence know, invented the flushing toilet in 1596. Sadly for Sir John, a witty courtier, godson of Queen Elizabeth I, the main short-term result of this was that he was banished to the army in Ireland for writing of his contraption in terms more Rabelaisian than mechanical. As will be seen shortly, for various reasons his invention did not take off for another two hundred years or so. Almost 350 years later, in 1943, what may be justifiably termed volume 2 of Harington's Metamorphosis was published by Reginald Reynolds, it having been written in the same

---

[1] An Elizabethan pun. Privie meant both toilet and private.

highly entertaining and informative style while the author was an air-raid warden during London's blitz.

Wright's (1960) well-written and researched 'Clean and Decent' provides 'the fascinating history of the bathroom' and outlines in detail the history and development of the modern toilet. Finally, Kira (1976) considers, in a more thorough, empirical, innovative and thoughtful way than any other and from an architectural point of view, the design criteria for meeting toileting needs.

HISTORY OF THE NEED FOR EXCRETA DISPOSAL SYSTEMS

For thousands of years, toileting procedures were probably similar to that described in the twenty-third chapter of Deuteronomy, the fifth book of the Old Testament:

> If there be among you any man, that is not clean by reason of that which chanceth him by night, then shall he go abroad out of the camp, he shall not come within the camp . . .. Thou shalt have a place also outwith the camp, whither thou shalt go abroad: and thou shalt have a shovel among thy weapons; and it shall be, when thou sittest down abroad thou shall dig therewith, and shalt turn back and cover that which cometh from thee: for the Lord thy God walketh in the midst of thy camp . . . therefore shall thy camp be holy; that he see no unclean thing in thee, and turn away from thee.

There is concrete evidence that 400,000 years ago, *Homo erectus*, the immediate predecessor of *Homo sapiens,* slept and ate in areas close to the hearth that were swept clean. Debris and waste materials, including human coprolites (fossilised faeces), are found away from such clearly designated living areas (Leakey and Levin 1977). In fact, it is standard practice to identify the living areas in early human camp sites by the low frequency of waste materials. It is reasonable to argue that excreta disposal for humans can only have become regarded as a problem after our species progressed from the hunter-gatherer type of economy to an agricultural economy about 10,000 years ago. Developments since then have been extremely rapid. Prior to that time hunting bands or groups of less than fifty individuals were the norm. Thereafter, with the possibility of specialisation of skills, the first towns and cities emerged. One of the main implications of this was that waste disposal had to be considered more systematically. One would imagine that this should hardly have stretched the imagination of *Homo sapiens* at either an intellectual or a technical level. However, the history of human excreta disposal suggests, lamentably, otherwise.

In general terms our society views very unfavourably that part of our diet processed and ejected as waste by our digestive system. Such waste, when naturally decomposed and brought back into the cycle of life as manure can be a valuable resource. Until water-borne sewage systems were introduced, 'night soil' was collected and used in manuring farm land until cities became too large. Chadwick (1842) outlines the economics of the transport costs as against the value of manure and demonstrates why, at that time, the cities simply had cesspits that were covered when permanently full. Indeed 'no refuse in London pays half the expense of removal by cartage'. The appalling state of the cities during the last century is well, though somewhat mildly, documented by Charles Dickens in many of his major novels. However, no concessions whatsoever are made to Victorian sensibilities in less well-known accounts in his weekly journal *All the Year Round*. In one such account (Dickens 1865), he describes a visit he made to a poor part of London, probably to gain material for his novels, with a party including the physician from a Fever Hospital and Parish Officers. Nothing is left to the imagination:

> . . . children at play in yards five feet by three, where the oozings of panless closets had saturated the black soil, where an open stagnant drain mingled its effluvia with that of rotting water (barrels) . . .. Here, the oozing and the soil from the closet . . . runs down the open window of the dwelling-room, where a boot-maker and his wife are at work . . .. There is a ghastly monotony about experiences such as these. Kennels in which no sane man would allow the least valuable of his animals to sleep, filled night and day with men, women and children.

It was in 1842 that Edwin Chadwick published his classic 'Enquiry into the sanitary condition of the labouring population of Great Britain' for the Poor Law Commission, which resulted in Parliament passing major legislation on public health. In contemporary accounts provided by observers such as Chadwick and Dickens, we read of enormous dunghills in crowded streets, of stench, of flies, of whole areas with cellars three feet deep with the overflow of cesspools, and of yards and streets covered to a depth of almost six inches from overflowing privies where bricks had to be placed for residents to step on. Wells were often close to, and contaminated by, large cesspits. Sewage was often dumped into rivers from which the drinking supply was obtained.

In spite of these conditions, it was still widely believed in the first half of the nineteenth century that the major causes of death, such as cholera and typhoid, were due neither to poor or non-existent sewage disposal nor contaminated water supply, but to bad air. 'The miasmic theory of disease, which held that infection was carried by bad air, predominated in the nineteenth century, even when the connection between cholera . . . and contaminated water was patently demonstrated.' (Calder 1977). Chadwick's objective and massive data-collecting exercise finally overcame the prevailing dogma, as he was able conclusively to demonstrate the links between dirt and death rates. The Public Health Act of 1848 took the first steps towards implementing some of Chadwick's recommendations and set up local Boards of Health with responsibility for sewage and piped water, particularly in cholera-ridden London. Work on improving sewage systems and water supplies was slow and variable. The middle classes, who were, of course, most likely to be benefitting from such facilities as did exist, did not take kindly to the idea of paying rates to provide improvements that would most radically affect the lives of others. Sewage was so much in evidence in early Victorian life that perhaps to a certain extent it was accepted as part of the landscape. That there might be ways of disposing of excrement efficiently, and removing the smells, the disease and the filth underfoot, came slowly to some (Calder 1977). Not until the 1870s was the London death rate to fall decisively: it would hardly be coincidence that this fall came within five years of the opening of the new drainage system (Wright 1960). This phase of the London sewerage involved the construction of 83 miles of intercepting sewers to drain 100 square miles of buildings. It was in this climate, with the provision of piped water and sewerage, that it was possible for Harington's water closet to develop and spread.

TYPES OF EXCRETA DISPOSAL SYSTEMS

Excreta disposal systems can be most easily divided into two types: those that are water-borne and those that are not.

Non-water-borne systems

Non-water-borne systems have historically ranged from that referred to earlier in Deuteronomy to the cesspits and dunghills of the early Victorian cities. In medieval castles, the contents of the garderobes or latrines were discharged directly into the castle moat, which was usually not water filled. Either way, as Kira (1976) has noted, it must have taken more courage to swim a moat in real life than any Hollywood hero could imagine. Reynolds (1943) provides a picturesque account of Noah's non-water-borne system. Reynolds alleges that Noah had, understandably, a considerable problem with the disposal of animal dung aboard the Ark. He was very loath to part with this valuable manure, as he knew how useful it would be when the flood waters receded. To accommodate the manure he therefore had a special bulkhead constructed in the stern of the Ark into which he regularly shovelled the manure. Gradually, however, the cargo of manure became heavier and heavier, and the stern of the Ark began to settle dangerously low in the water. Reluctantly he realised he would have to dispose of the manure, so he began to unload it over the side. There was so much of it that the manure formed an island that rose out of the water. Eventually this island formed a whole new continent. And do you know, there it stayed until Columbus discovered it?

Modern non-water-borne disposal systems are usefully discussed by Savage (1975) and earlier systems by Wright (1960). Typically, town dwellers before modern sanitation disposed of their waste in cesspits. Obviously, in such large quantities excreta quickly became infected and posed a major health hazard. There were other hazards too. Wright (1960) records the sinking of a carriage into a nineteenth century cesspit. Indeed, legislation governing the construction of cesspits has existed in England since the twelfth century. A housing ordnance of 1189 required that 'garderobe pits, if not walled, must be at least 5.5 feet from the party line' (Wright 1960). Strangely the immensely popular earth closet was not thought of until its invention by the Reverend Henry Moule in 1860. It remained in use in parts of rural England until the 1950s.

Water-borne systems

The development of modern excreta disposal systems is strongly linked to the development of piped water supplies. Water-borne systems had been in use in various historic and prehistoric civilisations (Wright 1960; Kira 1976). Indus civilisation sites, excavated by Sir Mortimer Wheeler and dated around 2300 BC, have been found to have at least one bathroom for every house. There is also evidence of lavatories, the wastes from which were carried by a drainage channel to a chute built within the thickness of the wall and which discharged into street drains. Latrine-like receptacles with crude drains have been found in the Orkney Islands in neolithic stone huts considered to be 10,000 years old. The Minoans in Crete during the second millenium BC had water-borne sewage systems. The toileting and bathing facilities at the Palace of Knossos were remarkably luxurious and modern in appearance. They used such sophisticated plumbing techniques as 'parabolic curves in water channels, and the precipitation of sediment in intermediate cesspits'. The Ancient Romans, of course, are famed for their public engineering feats and hygiene facilities, including piped hot and cold running water, water-flushed sewage systems and steam rooms. In the fourth century AD, Rome had '. . . public baths . . . as well as private water-flushed latrines, there were plenty of public ones; Rome in AD 315 had one hundred and forty-four' (Wright 1960). At the risk of parodying Gibbon, as Rome declined and fell, so Europe began to smell. Worse, the lavatorial Renaissance lagged behind the political and artistic Renaissance.

It is important to ascribe accurately the birth of the modern water closet. Many (e.g. Graham 1977) are under the impression that the flushing toilet was invented by Thomas Crapper. Kira (1976) ascribes this to US troops in Europe during the First World War who noted the inscription T. Crapper & Co. inside many toilet bowls. Not so; for the modern flushing toilet, as we know it, was essentially devised by Sir John Harington in 1596. For various reasons, it is worthwhile briefly to outline some details of the man, his invention and his remarkable book.

Sir John Harington (1560–1612) was an Elizabethan courtier, translator, author and wit. His father had enriched the family by marrying one of Henry VIII's illegitimate daughters and his second wife was an attendant of Queen Elizabeth. Elizabeth was actually godmother to Sir John and when he invented his flushing toilet he installed one in the Queen's Palace at Richmond. Sadly, no trace of this now exists. Harington's book is outstanding. He provides a thorough, informative, amusing and irreverent review of the problem of toileting and excreta disposal and attitudes towards these issues. Much of it remains applicable today. Harington, as was the fashion in his day, delighted in puns and double meanings. This topic, of course, lends itself easily to this sort of treatment and he exploited this fully. Even the title of the book *The Metamorphosis of Ajax* was a pun, a jakes or jax being a slang term for a privy or private place. He published the first edition under a pseudonym and went to great lengths to justify his full and open discussion of the subject.

His use of a pen name was to no avail and Harington was banished by Elizabeth for his indelicacy. Like an out-of-favour cabinet minister in more recent times, he was sent to Ireland. There during a military campaign he redeemed himself, killing Irishmen and winning a knighthood in 1599.

The diagram originally supplied with the description of Harington's water closet together with an illustration of the 'godly father sitting' and one of Harington's more respectable poetic celebrations is given in Figure 2.1.

Sadly, this great invention was not fully exploited and in widespread use for another two hundred and fifty years — mainly because of the lack of a piped water supply. Those few water closets installed in the seventeenth and eighteenth centuries were in large country mansions with their own water supplied (Girourd 1978), but even these were rare, as servants to remove and empty chamber pots were cheap. It is important to appreciate the context in which the design of contemporary toilets developed, as their design influences our behaviour and attitudes towards toileting.

It is to the entrepreneurial spirit of George Jennings that we directly owe the design and rise of public toileting facilities (Wright 1960; Kira 1976; Lambton 1978). With one eye on public need and the other on a good business opportunity, Jennings launched a vigorous crusade on a subject that hitherto had not been openly discussed. Jennings (in Wright 1960) describes how his ideas for halting stations or 'retiring rooms', or what we now call 'public conveniences' were originally:

> declined by Gentlemen (influenced by English delicacy of feeling) who preferred that the Daughters and Wives of Englishmen should encounter at every corner, sights so disgusting to every sense, and the general public suffers pain and often permanent injury rather than permit the construction of that shelter and privacy . . .

In 1851, Jennings installed public toilets in the Crystal Palace for the

Figure 2.1: Harington's water closet

A godly father sitting on a draught,
To do as neede, and nature hath us taught;
Mumbled (as was his manner) certain prayr's,
And unto him the Devil straight repayr's:
And boldly to revile him he begins,
Alledging that such prayr's are deadly sins;
And that it shewd, he was devoyd of grace,
To speake to God, from so unmeete a place.
The reverent man, though at first dismaid;
Yet strong in faith, to Satan thus he said.
Thou damned spirit, wicked, false & lying,
Dispairing thine own good, & ours envying:
Ech take his due, and me thou canst not hurt,
To God my pray'r I meant, to thee the durt.
Pure prayr ascends to him that high doth sit,
Down fals the filth,[58] *for fiends of hel more fit.*

Great Exhibition. They were a great success and over 800,000 visitors paid for their use. It is to Jennings that we owe the expression 'spending a penny' (Wright 1960). By the 1870s, public toilet facilities were accepted as part of the 'conveniences suited to this advanced stage of civilisation' and it is to Jennings also that we may attribute the familiar feature of public conveniences. He had the idea of putting these facilities discreetly underground in town centres and at railway stations so that they were both discreet and also economical in terms of use of expensive land in centres of population. 'Jennings' ideas were revolutionary: firstly many conveniences were built underground, with cast iron arches, railings or pergolas to mark their whereabouts. Those built above ground were distinctive little buildings in their own right, with their filials, pillars, panels and enhancing lamps' (Lambton 1978).

During the second half of the nineteenth century and the early part of this century, Harington's basic invention went through a number of modifications, to improve hygiene and reliability (Wright 1960; Kira 1976; Latham 1908). There were hopper closets, valve closets and washout closets, before the washdown closet finally became firmly established. By the turn of the century, names like Bramah, Armitage, Twyfords and Shanks were, literally, household words. Many Victorian toilets were splendid works of art and many surviving examples have been lovingly catalogued by Lambton (1978).

PROBLEMS IN MODERN TOILET DESIGN

The modern bathroom, of which the toilet or lavatory is part, attained its standard form by the 1920s (Gideon 1948). Gideon describes the 'rigid layout of the bath, basin and toilet, and their comparison within a minimum space' as the compact bathroom. It is more accurately and popularly referred to as 'the smallest room' and Kira (1976) discusses how odd it is that such an important room in the house, where such a large proportion of time is spent, has been given so little prominence, thought and space by architects. It is even worse in settings such as schools and hospitals. Little has changed since 1907 when Latham recommended that:

In large dwellings and public buildings such as hospitals, workhouses and hotels it is desirable that the water closets should be separated from the main buildings and be approached by a corridor with doors at either end, and having through ventilation, so as to cut off the direct communication of the closets from the rest of the building.

The toilets in many schools and hospitals now are direct descendants of this model — annexes tacked on as an afterthought.

Another feature of modern 'civilised' toilets needs to be touched on. Throughout most of Western society toilets are designed for sitting on in the same way as a chair. These are called pedestal toilets and their use can be traced back to Roman toilets, close stools and water closets. This contrasts with the squat posture adopted in many Third World countries (Pacey 1980; Feacham and Cairncross 1978). Although sitting is associated with water-borne disposal systems and squatting with non-water-borne systems, there is no logical connection between the two. Pacey (1978) comments that:

> Although the squat hole is very widespread, people in some parts of Africa and the Caribbean are increasingly expressing a preference for the raised seat. In the latter region where both types of latrine co-exist a higher standard of living is associated with the 'sit-down' toilet. Advantages are claimed for it . . .

This is indeed unfortunate as sitting at toilet is one factor, together with diet, that is blamed for the Western diseases of constipation and piles. With the squat posture, the appropriate muscle groups can be used more efficiently with less ineffective and potentially damaging straining.

It is easy to see and to understand how problems with the design of the modern pedestal toilet present themselves. First, there is the problem of the use of the sitting posture mentioned immediately above. Secondly, there is a whole range of problems confronting elderly, handicapped or disabled people with special continence needs. The bathroom in most houses is small and usually upstairs. 'Public conveniences', frequently being sited underground, are neither public nor convenient to disabled people. It is only relatively recently that legislation has been introduced to begin to guarantee the right to access for handicapped people to public conveniences and to toilets in buildings that are open to the public (Boswell and Wingrove 1974). Sadly, many elderly, mentally handicapped or physically disabled people are still cared for in institutional settings, where cold, draughty, echoing and impersonal toilet annexes down lengthy corridors and through sets of double doors are Latham's legacy. The miasmic theory of bad air still seems to have a disproportionate effect despite vastly improved infection control in a host of ways.

One of the few thorough and scholarly studies of both physical and psychological criteria for toilet design has been carried out by Kira (1976). Kira urges that:

> perhaps most important(ly), the architects and builders — who actually are the purchasers and who actually are responsible for the design of our bathrooms — must begin to think of hygiene facilities as an important part of our daily lives rather than as a necessary evil to be accommodated according to the dictates of some obsolete handbook or drawing template in whatever space is left over with whatever part of the budget is minimally required to meet legal standards.

Harington took two or three hundred years to make an impact; Jennings took twenty or thirty years; it would be pleasing to think that Kira's impact will be sooner rather than later.

HISTORY OF INCONTINENCE AS A PROBLEM

One of the curious things about the history of incontinence as a problem is actually the change in meaning of the word itself. Commonly, incontinence is now taken to refer to urinary or faecal incontinence; not so long ago it was more commonly taken to refer to sexual incontinence. At some point the popular meaning of the word has changed but it is difficult to determine precisely when or how this change occurred. One of the most interesting ways to start looking at the use of the word is to consult the folio editions of Samuel Johnson's Dictionary, first published in 1755. Here, 'continence' is defined largely in terms of restraint, chastity and moderation of lawful pleasure and incontinence in terms of immediacy, lack of restraint of the appetite, indulging in unlawful pleasure, or unchaste. Johnson provides examples from English literature to illustrate the various uses: thus, when Shakespeare declares during Othello that 'He will return incontinent', we realise that his reappearance should be swift rather than damp.

'Continence' can be traced back through Old English to its Latin root and means literally to contain. Finkenstaedt, Leisi and Wolff (1970), in their study of the earliest known occurrences of 80,000

Figure 2.2: Public 'conveniences' still owe much to Victorian design concepts

"As far as I'm concerned it's neither public nor convenient."

THE SPASTICS SOCIETY

It's not that people don't care, it's just that they don't think.

English words, list both the words continence and incontinence as being in use in literature by the period 1150 to 1450. A survey of eighteenth and nineteenth century dictionaries demonstrates that throughout this period incontinence retained chiefly sexual associations. Even up to 1964, the Concise Oxford Dictionary defined incontinence primarily as 'wanting in self restraint, especially in regard to sexual appetite'. Only in medical dictionaries was incontinence used to refer to a lack of bladder or bowel control. Yet, somewhere between the 1930s and the 1970s, the popular use of the word changed. In 1933, the vast majority of literary quotes used to illustrate the use of the word incontinence in the Complete Oxford English Dictionary referred to sexual promiscuity. In the supplement to this, published in 1976, the only further examples of the use of the word are of urinary and faecal incontinence. What caused this change in the language is not at all clear, but it is important to remember that the change is relatively recent. Professionals should be cautious when using the word with elderly clients, for some of whom it may have quite a different and morally shocking meaning.

The first mention of incontinence of urine as a problem comes in 1500 BC in the Papyrus Ebers, when a remedy consisting of juniper berries, cyprus and beer was recommended (Glicklich 1951). Probably the first mention in English of toilet training problems comes from Thomas Phaire in 1553 when, in his *Boke of Chyldren*, he included a section entitled 'Of Pyssing in the Bedde'.

In one sentence, Phaire mentions the problems of day and night incontinence in children and in old age. The treatment that Thomas Phaire recommended was a powder made from the burnt trachea of a cock. If this were not available, then a powder made from the testicles of a hedgehog or the claws of a goat would suffice. It is fairly obvious, that for incontinence, Phaire was following the writings of Paulus Aegenita (625–690 AD) who in turn based his work heavily on earlier Greek physicians such as Galen, Oribbasius and Aetius. In general, Paulus Aegenita had a large influence on medieval medicine. On incontinence of urine, he wrote:

Relaxation of the muscle of the neck of the bladder occasions this affliction and therefore it happens most frequently to children. Our general treatment ought to consist especially of tonics, such as hot wine and oil and the like, abstaining from all things which are powerfully refrigerant and rather as much as possible using calefacients; for cold produces a resemblance to paralysis. The following things are naturally efficacious: Burn the crop of a cock

27

and give to the patient to drink in tepid water, when fasting, or the flowers of the white eye-ox (chrysanthemum) in like manner, or, shave down the testicle of a hare into fragrant wine and give to drink; or, give calamint and myrrh in a draught before supper; or, give the toasted seed of wild rice to drink every third day. Let the privy members be anointed with cimolian earth, mixed with the juice of perdicias.

None of the above remedies have, to the authors' knowledge, been subjected to double-blind, controlled trials.

One of the earliest references to incontinence in a handicapped person comes from Martin Luther (1483–1546), who thus described what appeared to be a severely or profoundly mentally handicapped child:

Eight years ago, there was one at Dessau whom I, Martin Luther, saw and grappled with. He was twelve years old, had the use of his eyes and all his senses, so that one might think he was a normal child. But he did nothing but gorge himself . . . He ate, defaecated, and drooled . . ..

Luther's remedy was somewhat more drastic:

So I said to the Prince of Anhalt: 'If I were the Prince, I should take this child to the Molda River which flows near Dessau and drown him'.

Luther notes that his recommendations were not carried out.

Glicklich (1951) reminds us that:

The Middle Ages were . . . a time of supplication and prayer. In Transylvania, St Catherine of Alexandria was believed to be helpful in enuresis and on her nameday, November 25th, was particular implored for help. In southern Germany St Vitus was appealed to for relief.

He was also a patron of those suffering from the 'dancing mania' and constipation.

Both cauterising the urethra and dilating the urethra with bougies were popular approaches to treatment in the eighteenth and nineteenth centuries. 'If these methods of treatment produce any effect, I suspect that it is simply by annoying the patient, and by giving him that strong desire to be relieved, which . . . (is) the first step towards recovery' (Brodie 1842).

Arnaud (1763) popularised the use of the bougie, a flexible cylindrical instrument, used to dilate a stricture. In describing a man who, in 1752, had an enlarged prostate, Arnaud:

> Made him begin with the dilating candles and to continue using them for several days after which . . . they found a free passage to the bladder: in less than eight days a very plentiful suppuration was brought on. The incontinence of urine ceased during the night; it afterwards diminished insensibly, in the day time; and in ten weeks the Patient was cured.

The use of both bougies and catheters in many cases of incontinence increased following such descriptions.

In the long history of incontinence as a problem, even where attitudes towards the problem may have seemed compassionate, the treatment may have been less so. Chambers (1846) in Dickensian style, described the case of a 17-year-old girl who was nocturnally enuretic and:

> was rendered incompetent of undertaking a situation and had become a burden on her friends . . . (who had) accepted the situation of a servant a week before her admission into the Hospital; and during the whole of that week she never undressed or went to bed, but remained on a chair by the kitchen fire in order to conceal her affliction from the family. Is it then likely that in one so much alive to her state, ridicule or punishment could effect any alteration?

Chambers' first line of action was 'a blister . . . applied occasionally to the sacrum . . . (to) act as a stimulant to the bladder, and . . . prevent the patient from sleeping on (her) back'. When this failed 'I had the orifice of the urethra cauterised with the nitrate of silver. The operation has been twice performed as the first was not sufficiently powerful.'

Charles Mercer in his standard textbook *Lunatic Asylums* (1894), although fairly humane in his time, could also be strict with his incontinent patients:

> There is a class of uncleanly patients whose faulty habits are due to sheer laziness and indolence. Such a patient will pass water in

bed, because of the two evils of lying on a wet sheet or getting out into the cold to pass water, he prefers the former. Others again are dirty from a malicious desire to give pain and trouble. They have a grudge against either a particular attendant or against mankind in general and they take this means of doing that which they know to be offensive and objectionable. Lastly, there are those who not merely pass their excrement under them, but who proceed thereupon to kneed it with their hands and to daub it all over their persons, their clothing and their apartment. These superlatively filthy patients are again of two classes — first, those whose dabbling in filth is the result of stupidity, who are dazed and demented, and whose action may be due to some futile intention of cleaning the mess away, or to non-appreciation of its nature; and, secondly, those who know quite well what they are doing, and taken an insane delight in the filthy occupation.

The ways of dealing with uncleanly habits will, of course, differ to some extent according to which of the above categories the patient is to be placed in . . .. The . . . class of patients . . . who are dirty from sheer indolence can always be cured. The mode of treatment is to make it more troublesome to be dirty than to be clean . . .. These are suitable cases for holding out inducements to cleanliness by withdrawing some privilege, and making its restoration contingent on an improvement in the habits.

Patients who are dirty from sheer malice and from a desire to give trouble are a very difficult class to deal with . . . in no case is the task a very hopeful one and they will often continue their habits in spite of all that can be done.

The last category of patients comprise the most objectionable of all. Such patients are always made the tenants of single rooms, in which they are for the most part left during the night to their own devices, and discovered in the morning in a condition of indescribable filth . . .. But in an ideal asylum . . . such patients would have a special attendant to remain with them at night and to prevent their indulgences in such practices.

By contrast, during the same period, the law specifically allowed the driver of a hansom cab in London to urinate against the offside rear wheel of the cab. Apparently, this law has never been repealed (Millard 1979).

Still, there were those during this period who also inclined towards psychological approaches for explanation and treatment of some forms of incontinence. Charles Bell (1820) asks 'Is it beneath the dignity of the subject (incontinence of urine) to inquire why children pass urine in bed. Many a little urchin may be spared his flogging if the very simple cure was known.' He cites some of the horrible methods used of frightening children in order to break the habit of wetting the bed. These include being forced to crush live mice in their hands or being forced to sit by the bed of a dying person. Brodie saw one child whose nurse had tied a cord around his penis to stop his bed wetting and which had cut through the urethra. Bell's explanation and remedy are simple. He argued that the:

> Master spring of the muscles of the bladder . . . (is a) sensible spot a little behind and below the orifice of the bladder . . . when he lies on his back it presses upon this sensible spot and distends that part of the bladder . . .. When a child wets the bed, it is in consequence of a dream, excited by the irritation of this sensible spot of the bladder, by the urine resting there and stretching the bladder; it is cruel to chastise the child; and raising it frequently to make water does not mend the matter . . .. The cure is a simple one: he is to accustom himself to sleep upon his face, or side.

John Shaw, an editor of Bell's work adds an interesting footnote.

> It must not be forgotten, however, that there are cases in which a boy makes water very frequently, even through the day, without suffering much irritation. In such a case, the boy may be obliged to retain his water longer, by compressing the urethra: by a careful distension of the bladder and by gradually increasing the interval of making water, the bladder may be at last brought to its natural quantity.

This is the earliest mention in the literature of retention control training. The first mention of fluid restriction came around the same period from Chambers in 1846, also around the same period.

Glicklich (1951), in her historical review of enuresis, comments that attitudes towards enuresis have mirrored the basic medical opinions and fashions of successive ages. She astutely concludes that:

> When one reads of the number of medicaments, implements and methods, all used in the name of science, he is inclined to believe

that when all these were turned on a specific case of enuresis the disorder just 'upped and died' because it was outnumbered.

A wide range of medical and surgical remedies have been proposed and the 'unfortunate male child with his exposed penis . . . (has been) the subject of numerous manipulations and gadgets'. Most of the early psychological approaches have focused heavily on punishment in one way or another. Beatings, shame and ridicule have lasted well into the twentieth century, and are still common. Remarque in *All Quiet on the Western Front* describes how army recruits are sometimes treated. 'Piss-a-beds' were paired off to sleep one above another in bunks with no mattresses so that they wet on each other. There is no evidence that such an approach has any good effect.

3

The Function of Micturition

It is said that the Roman Emperor Vespasian
(AD 9–79) when asked for this justification
of a new tax on public urinals answered
'Pecunia non olet' (money does not smell).

SCENT MARKING

It is widely assumed that the function of micturition is a purely
physical one, that is to discharge waste products of the body clear
of the skin. This is not wholly sufficient. In mammals, scent marking is another important continence-related behaviour, and some of
the ways in which scent marking is performed contrast markedly
with a 'discharge clear of the skin' definition of the function of
micturition. For example, urine washing is a reliably documented
phenomenon in some species of monkey (Rowell 1972), where urine
is smeared on objects in the environment through contact with the
monkey's hands and feet.

Chemical communication in animals in general, and scent marking in particular, are well reviewed by Eisenberg and Kleiman
(1972) and Ralls (1971), respectively.

Does scent marking, or something similar, occur in humans?
Scent obviously plays a less important role in humans, as the olfactory part of our cerebral cortex is relatively small. On the other
hand, that scent is still important to humans is clear from our multi-
million pound perfume industry, the many taboos that surround
natural body odours and wastes and the use of incense in religious
ceremonies.

One prerequisite skill for scent marking must be the ability to
differentiate own from other urine. Smith (1979b) found this ability
in a profoundly mentally handicapped man who had been resistant
to long-term improvement in toilet training and who, it seemed
likely, liked to sniff his own wet clothing.

It is often assumed that the purpose of scent marking is territorial,
that is, the scent marks out a territory which the individual will

33

defend against others of the same species. Whilst such an interpretation of this behaviour applies in some instances, the motivation and functions of scent marking are generally wider and more complex than this. As Eisenberg and Kleiman (1972) comment,

> The release and deposition of scent serves many functions. It permits the exchange of chemical information among animals that live with overlapping home ranges, but tend to move and forage alone. It gives information with respect to age, sex and reproductive conditions . . . .. We must divorce ourselves from considering scent marks as a means of territorial defence; rather, we should think of scent as a means of exchanging information, orienting the movement of individuals and integrating social and reproductive behaviour.

TERRITORIAL BEHAVIOUR

There is increasing, though not extensive, evidence that territorial behaviour occurs in humans. This phenomenon has been demonstrated in 'abnormal' individuals, including mentally handicapped or psychiatrically disturbed people in ward settings (Palluck and Esser 1971; Esser 1973). Much of this work has been most concerned with the relationship between the use of space by residents on wards and with ward dominance hierarchies or pecking orders.

Territorial behaviour and micturition

Hereford, Clelland and Fellner (1973) hypothesised that increase of available territory should lead to a decrease of nocturnal wetting and soiling in nine profoundly mentally handicapped adult males. Their results appear to support impressively the view that decrease in crowding and the clearer demarcation of sleeping space reduce the amount of nocturnal enuresis and encopresis in these particular individuals. Sadly, a major criticism of this study must be the four- to five-day observation and récording phases: many behaviours, including incontinence, show considerable within-subject variance in frequency over time and thus four- to five-day time periods cannot be considered sufficient reliably to assess the incontinence rates in different phases (Smith and Wong 1981); secondly, since hospitalisation results for most people in decrease of sleeping space, one would expect, according to Hereford *et al.* (1973), an increase in nocturnal wetting. In fact, it is well established that a change in sleeping situation such as occurs with hospitalisation or on holiday, results in a reduction in nocturnal enuresis (McKeith, Meadow and Turner 1973). Hereford *et al.* make a further attempt to link 'incontinence' with territorial behaviour; they note that scent marking occurs more often among male mammals when the object involves aggression and further make the connection between this and the fact that, in humans, enuresis and encopresis are twice as common in males. However, male children show a higher incidence of very many other disorders, the male of our species being more at risk generally (Rutter, Tizard and Whitmore 1970). Smith (1979b), in a survey of over 1300 mentally handicapped hospital residents, found a small but interesting sex difference in incontinence. This survey included ratings of daytime wetting and soiling frequencies and degree of independence at toilet. There was a significant sex difference for both measures of incontinence but not for dependence upon staff, males being more incontinent but not more dependent.

However, in support of Hereford *et al.* (1973), evidence of the effect of change of environment on incontinence in profoundly mentally handicapped adults has recently been presented by Shrubsole and Smith (1984). They recorded incontinence in 13 subjects over four-week periods in two different living situations. The first situation was in an overcrowded and impoverished hospital ward and the second was following 'upgrading' of this accommodation to provide less crowded facilities and better living conditions, including improved toilet facilities. Without the introduction of any new specific toilet training programme, there was a 30% reduction in the frequency of incontinence. This, however, could be due in some subtle way to improved staff morale and better nursing techniques. Recently, also, Duker (1983) has reported the results of a multiple regression analysis of several environmental variables on degree of bladder control in two hundred hospitalised mentally handicapped residents. He found size of living group and access to toilet significantly related to degree of bladder control.

Function of 'incontinence' in humans

Thus it can be seen that the possibility exists that micturition in humans might have functions other than that of discharging waste products from the body. Scent marking may be at least a plausible explanation of some instances of incontinence in mental handicap. There has, however, as yet been very little serious study in this area, but consideration should be given to the possibility that an apparent incontinence problem may have a function.

4

Theoretical Models, Component Skills and Developmental Sequence of Continence

> To begin my life a speechless babe,
> hairless, incontinent . . . a nurse's
> nuisance.
> > George Bernard Shaw (1901)

THEORETICAL MODELS

The purpose of this section is to discuss theoretical models that may be used to describe the phenomenon of urinary continence at a behavioural level. What is already known or believed about the processes underlying normal bladder function and urinary continence at a physiological and anatomical level is well covered elsewhere (Kuru 1965; Yeates 1973; Milne 1976; Stanton 1977; Feneley 1986) and no attempt will be made to summarise this here. It is argued that a far better understanding of the behaviour itself is required. Many incontinence problems, especially with otherwise normal or with mentally handicapped children, have no underlying physical or physiological cause: it is the behaviour of going to the toilet or passing urine in the toilet that we are often concerned with. Models have been constructed at the physiological level to describe the functions of the lower urinary tract but little serious attention has been paid to analysing the behaviour concerned. With only one or two exceptions (Ellis 1963; Bettison 1978, 1980) this is usually touched upon briefly at a 'common sense' level. An attempt is made here to discuss and apply relevant psychological concepts and processes to understanding the behaviours involved in becoming and remaining continent of urine.

One of the better models, integrating what is known by urologists about bladder function and presented as a practical visual aid, is Yeates' (1972, 1973) model of the micturition cycle. According to this model, sophisticated bladder function is simplified to be viewed as a cycle comprising five main phases. These are bladder filling, the awareness of the desire to void urine, postponement of voiding until an appropriate toileting situation is reached, initiation of voiding through contraction, and the maintenance of bladder contraction during emptying. Disorders of bladder function can usefully be classified according to the five main phases of the micturition cycle. From a behavioural point of view, however, such a model is of limited value, especially if one is viewing the process developmentally, as is necessary in toilet training a normal child or a mentally handicapped person. A learning theory view of this process is therefore taken here for the moment, to see what learning models can be proposed to account for continence at a behavioural level. The three main learning theories considered here are classical conditioning, operant conditioning and stimulus–response (S–R) theory.

Classical conditioning

This was the first learning theory to be applied to the acquisition of continence. It is also the most widely known form of learning. Briefly, classical conditioning involves an association between an unconditioned and a conditioned stimulus through repetition. The buzzer or bell and pad treatment for nocturnal enuresis was interpreted in this way by Mowrer and Mowrer in 1938, which interpretation was and still is, widely accepted, where:

$$CS \longrightarrow UCS \longrightarrow (U)CR$$

$$\text{bladder} \longrightarrow \text{bell} \longrightarrow \text{waking/contracting}$$
$$\text{distension} \qquad\qquad\qquad \text{of sphincter}$$

Lovibond (1963), however, criticised this model on the grounds that repeated presentation of the conditioned stimulus (bladder distension) in the absence of the unconditioned stimulus (bell) would eventually lead to extinction of the conditioned response (waking and contracting of sphincter muscles). Lovibond (1964) considered alternatives to the classical conditioning model on the basis that the treatment had been shown to be effective and that, if a completely appropriate learning model could be uncovered, this would lead to even more effective treatment methods.

In accordance with the spirit of that period, aversion learning was considered a possible model. Electric shock was tried to replace the supposedly neutral stimulus of the bell, but a controlled trial failed to demonstrate any significant improvement in outcome (see Lovibond 1964). Not surprisingly, this was complicated by the reluctance of parents to use such methods. But Lovibond himself hypothesised avoidance learning to be the model, as conditioned avoidance responses are more resistant to extinction, so he devised a 'twin signal' system. When the child wet the bed, a relatively soft tone sounded first. If the child inhibited voiding, woke up immediately and switched the alarm off, he was able to avoid the onset of a second, louder, more unpleasant, klaxon-type of alarm that would otherwise blast him awake. Attractive as this system appears, there was unfortunately no significant difference in effectiveness between this and a standard bell and pad control group. Thus, for the acquisition of nocturnal continence under overt training conditions, it has not been possible to establish the most likely learning model.

Operant conditioning

In a classical conditioning model of bladder training, the child or adult retains a passive or respondent involvement in the learning process. By contrast, broad psychological theories of child development view the child as playing an active role in learning: the child is seen as acting or operating upon, enquiring about and testing and changing his environment. This is one of the reasons why operant conditioning has become increasingly popular and acceptable as a model on which to base toilet training and other types of training programmes. In recent years, daytime toilet training has been viewed almost exclusively in operant terms. The approach taken is basically to reward appropriate toileting behaviour (e.g. passing urine into toilet) and not to reward, or even to punish, inappropriate toileting behaviour (e.g. wetting pants). More detailed accounts of operant conditioning toilet-training procedures, which are much more sophisticated than may appear from the crude account given here, are provided by Azrin and Foxx (1974), Foxx and Azrin (1973a) and Bettison (1982) and are reviewed in some detail later. Although in practical terms operant conditioning has had a great influence on training programmes, further theoretical discussion of this and its relation to classical conditioning is best included in the next section.

Stimulus–response theory

Learning theory models readily accommodate change in the stimuli and responses link during learning. For example, when the stimulus (S) is bladder distension and the initial response is voiding, the response (R) after learning might be toilet approach followed by voiding. In practice, these changes are provided for by the training procedures of shaping, prompt and fade, and chaining. Fading is change in stimulus (e.g. when the stimulus is provided by guiding the child to the toilet, this guidance is gradually reduced or faded) and shaping is change in response (e.g. pulls pants down from below knees, pulls pants from knees, pulls pants down from above knees etc). Chaining occurs where, in a series of responses, one response leads to the next (e.g. toilet approach, removal of clothes, sitting on toilet, voiding in toilet). As conditioning progresses in any learning model, more automatic relationships between stimuli and responses develop. The relation usually strengthens with repetition and previously neutral stimuli may lead to specific behaviours. With the two events of stimulus and response, we have four possible pairs of sequence combinations:

$$S \longrightarrow S \qquad S \longrightarrow R \qquad R \longrightarrow S \qquad R \longrightarrow R$$

The first relationship, $S \longrightarrow S$, is typically considered to occur in classical conditioning situations where an unconditioned stimulus (e.g. buzzer) is paired with a conditioned stimulus (e.g. bladder distension). The second relationship, $S \longrightarrow R$, is also usually considered to be characteristic of a classical conditioning paradigm (e.g. buzzer $\longrightarrow$ waking). However, operant conditioning can also be viewed in terms of stimulus–response theory, as a discriminative stimulus may signal responding and the response may elicit a reinforcing stimulus (e.g. voiding on potty $\longrightarrow$ mother's praise). The third relationship, $R \longrightarrow S$, is therefore considered most typical of operant conditioning, where the response is followed by a reinforcing stimulus, as the individual in this case is controlling the environment through his response. The $R \longrightarrow R$ relationship, or response chain, gives information about the 'dynamics' of the behaviour itself, in the same way that the $S \longrightarrow S$ relationship can give information about the environment.

Ellis (1963), in his frequently cited article, was the first to apply stimulus–response analysis to toilet training. Prior to the development of continence, the stimulus of a full bladder leads to the

Figure 4.1: Stimulatory-response analysis of toilet training

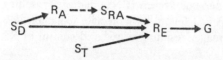

$$S_D \longrightarrow R_E$$

where

S_D	is discriminative stimulus (full bladder)
R_E	is eliminatory response
G	is reduction of S_D and reward
R_A	is approach response elicited by S_D
S_{RA}	is cues generated by R_A
S_T	is cues associated with toilet

response of elimination, as shown in the upper part of Figure 4.1.

Following toilet training, it is proposed by Ellis that the mechanism shown in the lower part of Figure 4.1 operates. The discriminative stimulus of bladder distension ($S_{\hat{D}}$) is no longer simply linked with elimination, but also with approach responses to toilet ($R_{\hat{A}}$). These approach responses themselves form cues that constitute stimuli for the elimination response in the toilet ($R_{\hat{E}}$), as do the stimuli associated with sitting on the toilet itself ($S_{\hat{T}}$). $R_{\hat{E}}$ is strengthened by G in terms of reduction in the initial $S_{\hat{D}}$ and social or other rewards.

The Ellis model is basically a useful model, but there are some theoretical difficulties. For example, S_D (bladder distension) may act as a discriminative stimulus in that it comes to signal to the individual that reinforcement is available if it emits the operant behaviour. However, the reduction of a discriminative stimulus in experimental terms is not rewarding, but usually leads to experimental neurosis. Thus, $S_{\hat{D}}$ should perhaps be viewed more as an unpleasant stimulus (S–), the reduction or removal of which is negatively reinforcing. However, the Ellis model is immensely important as it stimulated a number of practical attempts to devise toilet-training programmes for the mentally handicapped. Ellis himself saw two main uses of his model. The first was in analysing why continence had not developed and the second was in designing a toilet-training programme. In terms of his model, he cites four possible areas of difficulty or disorder in developing continence.

1. Lack of training or opportunity to establish the S–R links.
2. Decreased learning ability, resulting in less associative strength between S–R links.
3. Central nervous system (CNS) damage, resulting in impoverished $S\hat{D}$ and failure to appreciate reduction in $S\hat{D}$.
4. CNS damage, resulting in reduced control of $R\hat{E}$.

The programme that Ellis designed and proposed in some detail revolved around determining the temporal locus of $S\hat{D}$: 'The patients should be observed . . . and a *precise* record made of the *frequency* and *time* of $R\hat{E}$ occurrences over an interval of, perhaps, 30 days . . . .' The success of the project would appear to hinge critically upon the accuracy of these records for the provision of information pertaining to the temporal locus of $S\hat{D}$, i.e. when the child needs to go to the toilet. The procedure then involved taking the individual to the toilet around the time of an expected $R\hat{E}$, and rewarding him substantially for eliminating in the toilet.

A third very important use of the Ellis model, however, is that it can provide us with a basis for classifying different methods of toilet training. Classification is necessary in order to try to interpret and compare the effectiveness of the many different studies of and packages for toilet training that will be reviewed later. The approach to training that Ellis advocates involves intervening in the model initially at S_D. An alternative approach can involve intervening in the model initially at $S\hat{T}$, by ignoring the times of hypothesised full bladders and simply toileting the child at arbitrarily set intervals of time. The former approach can be called a 'timing' approach and the latter a 'regular toileting' approach. This is also discussed in more detail later.

The point has often been made that, in laboratory studies with animals, it is relatively easy to distinguish between classical and operant conditioning, the former being more concerned with the antecedents of behaviour, the latter with consequences.

It has traditionally also been believed that classical and operant conditioning are two distinct phenomena related to two distinct neurophysiological mechanisms: the involuntary visceral responses (including the functioning of bladder and bowel), which are controlled by the autonomic nervous system, have generally been considered susceptible to classical conditioning; the voluntary skeletal muscle responses (such as walking to the toilet, handling of clothes and sitting down), which are controlled by the CNS have generally been considered modifiable by operant conditioning. However, Miller and Di Cara (1967) demonstrated conclusively that heart rate in the rat could be modified in an operant paradigm using pleasurable consequences. Less well-known, but of extreme importance to the present discussion, is that operant manipulation of both bladder and bowel had been demonstrated in the rhesus monkey. By catheterising bladder or bowel, the pressure in bladder/bowel has been controlled and used successfully as the discriminative stimulus in bar pressing tasks (Slucki, Adam and Porter 1965; Slucki, McCoy and Porter 1969; Soldoff 1971; Soldoff and Slucki 1974).

COMPONENT SKILLS OF CONTINENCE

Having considered possible learning theory models (and problems) for the development of continence viewed in a rather simple sense, we shall now attempt to review the situation, viewing toileting as a more complex task. Exactly what component skills, at a behavioural or molar level, are involved in fully developed self-care at the toilet? There has been very little empirical study of continence-related behaviours to establish exactly which factors are important and what is the exact role of these factors. The following are simply presumed to be of importance.

Muellner (1960) states that four steps occur in the acquisition of full control over micturition:

1. The child must be aware of the sensation of a full bladder.
2. He must have the ability to 'hold' urine for a brief time when the bladder is full.
3. He must be able to initiate the urine stream when the bladder is full.
4. He must be able to pass urine in the absence of a full bladder, i.e. pass small amounts of urine at will (discussed more in the next chapter).
   To this list a fifth skill of bladder function may be added (Yeates 1972, 1973).
5. The child must be able to maintain the urine flow through bladder contraction after the urine stream has been initiated.

We may then add a list of non-bladder function skills, which are nevertheless important and are emphasised in many toilet-training programmes (e.g. Mahonen, Van Wagenen and Meyerson 1971; Foxx and Azrin 1973a).

6. The child must be able to remove and replace clothing as necessary at the toilet.
7. The child must be able to get up and walk to the toilet, or ask to be taken there, or ask for access to the toilet.
8. The child must be able to ask about and plan ahead for the use of toilet facilities, whether the bladder is likely to be full or not.

Tierney (1973, 1976) discusses some of the above in more detail and provides a breakdown of toileting skills into the four main areas of: handling of clothes at toilet; going to toilet; sitting on toilet; continence (Figure 4.2). The development of each of these abilities is then broken down further into four steps or stages. This model is intended for use in assessment of toileting skills as a basis for a training programme and will be discussed further in a later chapter.

Bettison (1979) provides a useful further analysis of the development of continence in S–R terms, viewing it as a somewhat more complex set of behaviours than Ellis' (1963) model. In this analysis, some of these behaviours occur in a chain and some occur concurrently (Figure 4.3).

It would certainly seem that, although there have been few attempts to produce possible models for continence at a behavioural level, an S–R analysis encompasses the possibility of either or both classical and operant learning (if they are fundamentally different in the first place) and offers the opportunity for a detailed analysis of the component skills involved. One of the aspects of continence that has not really been stressed so far (except perhaps in the Bettison model) is the inhibitory effects that many behaviours must have, e.g. the stimulus provided by wearing clothes leads to the response of not voiding. In S–R terms, it does not really matter whether a behaviour is elicited or inhibited, both are regarded as responses; but in models of continence, more account should be taken of inhibitory relationships between stimuli and responses. From this theoretical discussion of continence and from subjective experience of toilet-training programmes, a more complete S–R type of analysis is presented in Figure 4.4. It should be stressed again that the components of the model are merely postulated and not necessarily validated from direct observational studies. There is a need for detailed empirical study of how continence normally develops.

Figure 4.2: Model for shaping toileting behaviour

	Continence	Sitting	Dressing	Going
Final Target Behaviour	4 Child urinates only in the toilet and is otherwise continent	8 Child sits on toilet independently	12 Child removes his clothing independently	16 Child goes to the toilet independently
	3 Child urinates in toilet regularly and has only infrequent incontinent episodes	7 Child is helped to sit on toilet and sits unrestrained	11 Child removes or actively attempts to remove some of his clothing	15 Child 'asks' to go to the toilet
Intermediate Target Behaviour	2 Child has established some regularity and uses toilet more frequently than is incontinent	6 Child is placed on toilet and sits unrestrained	10 Child actively assists when clothing removed	14 Child indicates need to urinate
Base Target Behaviour	1 Child uses toilet when placed on it and is incontinent at all other times	5 Child is placed on toilet and is restrained to sit	9 Child co-operates passively when clothing is removed	13 Child is taken to toilet

Based on a figure by Dr Alison Tierney. Reproduced by permission of *Nursing Times*, where the original first appeared in December 1973

Figure 4.3: Bettison's (1979) model for continence

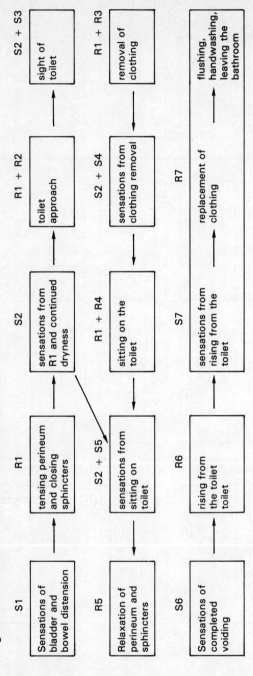

Figure 4.4: More complete S–R model of continence

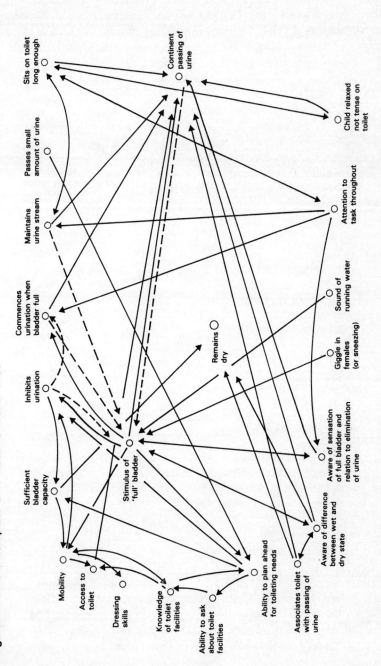

The three primary components involved in this model of continence are considered to be the stimulus of a full bladder, remaining dry and the continent passing of urine. Related to these conditions are a larger number of component factors listed below for convenience under four main headings:

Bladder and sphincter factors

— Sufficient bladder capacity
— Ability to inhibit micturition ⎫
— Ability to commence micturition ⎬ sphincter control
— Ability to maintain urine stream ⎭
— Ability to pass small amount of urine in the absence of full bladder

Independence factors

— Sufficient mobility
— Access to toilet
— Knowledge of toilet facilities
— Ability to ask about toilet facilities
— Ability to plan ahead for use of toilet facilities
— Sufficient dressing skills

Associative factors

— Association between toilet and passing urine
— Ability to discriminate differences between wet and dry state
— Awareness of sensation of full bladder and relation to response of elimination

Interference factors

— Short attention span (unable to attend to task throughout)
— Running water, giggling or sneezing (especially in females)
— Behaviours incompatible with continence (e.g. not wanting to leave a meal or warm situation to go to cold toilet)
— Tense, unable to relax sufficiently on toilet.

The interrelationships between these components are shown in Figure 4.4. (Inhibitory relationships are shown as dotted lines in order to avoid treating the inhibition of a response as a separate behaviour. Double-headed arrows indicate either reciprocal relationships or behaviours that may arise concurrently.) For the sake of brevity this is not in fact a proper S–R model, as the stimuli and responses are not defined and many further stimuli arising from some of these behaviours are not included (e.g. see Bettison's model, Figure 4.3). Various further factors have not been included in this model; for example, modesty training and the need for privacy in toileting, which normally develop after continence has been at least partly achieved. Also, behaviours that normally follow appropriate use of the toilet, such as flushing the toilet and washing hands are not included. In dealing with continence at a behaviour level, we have also not included other factors that possibly affect the micturition process, such as temperature, fluid intake, etc.

The main point to be grasped from Figure 4.4 is that the development and maintenance of full continence is complex. In learning terms, its acquisition cannot be adequately accounted for through a simple operant process of seating a child on the toilet or pot and rewarding him if he passes urine. Language, modelling and cognitive factors, together with some minimum level of maturation, are assumed to play a large part in the development of continence in normal children. However, neither an appreciation of the probable importance of the above factors, nor an appreciation of the complexity of the task is of much practical help when faced with the task of toilet training a non-verbal, mentally handicapped or otherwise developmentally delayed or disabled person. In the absence of a more thorough factual understanding of the development of continence, the models of Tierney, Bettison and in particular Ellis, must retain the most heuristic value.

Finally, with respect to the physiological basis of micturition, Yeates (1972) has commented honestly that, 'Although in recent years there has been a great deal of research into the function of the bladder, its inlets, its outlets, and its control, much must remain very imperfectly understood'. How much more is this the case at the behavioural level, where the models we are able to produce are wholly theoretical and not at all empirically based? We need to know with more certainty what the behaviours really are for which we are trying to construct models.

IS THERE A DEVELOPMENTAL SEQUENCE IN THE ACQUISITION OF CONTINENCE?

Although the components of continence are as yet imperfectly understood, the question arises as to whether there is a developmental sequence among the presumed components. Urologists, such as Muellner (1960) and Yeates (1973), presume that for basic bladder function skills there is such a sequence and although there is disagreement over detail, there is broad agreement about the nature of the sequence overall. This is most succinctly summarised by Bettison (1978, 1979) as:

1. Reflex micturition in infancy.
2. 1–2 years — awareness of full bladder and brief holding of urine.
3. 3 years — holding urine for prolonged periods thus increasing bladder capacity.
4. 3–4 years — able to initiate urine stream with full bladder when seated on toilet.
5. 6 years — able to voluntarily commence urine stream without full bladder.

Knowledge about the developmental sequence in which continence is gradually acquired and the age at which full continence is normally achieved is of considerable practical importance for prompting the acquisition of continence in developmentally delayed and other children. There are two major criticisms of the work regarding the development of continence.

The developmental sequence

The first is that, although the authoritative statements made regarding the developmental sequence of continence skills are supposedly based on studies of large numbers of children, no data are actually presented (e.g. Gesell and Armatruda 1941; Muellner 1960). Furthermore, more recent publications tend to refer back to these authors without question. One recent urological study is, however, an exception to this and does present data on bladder capacity and ability to retain and pass urine (Hjalmos 1976). Unfortunately, the data were collected under artificial, clinical laboratory conditions with children being catheterised and requested to hold or pass urine.

Under such clinical conditions, anxiety must become a factor in responses. There have been no observation and recording studies of bladder function skills in normal children carried out under day-to-day living conditions. However, in one study where data were recorded longitudinally with mentally handicapped children on toilet training programmes, the findings on passing urine in the absence of a full bladder were not wholly consistent with the model described above, the ability to pass urine in the absence of a full bladder being an early acquired skill and not the last skill to be achieved (Smith and Wong 1981).

Smith and Wong (1981) and Fielding (1982) have voiced the suspicion that the ability to empty the bladder completely may be an important skill, yet one that is not included by others in their analyses.

Hints that bladder filling and emptying may not be as straightforward as it is widely assumed may be extracted from a few scattered brief reports. Visser *et al.* (1981), in their study of cyclic filling and emptying of the foetal bladder, comment that 'on some occasions . . . (emptying) occurred over a few seconds, while in others voiding was stepwise over a period of approximately 20 minutes'. Duche (1973), in a study of babies aged one to seventeen months, states that 'the volume of urine passed seemed to be extremely variable, and seemed unrelated both to time of night when micturition took place and to age and weight of the infant'. Similarly, McGraw (1940), in discussing one baby studied over a ten-month period concluded that her data 'cast doubt on the alleged functioning of a physiological rhythm. A scattergram of the number of voidings . . . during each hour of the day for the first 300 days of life fails to exhibit a definite rhythmic tendency.'

Age of achievement of full continence

The age at which daytime bladder control has been attained has been recorded in a number of different ways. Largo and Stutzle (1977a) estimated degree of bladder control by day for over 400 children, at intervals for the first six years of life (Table 4.1). Total bladder control, except for a few lapses, is achieved by the majority of the children in their sample between the second and third year. Overall, although definition and methods of rating vary, these results are broadly consistent with the outcome of studies of other large samples in contemporary western populations (Newson and Newson 1963;

Table 4.1: Percentage of children with different degrees of daytime control by age

	9/12		1		1½		2		3		4		5		6	
	m	f	m	f	m	f	m	f	m	f	m	f	m	f	m	f
0%	97	92	90	78	56	43	26	24	2	0	1	1	2	2	1	1
1–30%	3	4	8	11	15	29	10	10	1	1	1	0	0	1	2	0
30–70	0	2	2	2	7	5	11	15	2	3	0	1	1	1	3	1
70–95	0	0	0	0	12	7	36	39	78	78	9	9	5	4	3	1
100	0	0	0	0	10	16	17	22	18	18	89	89	92	92	97	97

Source: Largo and Stützle 1977a

Brazelton 1962; Oppel, Harper and Rider 1968a; De Jonge 1973; Weir 1982). The majority of children achieve a substantial degree of daytime dryness between their second and third years, although there are considerable individual differences.

The achievement of daytime bladder control is one aspect of the achievement of diurnal control required over both bowel and bladder for full continence. The sequence accepted by most (e.g. Bettison 1979) for the development of day and night bladder control is: bowel control at night; bowel control during the day; bladder control during the day; and finally bladder control at night.

The data that Largo and Stutzle (1977a) present are largely in accordance with this. However, they go on to note that 'about 8 per cent of the children had a different pattern in their development of bowel control and bladder control. Thus quite a few children are exceptions to this rule'. Brazelton's (1962) account of 1170 children in his paediatric practice, however, is definitely not in accordance with the accepted view. He found '12.3 per cent achieved bowel training first, 8.2 per cent were trained for urination first and 79.15 per cent were reported as training themselves simultaneously for bowel and bladder control'. One major difference between Brazelton's study and the others is that all the parents of children in his sample received advice from him on toilet training.

A major criticism of the work regarding the development of continence is that such knowledge as exists has thus far tended to be derived from questionnaire studies where mothers have been asked to give their opinion, often retrospectively, of their child's functioning. Such studies are subject to all of the problems of unreliability inherent in the more subjective and indirect methods of studying behaviour.

Furthermore, cross-cultural and social class differences in attitudes to toilet training are well documented, so that studies based on mothers' reports will be heavily influenced by the prevailing toilet training fashion. For example, information on toilet training from 25 different societies throughout the world indicates that the average age at which toilet training is said to begin is two years, with a range of from two or three months for the Tanala of Madagascar to five or six years for the Siriono of South America (Whiting and Child 1953).

Within Western Europe, national and social class differences are reported concerning the age at which training commences. Hindley (1965) reports that mothers in London start training before mothers in Paris, who start training before mothers in Stockholm. Newson and Newson (1963), in a survey of over 700 babies in Nottingham in England, reported social class differences in numbers of mothers who had started toilet training by the age of twelve months: there was a marked difference between social class V mothers and mothers in social classes I-IV in two respects, namely that fewer social class V mothers had started training by the age of twelve months and that of those who had started training, fewer reported any progress.

Apart from such cross-cultural variation, one can find extreme swings in attitudes towards toilet training within a society over a decade or so. Lieberman (1972) provides a fascinating survey of the advice given on toilet training over the period 1927 to 1964 in the American magazine *Parents*: in 1929, mothers were advised to begin bowel training within weeks of birth 'as soon as the umbilicus has healed' and to begin bladder training in the second half of the first year of life; several years later, in 1936, this earlier advice was being contradicted by advocating that training should be left until later within the first year, with the notion that children would more effectively train themselves when they were more ready; by 1940, *Parents* advised mothers to delay toilet training further until after the age of two years. By this time the influence of Freud was spreading and the supposed dangers of early or strict training were being stressed.

Thus, interpretation of results from surveys can only be made within the context of the situation in which the particular survey was taken. There is a need to replicate, with normal children, the method of data collection and type of study reported by Smith and Wong (1981).

5

The Roles of Maturation and Learning

Almost every healthy baby, boy or girl,
can be trained so that he or she will not
soil diapers after 8 weeks old.
Parents magazine (1929)

We can now move on to give more consideration to the roles of maturation and learning in the development of toilet training. We are not, of course, considering here the associated toileting skills (e.g. it is unlikely that the specific ability to flush a toilet is genetically encoded), but are considering only the basic ability of not soiling or wetting oneself and of voiding in a socially prescribed place. The terms 'development' or 'acquisition' of continence have been preferred here rather than the more usual term 'toilet training' as the latter implies a learning process.

Consideration of the respective roles of maturation and learning is not, however, without its difficulties. Few studies address themselves specifically to this question. Those that do tend to involve small numbers. Also, cognitive-mediated learning processes cannot be ruled out. Some survey-type studies using large numbers do address themselves to some extent to the role of 'training', but these tend to use less reliable, and often retrospective, parents' reports rather than direct observation.

Differing views can be found on the subject. For example, Bettison (1979) considers that 'the development of continence appears to be a maturational process for most people'. McKeith, Meadow and Turner (1973), on the other hand, are not so certain and '. . . consider it reasonable to accept the idea that training is important in the development of daytime dryness but look sympathetically at the idea that night-time dryness emerges spontaneously without teaching'. They also point out that 'there is ample opportunity for the child to learn daytime bladder control in the absence of any systematic attempts to potty train', that is to say that, even where potty 'training' is not carried out, the child may learn in other ways such as through imitation learning, latent learning, etc.

As with many other aspects of child development, the issue of whether continence is 'learned', or develops spontaneously as a process of natural maturation, or is the result of an interaction between the two, is a fundamental one.

ROLE OF MATURATION

Davis (1947) and Koluchova (1972) have looked at many aspects of development and learning in children reared in complete social isolation. Any evidence of rudimentary continence behaviour in the absence of toilet 'training' or opportunity for other forms of learning, such as imitation, modelling, latent learning, etc., would provide strong evidence for an innate development of continence. One of the aspects of behaviour, unfortunately little commented on, is that of toileting behaviour. Davis (1947) implies that proper toileting behaviour was established in one formerly isolated child after the child had been removed from isolation, but gives no further details. Koluchova (1972) comments that, following the removal of twins from their deprived and isolated situations 'there was evidence of considerable progress in habit formation'. Thus, such studies shed little light on this issue.

One piece of evidence purporting to support a maturational view of the development of continence in humans is contained in an interesting but little known paper by McGraw (1940), according to whom 'the proposition that sequential changes in behaviour and activities of the growing infant reflect different levels of neural organisation should meet with no serious objection'. McGraw carried out one of the very few longitudinal studies of the development of continence to be found in the literature. The subjects of her study were two sets of identical twin boys who attended a university nursery five days a week. One child from each pair of twins was placed on the pot every hour from the early months of its life and the other child in each pair was not 'potted' until considerably later. The percentage times that these children passed urine on the pot was recorded. The two set of twins were studied for 17 and 28 months respectively, and overall, the results indicate that hourly 'potting' from early in life had no appreciable effect, as the late-trained children showed similar success rates to their identical twins. McGraw interprets these data as showing an initial steady decline with the children least responsive between six and ten or eleven months. From there, there is a rapid improvement in both cases.

But when 'potting' at hourly intervals was introduced for the second child of one pair of twins at the age of about 14 months, that child's success rate was only 10 per cent below his brother's. Recording for that pair of twins was discontinued at this point. The early toileted child in the second pair of twins then showed a clear decrease in success rate. When he had improved substantially again around the second year of age his identical twin was then introduced to the pot and the success rate for the two was identical.

Two points are worth making here: first in two sets of identical twins, using direct observation and recording, there is no evidence that 'potting' from a very early age resulted in any 'training' or 'learning' early on; however, the fact that the second 'unpotted' twin of each pair showed similar success rates when introduced to the pot at a later age does not necessarily argue a strong case for maturation, as the second twin presumably could have learned through imitation, modelling etc.

However, these data are hard to explain using a *simple* mechanical learning view of toilet training. The evidence here is more consistent with the view that continence either develops spontaneously, given the opportunity, or through more complex learning processes mediated by cognitive processes. Indeed, McGraw does comment that the late trained twin in the second pair of twins did have the opportunity to previously 'observe other children urinate in a vessel'. She suggests that toilet training be delayed 'until the child's general behaviour indicates cortical participation in the act of micturition'. This seems sensible advice, but in the case of delayed continence it poses two problems. First, as McKeith *et al.* (1973) admit, 'we know of no way of finding out, in any child at any particular age, whether the CNS mechanisms for bladder control have matured'. Secondly, if we wait for some handicapped children to mature sufficiently before implementing training, we may wait forever. It is with developmentally delayed children that toilet training is such a major problem.

A study by Newson and Newson (1968) of large numbers of children by using questionnaires and rating scales yields results that must be interpreted in a similar manner (Tables 5.1 and 5.2).

All of the mothers in their early study (Newson and Newson 1963) who had started training by the age of 12 months were asked what success they had. Neither age at start of training nor ratings of progress in toilet training at an early age are significantly related to the situation at age four years. Newson and Newson (1968) conclude from these and other results that:

Table 5.1: Age toilet training started compared with outcome at age 4 years

Outcome	Age			
	0–2 months (*n* = 75)	3–8 months (*n* = 93)	9–12 months (*n* = 61)	12 + months (*n* = 46)
Reliable at 4 years	65	63	54	54
Residual toilet problem	35	37	46	46

Source: Newson and Newson 1968
Note: Data are per cent outcome. Differences not significant.

Table 5.2: Progress in toilet training at 12 months compared to reliability at 4 years

Outcome	Progress		
	Often successful at 12 months (*n* = 48)	Occcasionally successful at 12 months (*n* = 119)	Never successful at 12 months (*n* = 61)
Reliable at 4 years	58	61	64
Residual toilet problem	42	39	36

Source: Newson and Newson 1968
Note: Data are per cent outcome. Differences are not significant.

toilet training is one area where the mother can do what suits her in the short term, without worrying whether she is endlessly extending the long term process by her choice of an early or a late start . . . .. So long as they realise that they are choosing between here and now emphases on potting or on washing, without any built-in guarantee for the future, they may as well please themselves.

Some evidence of very slight effects of potty training on different aspects of the development of continence is presented in a study by Largo and Stutzle (1977b). Their subjects were grouped according to whether potty training was started between one and six months or between eight and twelve months (both rather early). The children were rated for overall bowel control and bladder control separately for day and night, both at twelve and eighteen months. Again their

Table 5.3: Age at beginning of toilet training in relation to degree of control at 1 and 1½ years. Group A = training period started between 1 and 6 months; Group B = training started between 6 and 12 months

Bowel/bladder control	Rating of Control					Significance
	0%	1–30%	30–70%	70–95%	100%	
Bowel control						
At 1 year						
Group A, $n=30$	1	1	3	9	16	$\chi^2 = 12.1$
Group B, $n=33$	7	5	5	10	6	$P = 0.05$
At 1½ years						
Group A, $n=51$	1	4	2	15	31	$\chi^2 = 5.0$
Group B, $n=49$	3	6	6	8	26	$P = 0.1$
Daytime bladder control						
At 1 year						
Group A, $n=30$	20	2	4	4	—	$\chi^2 = 4.9$
Group B, $n=33$	24	3	6	—	—	$P = 0.1$
At 1½ years						
Group A, $n=51$	27	10	5	2	7	$\chi^2 = 4.01$
Group B, $n=49$	37	7	5	7	3	$P = 0.1$
Night-time bladder control						
At 1 year						
Group A, $n=30$	28	2	—	—	—	$\chi^2 = 0.5$
Group B, $n=33$	32	1	—	—	—	$P = 0.1$
At 1½ years						
Group A, $n=51$	39	5	4	3	—	$\chi^2 = 4.4$
Group B, $n=49$	36	8	2	1	2	$P = 0.1$

Source: Largo and Stutzle 1977b

rating scale is in terms of: 0 per cent = no control; 1 to 30 per cent = partial control approximately one-third of time; 30 to 70 per cent = control during one-third to two-thirds of time; 70 to 95 per cent = total control except for a few lapses; 100 per cent = total control. The results are presented in Table 5.3. At the age of one year, the first group showed a significantly higher degree of bowel control than those in the second group, but this difference had disappeared by the age of eighteen months. There was no difference between the two groups either at twelve or eighteen months in bladder control by day or night. Largo and Stutzle (1977b) conclude that 'whether a child is put on the pot at the beginning or at the end of his first year, there is merely a short-term difference for bowel control and none at all for bladder control by day and at night'. On the face of it, although a slight effect of training may be occurring here, this would hardly seem to constitute strong evidence for a major role for learning in toilet training. On the other hand, firstly, it is likely that the 'training' procedures used by most parents are relatively weak in learning theory terms, and secondly, one cannot rule out learning such as imitation learning in the supposedly 'untrained' children. As can be seen from the later presented studies on the role of learning, those in which clearly specified, consistently applied, operant techniques are used show clear evidence of training effects compared to those where 'potty training' or 'habit training' is referred to in a vague sort of way. Thus, although those studies presented above tend to support a maturational view, the possibility that continence can be learned cannot be negated due to weaknesses in the studies.

Kolvin and Taunch (1973), in a discussion of the main theoretical issues underlying the problem of nocturnal enuresis, summarise the evidence for a maturational view of that disorder. This includes:

1. The half bell-shaped appearance of the age prevalence curve, indicating that age is the crucial factor in achieving night-time dryness.
2. The strong tendency to spontaneous improvement.
3. The evidence that genetic factors influence the age of becoming nocturnally dry.
4. The evidence of immaturity of bedwetters, e.g. low birth weight, etc.
5. Sex differences.

The same sorts of evidence and arguments can be applied to daytime wetting. Weir (1982) takes a similar view from his study of 700 three-year-olds. He found that male sex, presence of night wetting, presence of daytime soiling, low general developmental score, poor language development and the presence of behaviour problems were all associated with daytime wetting, although body size and low-birth-weight were not. Conversely, environmental factors such as social class, housing conditions, single parent families, family size, general health, various measures of stress, social contacts and sibling relationships were not associated with daytime wetting.

Overall, Weir (1982) considers the development of continence to be 'largely implemented by maturational factors'. However, the interpretation of such evidence, such as that on sex differences and genetic factors, is complex (Rutter 1973): for example, there is evidence that parents have earlier expectancies of the appearance of continence in girls (Stehbens and Silber 1971). Also, certainly with respect to nocturnal enuresis, there is considerable disagreement as to factors of possible aetiological significance, with some purporting to show evidence of delayed maturation and others not.

ROLE OF LEARNING

We shall now look at what evidence does exist for the learning of daytime continence.

Clark Hull (Hull and Hull 1919) was the first to take a learning view of bladder control and an interest in 'systematic studies of the learning processes concerned with urinary control'. Although their conclusions are the exact opposite of those of McGraw (1940), the Hulls' (1919) report is the only other longitudinal study of acquisition of bladder control in the literature. The subject of their study was female and the data presented covered the eleventh to the thirty-second month of life. The child was potted regularly from the end of the eighth month and percentage successful elimination was recorded. The Hulls' method of determining success rate is some-what idiosyncratic but probably does not affect the overall picture. Their interpretation of their data is that:

the general shape of the curve proves to be that of the familiar learning curves for skill and for the simpler mental processes, rising more rapidly at the beginning of the learning process and continuing progressively slower as the score approaches the limit of perfection.

The overall picture is not too dissimilar to that reported by McGraw, who, with additional evidence of identical twin controls, places a wholly maturational interpretation on such data. In discussing their data further, the Hulls contend that 'its most striking characteristic is the pronounced plateau beginning at the eighteenth four-week period and continuing without perceptible improvement throughout nine lunar months'. In the data presented by McGraw (1940) a marked regression rather than a plateau is apparent at a similar period and is commented on. The Hulls propose that a 'plausible explanation is suggested by the fact that the difficult early stages of talking coincide exactly with the beginning of this plateau. It is possible that learning to talk has in this case interfered with the acquisition of voluntary control of the bladder.' In fact, one might rather have expected the opposite to be true: that cognitive and linguistic factors should facilitate rather than inhibit the acquisition of continence (especially if one takes a learning standpoint).

Several years after the Hulls' (1919) paper, Bott et al. (1928) took the first explicit learning theory approach to the treatment of both day and night-time enuresis in children. Although inadequate data are presented, their discussion of the issues involved is particularly appropriate. They consider that 'the plateaux in the learning curve of bladder control present all the obstacles toward sustained effort on the part of the subject that characterise other types of learning'. Surprisingly, they continue by stating that:

knowledge of even the most elementary facts concerning the normal learning process has not yet, unfortunately, been grasped by the general public and until such facts become incorporated into the body of common knowledge, child training . . . must proceed . . . at least as best it may.

It is sobering to realise that such a statement was made over 50 years ago. Applied psychologists still have considerable difficulty in stressing to those directly involved in dealing with childhood problems the need to appreciate the continuing nature of a learning curve, as opposed to expectance of sudden changes in level of behaviour. Such a statement must surely have been over-optimistic at a time when learning theories were in their infancy and when psychoanalytical influences on views of child development had not even reached their peak. The Hulls' paper thus remains an historical oasis. Learning theory applications to daytime toilet training did not reappear in the literature until the mid-sixties, although applications of a conditioning approach to nocturnal enuresis began appearing in 1938 (Mowrer and Mowrer).

Brazelton's (1962) much praised paper (see Kolvin *et al.* 1973) stresses various practical and plausible factors in training of children. His view is that 'there is little innate in the child that leads him to want to be clean and dry, it (toilet training) must be understood as a kind of compliance to external pressure'. Brazelton provided all of the parents of young children in his paediatric practice with fatherly, reassuring advice on toilet training and his 16 (1.4 per cent) out of 1170 children with residual toilet problems at age five years is considered inspirational. Unfortunately, his study is uncontrolled and one suspects his population is predominantly middle class. Social class differences in prevalence of nocturnal enuresis, at least, are well established (Newson and Newson 1968; Kolvin *et al.* 1973).

A number of single case studies with young children who were systematically rewarded for passing urine when placed on the pot were published around the same time as Brazelton's report (Pumroy and Pumroy 1965; Peterson and London 1965; Madsen 1965). Where data are presented (Pumroy and Pumroy 1965), they are indeed reminiscent of learning curves and all of the authors conclude that continence may be trained speedily by means of appropriate reinforcement procedures. Clearly, without proper controls these single case studies, although suggestive, are not methodologically satisfactory, as continence may have developed spontaneously and coincidentally.

A more methodologically satisfactory single case study of a seventeen-month-old girl was carried out a few years later by Brown and Brown (1974) using a multiple-phase design varying the contingency of the reinforcement. The systematic nature of their training programme and their reinforcement procedures was enhanced by the use of a pants alarm to detect wetting accidents. During the baseline period, the child was reinforced for indicating the need to go to the toilet, was not prompted to toilet and was reinforced substantially for urinating on her potty chair. She was never reinforced for anything associated with a wetting accident. During the reversal period the child was reinforced periodically throughout the day, but never in association with signalling the need to go to the toilet nor for passing urine on her toilet. Prompts to toilet every two hours were reimplemented as during the baseline. Following reversal, the reinforcement procedures were reinstated as before. Brown and Brown (1974) present their percentage success rate in terms of number of signalled eliminations in the toilet divided by the total of the signalled and unsignalled eliminations together with the number of wetting accidents.

In this case, bladder control is closely related to reinforcement. The relatively rapid changes in behaviour coinciding with the presence or absence of contingent reinforcement would seem to establish a stronger case for 'habit training than . . . (others are) willing to entertain'.

Probably the best experimental study of toilet training with 'normal' children that has been published is that of Madsen *et al.* (1969), who carried out a controlled comparison of different methods of toilet training normal children. The study was experimental in that variables were manipulated. Also highly specific, practical details, more often associated with later behaviour modification manuals, are given. Also, the study was not designed to train children completely to pre-set criteria, but rather to assess the effectiveness of different techniques over a set training period. The study was conducted over a one-week baseline period followed by four weeks' training and then one week post-training. Results are presented simply for pre- and post-training successful urination and wetting accident rates.

There were five different groups of children:

1. A maturational control group ($n=15$). Mothers in this group were instructed to carry out no training whatsoever during the four week period.
2. A parents' method control group ($n=13$). Mothers in this group were asked to attempt to train their children using whatever procedures they would have used normally.
3. A reinforcement schedule group ($n=16$). Parents were instructed in the contingent use of rewards. Time spent sitting on the potty was increased using 'shaping' procedures, and mothers were instructed on how to handle negative reactions and how to punish accidents. Instructions were set down explicitly in an eleven-page booklet, which the parents used as guidelines for the programme.
4. A pants alarm group ($n=14$). Mothers were provided with miniature urine alarms that sounded when the child had a wetting accident. Mothers took the child to the toilet as quickly as possible when the child had a wetting accident, but otherwise used their normal training methods.
5. Pants alarm plus reinforcement schedule group ($n=12$). Both

the preceding experimental methods were combined for this group.

The children were classified into four age groups. Table 5.4 summarises the outcome of analyses of variance by age and method of training for decrease in accidents and increase in successful passing urine on toilet. The main effects of age and method of training are all significant. Individual tests applied to the differences between individual methods, showed that, overall, the two reinforcement groups (groups 3 and 5) were significantly different from the other three groups (maturation control, parents methods and pants alarm alone), but were not significantly different from each other. The three experimental groups (3, 4, and 5) did not differ from each other in decrease in rates of wetting accidents but were significantly more effective than the two control groups (maturational and parents methods).

Table 5.4: Analysis of variance summary for decreases in accidents and increases in success

Outcome	df	f	P
Decreases in accidents			
Training methods (A)	4	9.83	0.01
Age of child (B)	3	5.77	0.01
Interaction (A × B)	12	1.74	n.s.
Increases in success			
Training methods (A)	4	4.99	0.01
Age of child (B)	3	5.93	0.01
Interactions (A × B)	12	1.00	n.s.

Source: Madsen *et al.* 1969
From 'Comparisons of Toilet Training Techniques' by C.H. Madsen, Jr., M. Hoffman, D.R. Thomas, E. Koropsak and C.K. Madsen. In D.M. Gelfand (Ed), *Social Learning in Childhood: Readings in Theory and Application.* Copyright © 1969 by Wadsworth Publishing Company Inc. Reprinted by permission of Brooks/Cole Publishing Company, Monterey, California.

There was a significant age effect throughout, with the older children improving more than the younger children, but there was no age × method interaction effect. Theoretically this is quite important, as it means that the experimental training methods were effective across all the age levels, which one would not predict from a maturational viewpoint, although they were more effective with older children.

In additition to these studies of toilet training, there have been a number of further single case reports which, through demonstrating immediate change in continence associated with the introduction of contingent reinforcement, purport to support the view that toilet 'training' is indeed the appropriate term (e.g. Bach and Moylan 1975; Lal and Lindsley 1968). However, these reports do not provide non-treatment controls nor make use of reversal designs, so they contribute little more to the question of maturation versus learning in the development of continence.

Without doubt the most widely known report on toilet training is that of Foxx and Azrin (1973b). Foxx and Axrin take the most explicit operant approach to daytime training of normal children and claim incredible success in data presented for 34 children. Very detailed procedures for their training method are described in the associated training manual (Azrin and Foxx 1974), which has also been published as a paperback aimed at the popular market. These procedures are based on their earlier work in mental handicap, which will be discussed more fully later. Only a brief outline of the main features of their procedures will be given here. The training programmes are intensive with a one-to-one trainer–child ratio. In summarising their approach, Foxx and Azrin (1973b) list 16 other features:

1. A distraction-free environment.
2. Increased frequency of urination by increased fluid intake.
3. Continuous practice and reinforcement of the necessary dressing skills.
4. Continuous practice and reinforcement in approaching the toilet.
5. Detailed and continuous instruction for each act required in toileting.
6. Gradual elimination of the need for reminders to toilet.
7. Immediate detection of acccidents.
8. A period of required practice in toilet approach after accidents.
9. Negative reinforcement for the accident.
10. Immediate detection of correct toileting.
11. Immediate reinforcement for correct toiletings.
12. A multiple reinforcement system including imagined social benefits as well as praise, hugging and sweets.
13. Continuing reinforcement for having dry pants.
14. Learning by imitation.
15. Gradual reduction of the need for reinforcement.
16. Post-training attention to cleanliness.

Foxx and Azrin's conclusions are quite exceptional:

> All 34 children were trained in an average of 4 hours; children over 26 months old required an average of 2 hours training. After training, accidents decreased to a near zero level and remained near zero during 4 months follow-up. The results suggested that virtually all healthy children who have reached 20 months of age can be toilet trained within a few hours.

At face value, Foxx and Azrin's results are most impressive. The fact that there was no control group would hardly seem important as, with a mean age of 25 months (range 20 to 36 months), they could not all have been expected to achieve spontaneous continence immediately. However, a note of caution is necessary. The way in which Foxx and Azrin present supportive data leaves something to be desired. The length of the baseline period is not stipulated nor the way in which the baseline rate was established or estimated. They present an unusual graph and it is initially difficult to establish exactly what it represents. Mean wetting accident rate is presented for the whole group for the baseline period. This is followed by a gap in the data for the training period, before the post-training data are illustrated. The graph gives the initial impression of being a continuous one — it is not. They also claim in their manual (Azrin and Foxx 1974) that they tested their training package with about 200 children but only formally recorded data on 34. It is a great pity that the opportunity to study data from such a large sample was lost. Also, the data for children during the training period itself would be of considerable interest in order to look at the pattern of acquisition of these skills. The impression one gains from Foxx and Azrin's work is that of a change in level of behaviour, rather than change in trend, which would seem to be less in keeping with a learning theory viewpoint.

Azrin and Foxx (1974) contend that their manual alone is sufficient to provide parents with an extremely rapid procedure for toilet training their child, virtually all in one go. Larger scale replication of their work is required. Matson (1975) reports that, in using their manual with parents of six children, some problems did arise, although the training was basically successful. 'Emotional outbreaks' and temper tantrums were not uncommon as an initial response to the training situation, and some mothers did have difficulty with these when using the guidelines in the manual alone. Extra help and advice was necessary for these mothers. The training period ranged from six to fifteen hours as opposed to the average of four hours reported by Foxx and Azrin.

Numerous reports of parents who had failed to toilet train their own children when using the book alone was one reason that prompted Butler (1976a) to provide considerable emotional support to parents using Foxx and Azrin's methods. He organised a series of three classes for parents in addition to required reading of the manual by the parents. The parents then each selected a training day for their child and Butler supported them by means of a telephone call on that day and on each day for the following two weeks. Support by telephone was than given once a week for eight weeks. Although some parents had difficulties in discontinuing the prompts at the appropriate time and in use of 'positive practice' procedures for wetting accidents, Butler reports that 77 per cent of 49 parents were able to successfully train their children. One has to conclude from the more detailed data provided by Butler that, although there are misgivings about the evangelical manner in which the original claims were put forward, this study does provide quite substantial support for the claims of Foxx and Azrin, provided there is quite substantial support for the parents. An attempt to separate the effects of the book alone from other variables in the training situation has been made by Matson and Ollendick (1977). They compared two groups of five children (aged 20 to 26 months), the first of whom was left to use the manual alone as their basis for training while the second was provided with additional training and support. The parents in the first group fared worse than the parents in the second group. Only one child was successfully trained by a mother in the first group, compared with four or five in the second group. Again, Matson and Ollendick comment that the mothers using the book alone experienced considerable difficulties in coping with the apparently almost inevitable temper tantrums that occurred during training.

PHYSIOLOGICAL EVIDENCE

Jones (1956), in an early study, reports using feedback to treat a case of frequency micturition due to anxiety in an adult psychiatric patient. The urge to pass urine was associated with a rather low bladder pressure and so bladder pressure was directly fed back to the subject to establish the association. Subsequently, the readings on the manometer were falsified so that gradually increased amounts of urine could collect in the bladder without the corresponding increase in pressure being seen by the patient. In this way she was taught to hold larger volumes of urine. More recent studies utilising biofeedback will be discussed later in this book.

In the rhesus monkey there is clear evidence that discrimination of both bladder and bowel pressure *can* be learned. A little-known but important series of studies has been carried out by Slucki, Adam and Porter (1965), Slucki, McCoy and Porter (1969), Soldoff (1971) and Soldoff and Slucki (1974), mainly to study one aspect of visceral stimulus functions and general psychophysiological processes, Slucki *et al.* (1965, 1969) have provided a useful methodology for studying the development of continence and related behaviours in animals and their results have important implications.

Briefly, they catheterised the bladders of rhesus monkeys and controlled the volumes of urine, or its equivalent in saline solution, in the bladder. They then used the interoceptive stimulus of fluid in the bladder as a discriminative stimulus for a bar-pressing task. It was found, first, that bladder distension can be used as a discriminative stimulus in a learning task using edible reinforcers. This is important as there are constraints on what kinds of behaviours can be learned in different reinforcement situations (e.g. Seligman 1970; Shettleworth 1972); for example, dogs cannot be conditioned to yawn using edible reinforcers. Secondly, it was found that after attempts to teach discrimination of small volumes had failed success was more easily established at a higher volume and then generalised to successful discrimination of smaller volumes and differences. Thirdly, under reversal learning conditions, with the monkey now being reinforced under a bladder-empty condition instead of bladder-full, it transpired that the important feature in discrimination was stimulus onset: the rhesus monkeys did not discriminate stimulus offset well in either condition and overshot markedly with their bar pressing. This seems to be a general characteristic of visceral stimulation. This effect was also recorded on internally implanted EEG electrodes placed in the reticular formation, midbrain and cortex: the stimulus onset could be picked out clearly on the EEG trace, but the stimulus offset could not. Thus, both behavioural and physiological evidence were in accordance and any explanation must be proffered at physiological level. One practical implication of this is that, in toilet training, reinforcement should be contingent upon initiation of the urine stream and not its termination. Overall, this work obviously does not demonstrate conclusively that bladder control is necessarily normally learned, but it is an unequivocal and objective demonstration that a form of bladder function can be learned in an advanced species.

The use of what effectively constitutes a biofeedback device for pressure in the bowel in humans was first reported by Kohlenberg (1973). The subject was a 13-year-old boy who had had a section of his colon surgically removed as he suffered from Hirschsprung's disease (incomplete innervation of the colon). He had been a continuous soiler throughout his life and a colostomy was being contemplated. A balloon was inserted into the lower end of the bowel. This was fixed to the end of a catheter which allowed the balloon to be inflated from outside and the internal pressure also measured. The resting pressure in the colon, caused by small random fluctuations in muscle tension in the wall of the colon, was measured over a baseline period. Thereafter he was reinforced contingent upon fluctuations in pressure level. Kohlenberg (1973) demonstrated clearly that the 'pressure changes were a function of the reinforcement schedule' and that the resting pressure tended to increase throughout the study. In a larger study of six patients (five adults and one child) with evidence of organic impairment of anal sphincter control, Engel, Nikoomanesh and Schuster (1974) used similar procedures to bring retrosphincter responses under voluntary control. During the study all of these patients showed 'objective evidence of learned sphincteric control'.

Thus, these studies on bowel training demonstrate that this aspect of continence can be brought under learned control, and Soldoff and Slucki (1974) showed the same to be true for both bladder and bowel in the rhesus monkey. Studies of biofeedback will be further discussed later on.

Finally, the highest degree of voluntary control of visceral functions in humans that has ever been claimed was exercised in a music hall act by Le Petomane in Paris during the period 1892–1900 (Nohain and Caradec 1967). Le Petomane, described as 'an extraordinary case of rectal breathing and of musical anus', could reputedly intake a large amount of air into the lower end of the bowel and then control its expulsion to such an extent that 'when the gas comes out with enough force and with a certain degree of tension from the sphincter, noises are produced of intensity, timbre and great variety'!

A ROLE FOR BOTH MATURATION AND LEARNING

Having reviewed the empirical evidence in favour of both maturational and learning views of the acquisition of daytime continence, we can see that it is possible to cite evidence in support of either view.

In particular, the survey-type studies (Newson and Newson 1968; Largo and Stutzle 1977b) seem to indicate that whatever method one uses at whatever age or whether one uses no method at all does not seem to make much difference to the end result. This, on the face of it, would seem to provide support for a maturational view, as would the study by McGraw (1940). However, even when no explicit training is used, one cannot rule out other forms of learning. On the other hand, the evidence of social and cultural effects on age of acquisition of continence and studies such as those of Madsen *et al.* (1969), Brown and Brown (1974) and Kohlenberg (1973), constitute strong evidence that the processes of continence can be manipulated by environmental factors.

What is apparent from these different studies, therefore, is that when a learning approach to toilet training is clearly specified and there is evidence of consistency and immediate contingent reinforcement, then effects of learning are reported. One such study (Madsen *et al.* 1969) showed that children reinforced during training did significantly better than the maturational control groups and the children trained by parents' own methods. Conversely, it is curious that when training procedures are simply not detailed at all, the results of such studies tend to show no evidence of 'learning'. For example, in the studies of McGraw (1940), Newson and Newson (1968) and Largo and Stutzle (1976), there were no details available of the supposed training methods: in McGraw's study, no mention is made of the use of reinforcement, just regular potting; in the studies of Newson and Newson (1968) and Largo and Stutzle (1976) the parents were left to use their 'common sense' methods.

In fact, it is all too often impossible to extract the sort of information, such as the application of a consistent theoretical framework, contingencies and schedules of reinforcement, the roles of cognition, language, modelling and imitation and so on, that is relevant to the issue of whether 'training' has any specific effect. This is because the literature on toilet training is swamped by the pervading psychoanalytical views of 'coercive' versus 'permissive' training, almost to the exclusion of other possibly important factors in training.

In such studies, 'coercive' versus 'permissive' are implicitly equated with 'early training' versus 'late start to training'; even some of the better studies, such as that of Newson and Newson (1968), seem to have been influenced by this, judging by the question mothers were asked about the age at which toilet training was begun. Some people might intuitively feel that training procedures based explicitly on an operant conditioning approach must necessarily be classed as 'strict' or 'coercive'. This is not the case: the important factor in operant procedures is consistency and it is quite possible to be consistent without being punitive.

So what may we conclude and how may we reconcile the apparently conflicting views? At face value, the most plausible proposition is that many children do 'learn' to be continent by day, but that this process would normally develop spontaneously anyway, simply being accelerated by learning. We would propose, as usual, that both maturation and learning are necessary to the development of daytime continence.

The question for most parents is whether or not it is worth the trouble of implementing an overt, clear, structured training programme when the child's cognitive, linguistic and imitation abilities will largely obviate this need later on.

THE CONCEPT OF SENSITIVE PERIODS

As has been stated previously, the existence of rudimentary continence behaviour in formerly isolated children would provide strong evidence for the role of maturation in the development of continence. The converse, however, would not necessarily be the case. There might be a 'sensitive' period for the emergence of daytime continence. Such a period could depend on maturational factors, but if at that time the appropriate environmental factors did not come into play, then continence might fail to emerge. McKeith, Meadow and Turner (1973) have argued for a 'sensitive' period in the development of nocturnal dryness, between the second and fourth years. Such a concept would tend to argue a role for both maturational and learning factors.

In future studies of the roles of learning and maturation in the development of continence, the methods of experimental design used by Madsen et al. (1969), observation of behaviour by Fielding, Berg and Bell (1978) and study of bladder function by Smith and Wong (1981) would be more fruitfully followed, rather than simply asking questions regarding those ill-formulated notions of late/early, coercive/lax coercive training.

6

Specific Factors in Toilet Training

The severely mentally handicapped (formerly
idiots) are wholly dependent. They cannot be
taught to keep themselves clean . . . nor communicate
. . .. In practice they are less intelligent than
domestic animals.

> Stafford-Clark and Smith 1978

Toilet-training methods have been specified most clearly in the field
of mental handicap, where delayed continence is one of the biggest
problems encountered. In this section, we shall review the
emergence of the key features of current toilet-training programmes.
There are now in excess of fifty reports over the last twenty years
that present some form of data on toilet training mentally handicapped people. The nature and quality of these studies varies
greatly, but there would be little to gain by presenting an annotated
bibliography that catalogued their main conclusions and deficien-
cies. Instead, we shall draw out the main features and themes that
have emerged and combined to form the basis of current toilet training practices. These include the use of operant learning theory as a
training framework, questions of effectiveness, problems of
maintenance and generalisation of results, the use of regular toileting
versus 'timing' approaches to training, the use of punishment
procedures, the use of equipment and group versus individual training. Fluid intake will be considered separately.

THE USE OF OPERANT CONDITIONING TECHNIQUES AS A TRAINING FRAMEWORK

Recent reviews of literature on behaviour modification approaches
to toilet training in mental handicap contrast sharply with the asser-
tion quoted above from Stafford-Clark (Bettison 1980; McCartney
and Holden 1981; Wilson 1980). We shall now look more directly
at the evidence from studies of toilet-training programmes.

As noted earlier, Ellis (1963) formulated the issue in S–R terms. His theoretical model stimulated a number of studies on toilet training, judging by the frequency with which he is cited in reports in the following years. From this point on, virtually all reports of daytime toilet training in mental handicap have been carried out within an operant or an S–R framework, with perhaps just one exception (Edgar, Kohler and Hardman 1975).

Apart from a few brief and unsatisfactory reports (e.g. Morris 1957; McMillan 1961), the first study worthy of serious consideration was that of Blackwood (1962), who first specified and discussed operant conditioning as a framework for daytime toilet training:

> The attendants were instructed as follows — at ninety minute intervals throughout the day, they were to walk through the ward and observe each member of the experimental group successively. If, when observed the subject was emitting one of the six classes of behaviour under study, he was to be ignored. However, if the subject was observed to be emitting any other response, he was to be reinforced. The assumption was that this would increase the strength of any existing responses competing with the undesirable responses.

This is the only report that includes a control group where no difference was found between experimental and control groups: analysis of variance on data recorded before and after an eight-week treatment period showed no difference between thirteen experimental and fifteen control subjects for behaviours including wetting and soiling. With the benefit of hindsight, current practitioners would find this hardly surprising. The training methods would be regarded as too crude and naive to have any impact and, indeed, it would not be accepted today as a true operant study because of this. No mention is made of reinforcement of other appropriate toilet behaviours nor of any toileting schedule. However, this study is of historical interest as it was the first to take a planned operant approach and the standard of evaluation was well ahead of its time.

The first to report systematic reinforcement for use of the toilet was Dayan (1964). The twenty-five boys in the ward concerned were toileted at regular, two-hourly intervals and not at the times wetting accidents were thought likely to occur, as was central to Ellis' argument (this issue of 'regular toileting' versus 'timing' will be discussed shortly). Baumeister and Klosowski's (1965) study remains of interest, including their discussion of the practical problems following their attempts to train eleven profoundly mentally handicapped males over a seven-week period. They isolated their trainees in a group in a dormitory and reinforced 'hits' while sitting on commodes. Both Dayan (1964) and Baumeister and Klosowski (1965) report improvement in continence as do subsequent reports. For example, Miron (1966) and Yoder (1966) carried out operant toilet training procedures on a larger scale with groups of severely and profoundly mentally handicapped people and report overall reductions in incontinence rates.

Hundziak, Maurer and Watson (1965) compared a small group of children using contingent reinforcement for eliminating on the toilet during training, a group using more routine non-reinforcement training methods and a group of children receiving no form of training at all. They found significant differences in favour of the experimental group in terms of elimination on the toilet.

Other controlled studies in which operant techniques were found to have an effect include Tierney (1973, 1976) and Kimbrell et al. (1967). Tierney compared eighteen profoundly mentally handicapped trainees on an operant toilet training programme with eighteen controls on the same hospital ward. Evaluation was carried out using rating scales and direct recording with respect to different aspects of continence. Of the eighteen residents in the experimental group, fourteen 'displayed a reduction of incontinence and the acquisition of varying continence and toilet behaviour', whereas 'the control group showed minimal improvement in the area of toilet behaviour'. Kimbrell et al. (1967) carried out an operant toilet training programme, in conjunction with providing a generally 'enriched programme', for 20 severely and profoundly mentally handicapped female trainees. They assessed the effects by using standardised and appropriately modified rating scales and compared them with similar assessment of 20 non-treated controls. Again the experimental group demonstrated considerable gains over the control group. Colwell et al. (1973) looked at improvement in forty-four children who had undergone operant toilet-training programmes. Although there was no actual non-treatment control group, they were able to compare the rated improvement obtained with the expected improvement during that period by using the age-related norms for the Catell Infant Intelligence Scale and found significantly greater improvement than would have been predicted.

Thus, although there is evidence that operant training is superior to no treatment, it should be additionally noted that Tierney (1976), Kimbrell et al. (1967) and Colwell et al. (1973) all found evidence of generalised, as well as specific, improvements. Anyone who implements an intervention project in an institution realises that there are many general changes that have to be made to the regular living situation which are not specific to the programme but which are necessary for it to operate effectively. These apparent generalised effects of training may in part be a function of this or they may be some form of response generalisation activated by the acquisition of a new skill. There have been no well-controlled studies to evaluate the effects of 'enrichment' alone on continence, but some studies have found that environmental factors such as improved accommodation, toilet facilities, etc., do effect improvements in continence (Shrubsole and Smith 1984; Duker 1983).

HOW EFFECTIVE IS THE TRAINING?

Having established that various operant toilet-training programmes can have an effect, the issue that now arises is how much effect do they have? The most widely known reports of Azrin and Foxx (1971), elaborated on in their manual (Foxx and Azrin 1973a), claim the greatest success. With nine profoundly mentally handicapped adults over a training period of median length four days, wetting accidents were reduced by 90 per cent. Similarly, the work of these authors with toilet training of normal children include the most rapid success rates (Foxx and Azrin 1973b, Azrin and Foxx 1974). Their studies with mentally handicapped subjects have no controls, their dramatic success apparently obviating the need for this, so the ensuing issue becomes one of replication. Foxx and Azrin's work stimulated many further reports, most of which have involved relatively small numbers (Barton 1975; Smith *et al*. 1975; Dixon and Smith 1976; Bettison *et al*. 1976; Butler 1976b; Singh 1976; Sadler and Merkert 1977; Trott 1977; Smith 1979a).

An attempt by Barton (1975) to train four profoundly mentally handicapped children who additionally suffered from severe epilepsy or behaviour problems, resulted in the overall conclusion that although 'the procedure was demanding of teachers' skills . . . (it) resulted in significant progress'. However, 'no child achieved complete dryness, though accidents were reduced to as few as one per week, one boy . . . showed a complete relapse. In all cases progress was erratic.' The period over which Barton reports improvement is in excess of several weeks.

Smith *et al.* (1975), in training five profoundly mentally handicapped adult males, found that whilst the frequency of self-initiated toileting had reached a peak by the second week of training, wetting accidents took several weeks to reduce by 84 per cent. Data from 13 cases were retrospectively analysed by Smith and Smith (1977). When the data were grouped, there were significant differences by chronological age and by 'social age'. An 80 per cent reduction in wetting accidents was obtained by the *younger* low social age trainees in 5 to 6 weeks; a comparable reduction took 8 to 9 weeks for the *older* low social age trainees. An 80 per cent reduction in wetting accidents occurred after around two weeks for the younger, *high* social age trainees, compared to six weeks for the younger, *low* social age trainees.

The report and discussion by Bettison *et al.* (1976) is of considerable interest. They provided intensive training over a four-week period for eight profoundly mentally handicapped trainees. Five of the eight showed substantial improvement within that period. Training with one 49-year-old woman was discontinued after five days because 'she was remarkably resistant to the programme and proved too difficult for the trainers to manage'. The remaining two trainees did not reach the required criterion of nine out of ten successive eliminations being self-initiated toiletings. One of these two individuals was trained for a further 21 days but did not improve further.

Without doubt the largest and one of the most impressive studies is that reported by Pfadt and Sternlicht (1980) and discussed further by Pfadt and Sullivan (1981), but which unfortunately is not widely disseminated. In a massive undertaking, 63 mentally handicapped residents entered their 'Continence Training Programme', which included a planned progression through the successive stages of intensive training, maintenance and long-term preservation.

The intensive phase of training involved the Foxx and Azrin training procedures aimed at establishing bladder control and independent, self-initiated toileting. The trainees left this phase after nine self-initiated toiletings occurred over two days, or four weeks' intensive training. Of the 63 trainees, eight failed to reach criterion in this time and 55 (87 per cent) proceeded to the next stage of maintenance. The aims of maintenance were first to maintain self-initiated toileting and reduce the frequency of toilet accidents and secondly to teach further toilet skills including washing hands and flushing toilet. Training here was under a 1:2 staff/trainee ratio. The trainees left this phase after:

maintaining self-initiated toileting and an accident rate of two or less per week over two consecutive weeks, and

essential toileting tasks were performed on command,
or
two months' training.

Of the 55 who entered maintenance, six were still on maintenance at the time Pfadt and Sternlicht reported, nine failed to reach the exit criterion successfully and 40 progressed to the 'preservation' phase.

The aim of preservation training was to prepare trainees to maintain their new skills in their long-term placements. Staffing ratios were 1:3 and instruction in yet further toilet-related skills were given. The trainees left this phase after:

two consecutive accident free weeks,
or
two months' training and an accident rate of one per week or less.

Of the 40 trainees who entered this stage, 31 left successfully. Thus, approximately 50 per cent of the trainees can be said to have become fully continent.

The single case studies using methods similar to Foxx and Azrin's (Butler 1976b; Singh 1976; Trott 1977) show similar findings to the above. There is also a thoroughly confusing paper by Sadler and Merkert (1977) involving fourteen severely and profoundly mentally handicapped children and three different training groups. This paper could well be of interest if it were presented in a form that could be readily understood.

From these reports following the work of Foxx and Azrin, a number of points are evident. The number of attempts at toilet training they have stimulated indicates that they have indeed provided a useful package. However, the time taken for training is considerably longer than in the original reports and there are reports of failure. Progress in training is not as smooth as implied and where data are presented during the training period, there is considerable fluctuation. There are other issues, too, such as relapse, which we will now consider in the remainder of this section.

LONG-TERM EFFECTS: PROBLEMS OF MAINTENANCE AND GENERALISATION

Strictly speaking, maintenance refers to the permanence of effects in the training situation, whereas generalisation concerns the spreading of effects across different situations.

Long-term follow up of the effects of training is justly considered to be an important issue and many of the studies of toilet training in mental handicap are deficient in this respect. Some of the conclusions by those who have tried to look at this are presented here.

These are two problems that arise with respect to follow-up data. One is that follow-up data need to be related clearly to the aims of the training programme. In some studies the aim of training is solely continence whilst in others it is both continence and independence at toilet. Yet data on follow-up are often only given with respect to frequency of incontinence. Notable exceptions include Bettison *et al.* (1976) and Pfadt and Sullivan (1981). The other is that the results of maintenance should be kept separate from the original, specific, experimental effects of the intervention procedures. It is possible to have a perfectly effective training procedure the effects of which are considerably reduced at a later date by environmental conditions. In fact, the further away from the intervention period, the less one is justified in claiming that performance at follow up is a function of the original intervention; it is more reasonable to presume that performance is maintained by contingencies in the intervening period. It is argued here that the effect of maintenance is a separate issue from the effects of the particular method of training.

Leath and Flournoy (1970) provide a three-year follow up on forty of the subjects of study of Kimbrell *et al.* (1967). In the intervening period there had been no further formal training. The results were quite straightforward: the initial gains reported had been maintained but there had been little further improvement. The effects of training here seem to be quite clear. On the other hand, when Baumeister and Klosowski (1965) suddenly discontinued their training programme and returned their trainees to the regular living situation, 'the effect was to practically erase the progress which had been made to that point'. Both Dayan (1964) and Yoder (1966) appear to have conducted training in the more regular living situation and they report that progress was maintained over an eleven-month follow-up period. As Bettison *et al.* (1976) have noted, in these instances it is possible that the same environmental conditions and contingencies were maintained to a greater or lesser extent during that period.

With more intensive programmes, Van Wagenen *et al.* (1969a and b) report successful maintenance for their nine children at follow-up of six to nine months. Azrin and Foxx (1971) report success in nine subjects over a 20-week follow-up period. Bettison *et al.* (1976) give more detail about follow-up for the Foxx and Azrin package and indicate that progress was substantially maintained over eight to eleven months after training. Foxx and Azrin (1973) emphasise the difficulties that can arise in this area by the detailed lists of procedures they directed towards maintenance. They implicitly acknowledge some of the problems of working in large mental handicap hospital settings by the large number of forms they produce that must be signed and countersigned at various levels of the hospital hierarchy, to try and ensure that simple procedures are carried out consistently by ward staff. Nevertheless, there can be occasions when, wittingly or unwittingly, some staff may perform in ways that are clearly not consistent with the maintenance of a newly acquired skill, such as shutting doors, use of ill-fitting clothing, prompting trainees to toilet. Those trainees who do maintain their progress sometimes seem to do so despite their conditions rather than because of them. The fullest discussions of the problems that arise in this area are provided by Pfadt and Sullivan (1981) and by Bettison (1982) and the importance of generalising training across settings has been illustrated recently by Dunlap, Koegel and Koegel (1985). The issue has also been discussed by Smith and Smith (1977).

FACTORS INFLUENCING EFFECTIVENESS OF TRAINING

Schedules of reinforcement and extinction

Although in animal studies it is typically found that the initial schedule of reinforcement does have an effect not only on rate of acquisition but also on later extinction, evidence for such effects in human studies is limited (e.g. Finley *et al.* 1973), possibly because in implementing programmes in practice it is often difficult to be sure exactly what reinforcement schedules are actually operating. There are no reports in the literature of objective evaluation of staff reliability in applying reinforcement schedules in training programmes, but reliability of equipment, a minor aspect of the overall issue here, was reported on by Smith (1977). In using a pants alarm to detect inappropriate urination during training, a record was kept of whether or not it operated properly on five children. With 194 wetting accidents, the alarm activated immediately on 179 or 89 per cent of occasions. A sophisticated intermittent or variable reinforcement schedule would no doubt be difficult to operate in a situation such as a daytime toilet-training programme.

Regular toileting versus 'timing' approaches to training

A method of classification using Ellis' (1963) S–R model was proposed earlier. This was based on the point at which a method of training initially enters the Ellis model. The prevailing view of bladder function, as we have seen, is one of evacuation of the contents when critical bladder pressure is reached (Ellis 1963; Yeates 1973). Under normal circumstances, bladder pressure is presumed to be proportional to volume in the bladder and rate of bladder filling. Methods of toilet training that intervene in the Ellis model at the stimulus of bladder distension are based on this view of bladder function. An example of this is where a child is toileted at the times of actual or predicted incontinence in an effort to associate bladder distension with the toilet. Such an approach may be regarded as a 'timing' approach. Conversely, the predicted times of full bladders may be ignored and the child toileted at regular, set intervals of time. This approach may be regarded as a 'regular toileting' approach and, in the Ellis model, intervention here occurs at the stimuli associated with the toilet.

The distinction can be readily discerned in many of the descriptions of toilet-training procedures in the literature. The best and clearest distinction comes between the methods of Foxx and Azrin (1971, 1973a and b), who use regular toileting, and Van Wagenen et al., (1969 a and b) and Mahoney, Van Wagenen and Meyerson (1971), who use a timing method. Further examples of studies that specify a 'regular toileting' approach to toilet training include Dayan (1964), Hundziak et al. (1965), Thompson and Grabowski (1972), Connolly and McGoldrick (1976) and Ando (1977), as well as those studies based on the work of Foxx and Azrin (Barton 1975; Smith et al. 1975; Dixon and Smith 1976; Bettison et al. 1976; Butler 1976a; Singh 1976; Sadler and Merkert 1977; Richmond 1983). Examples of studies that stress the importance of timing include Ellis (1963), Baumeister and Klosowski (1965), Yoder (1966), Kimbrell et al. (1967), Goldberg (1971), McNamara (1972), Waye and Melnyr (1973), Fewtrell (1973), Tierney (1973), Baroff (1974) and Litrownik (1974). Thus, 'timing' versus 'regular toileting' can be seen to constitute a major theoretical difference between methods of training within an operant framework. However, Smith (1979a) compared the effects of regular toileting versus timing approaches for five children in each group, and found no difference between the two in overall outcome. Some of the implications of this for models of bladder function are discussed by Smith and Wong (1981).

Problems of the timing approach

One feature of the timing approach is worthy of comment at this point. 'Timing' in training is usually arrived at by recording incontinence over a baseline period (sometimes rather a brief period) and determining any temporal pattern. The likely times of accidents are then used as the times for prompts to toilet. Despite the number of reports purporting to have used 'timing', no data have been presented anywhere of the validity of the procedure. There are clearly several problems here.

First, what statistical techniques should be used to determine times when accidents occur with significantly higher frequency in individual cases? There has been no discussion of this and it is not an easy issue to resolve. It is suspected that the main method used is visual inspection and there is therefore no guarantee that trainees are not simply being prompted at times of peak frequencies most easily accounted for by random variation.

Second, the problem of statistical vs clinical significance is particularly important here. Even if we can establish statistically significant times, what percentage of total accidents would this account for? It may be possible to establish only one or two significant times of the day, with a large number of accidents still unaccounted for. With a severely or profoundly mentally handicapped person with whom we are trying to establish an association, we should surely aim to present the association in as close to 100 per cent of trials as possible and not in a relatively low proportion of trials.

Third, the interval between checks that is used in baseline recording is important. The method of direct observation and recording of incontinence during baseline is usually interval recording, when the child is checked at set intervals (e.g. half-hourly or hourly) and whether he has dry or wet pants is recorded. This is not the same as event recording, when the event is recorded when it occurs. For interval recording it is therefore possible that more than one event could occur in the time interval. The main problem is that the accuracy of the timing method is dependent on the time interval used and timing to within an accuracy of half an hour may not be accurate enough. There is evidence that, as the bladder fills, bladder pressure suddenly rises very much more sharply with increase in volume (e.g. see Milne 1976). It is likely that it is the time period during which this phenomenon occurs that is of importance in determining the limits of timing.

Finally, the extent of individual variation in terms of whether temporal patterns of incontinence exist is uncertain. For example, temperature, fluid intake, etc., have not really been investigated with a view to increasing prediction. A few authors briefly mention the use of other cues that trainers have used to 'tell' when a child needs to go to the toilet. Again, no data have been presented nor investigations conducted to determine their validity. Too much rests on unsubstantiated clinical intuition. These comments apply to the majority of attempts to train by using timing methods. The exception to this is the work of Van Wagenen *et al.* (1969) and their later study (Mahoney, Van Wagenen and Meyerson 1971), in which baseline data are not used to determine times of incontinence, but rather attempts were made to teach the child to go to the toilet in response to the sound of an incontinence alarm at the time a wetting accident occurs. This approach neatly avoids all of these problems, but has not been used by any others, apart from a single case study by Litrownik (1974) and a small sample study included in the report of Smith (1979a).

The use of 'punishment' procedures

One difference between regular toileting and timing approaches is that the former lends itself to the use of punishment procedures more easily. The issue of punishment is not specific to behaviour modification programmes in mental handicap, but it is a controversial one and there is no escape from ethical questions. It is therefore important to be quite clear about the precise nature, purpose and effects of any punishing or 'deceleration' procedures used contingent upon incontinence. Studies that have reported using punishment procedures include Giles and Wolff (1966).

The procedures used by Giles and Wolff, although termed 'mildly aversive stimuli' by them, would not be regarded thus by others:

The aversive stimulus conditions include ignoring the subjects, terminating meals, attaching the subjects to the end of a ten foot rope, restraining the subjects in the crawl pen, allowing the subjects to remain in soiled clothing and placing the subjects in restraining jackets. These stimuli were modified for use with each individual.

Other advocates of the use of strong punishment procedures include Ando (1977) and Azrin and Foxx (1971). In training five children, Ando (1977) states that 'punishments for urinating outside the toilet, wetting pants on the floor, include . . . a couple of intense spanks on the buttocks . . .' Because of persistent difficulties with one child, however, 'we devised a special punishment for him. For three days, three times a day, and for ten minutes every time, we tied a plastic urine collecting bag round his urogenital organs'. Ando (1977) reports a good outcome for two children, a poor outcome for one child and some improvements for the remaining two.

Time-out from reward

Foxx and Azrin (1973) advocated 'time-out from reward' of up to one hour. While it is generally accepted in principle that 'time-out from reward' should be more effective than extinction, the theoretical basis of prolonged time-out periods must be questionable. In later papers this length of time-out period has been reduced. The effects of length of time-out period seem to be complex, but Hobbs and Forehand (1977), in reviewing evidence on very brief, moderate and lengthy time-out periods and on the effects of sequencing, present no evidence whereby it can be concluded straightforwardly that lengthy time-out periods are more effective.

Overcorrection

The 'overcorrection' component in the Foxx and Azrin (1973a and b) toilet-training package is chosen in particular by Pfadt and Sullivan as the component most in need of empirical investigation. Overcorrection in general has been reviewed a number of times (Judkins 1976; Murphy 1978; Tierney 1978; Axelrod, Brantner and Meddock 1978) and with respect to toilet training by Pfadt and Sullivan (1980). Overcorrection is a procedure developed by Foxx and Azrin (1973c) and Foxx and Martin (1975). Its precise theoretical basis seems rather uncertain, although it appears to be somewhere in the region of 'response cost'. The general rationale of the technique is (1) to educate the person to accept responsibility for his behaviour through restitutional, overcorrectional procedures that require him to restore that situation to a vastly improved state; and (2) to require the offender to practice appropriate modes of responding through positive-practice overcorrection procedures that require him to behave appropriately in the situations in which he normally misbehaves. In toilet training, this means briskly physically guiding the 'offender', through cleaning up the results of the incontinence, to restore the situation to better than it was originally and through repeated 'runs' to the toilet from the place of the accident. The procedure is claimed by Foxx to be a positive, educational, acceptable procedure. These claims are questionable. All of the reviews of the procedure cited above raise considerable problems with its use and urge caution. The use of this procedure with profoundly mentally handicapped trainees who cannot follow verbal instructions requires a high degree of physical guidance. As trainees do not often wish to comply, the necessary degree of physical guidance can be considered unacceptable (Smith *et al.* 1975). The procedure is exhausting for staff and would appear to be aversive to trainees. There seems little to commend it as a substitute for aversive procedures. More recently, Foxx (1977, 1982) has accepted that overcorrection has an aversive component and that ethical issues do have to be considered. Clearer evidence on the precise role of punishment in toilet training programmes is required. Certainly, the results of Ando (1977) are not impressive when compared with the results of Tierney (1973), who used only extinction.

EQUIPMENT

The use of equipment has been a prominent feature of toilet-training packages in recent years. There are two main types of equipment: the pants alarm and the toilet bowl alarm. The pants alarm is a small portable electronic alarm that signals the onset of incontinence and the toilet bowl alarm is a device attached to the toilet that signals when urine is passed in the appropriate place. The purpose of both these types of equipment is to aid immediate and consistent detection of the passing of urine, thus increasing effectiveness of rewards and/or punishments contingent upon continent or incontinent urinary events. That such equipment serves this purpose indeed seems likely, but again there has been no direct empirical study of the precise effect of the presence or absence of equipment in an overall training package. Commercially available alarms are catalogued by the Association of Continence Advisors (1986).

Pants alarms

Pants alarms for daytime toilet training are essentially miniature portable versions of the bell and pad apparatus widely used in the treatment of bedwetting. The first pants alarm for use in daytime toilet training was used by Van Wagenen and Murdoch (1966). A flurry of reports appeared in the literature in the early- and mid-70s giving the technical details for pants alarms. The practical issues in the use of a number of commercially available pants alarms available in the UK are outlined by Smith (1977). They do require a high degree of supervision in use — it is not possible to attach them to mentally handicapped children or adults and let them roam freely. Minor breakdowns are common, the electrode systems for detecting urine in the pants being most vulnerable. A more sophisticated development of the pants alarm, with a modification so that the alarm can be operated by radio control, has been described by Mahoney *et al.* (1971). However, the outcome of a small trial involving a comparison of different methods of training, one of which included such a device, does not encourage the use of such complex alarm systems (Smith 1979a).

The only experimental attempt to validate the use of a pants alarm is included in the study by Madsen *et al.* (1969) with normal children, previously described. Although there were trends in the right direction, with the reinforcement-plus-pants-alarm group showing most improvement, these differences did not reach significance.

Toilet bowl alarms

As has been said, the correct use of a pants alarm requires some practice and the close supervision of the trainee. On the other hand, the correct use of the toilet bowl alarm is quite straightforward.

The toilet bowl alarm is an electrical device that signals the instant continent urine is passed into the toilet. There are far more journal articles describing pants alarms than bowl alarms, and there are far more commercially manufactured pants alarms available than toilet bowl alarms. This seems to imply an unfortunate interest in the negative rather than in the positive side of toilet training. A toilet bowl alarm can be useful in detecting the passing of urine on the toilet, as such detection is otherwise unreliable, particularly in school or hospital settings where toilet areas are often noisy. Such an alarm avoids the undignified and unreliable procedure of peering and listening, hoping to see or hear when the trainee passes urine. More importantly, some trainees pass as little as two or three millilitres of urine at times during training and this is difficult to detect without an alarm. Toilet bowl alarms designed to aid parents train small children have been developed in the form of musical potties. The first toilet bowl alarm was described by Watson (1967), although there appear to have been a number of problems in using his system. Azrin, Bugle and O'Brien (1971) and Foxx and Azrin (1973a and b) outlined the type of alarm that has become more widely used, and further discussion and detail are provided by Smith (1977), Yonovitz and Michaels (1977) and Bettison (1982). There has been no empirical investigation of how much the immediacy and consistency of reinforcement is improved by a toilet bowl alarm over a no-bowl alarm condition, nor has there been any controlled comparison of the effectiveness of a bowl alarm in a training programme. It is our subjective opinion, however, that the proper use of a bowl alarm is of more value than a pants alarm. Passman (1975) has described a further development of the standard bowl alarm by the attachment of a dispenser to deliver small edible reinforcers mechanically.

Although these alarms aid immediate and consistent passing of continent or incontinent urine, such equipment does not, on its own, perform any training of the trainee.

Other types of equipment

As described in other chapters, equipment has been used more directly in a biofeedback manner (Jones 1956; Kohlenberg 1973; Engel et al. 1974). Further, Vincent (1964), following anatomical study of the bladder, has devised a device for inhibiting micturition that may deserve some further attention. He developed a device to apply pressure to the perineal muscles, consisting of a shaped balloon held in place against the perineum. When urinary incontinence occurs or is about to occur, the balloon can be inflated by a small rubber hand bulb and hence pressure applied to the perineum, which is said to inhibit micturition. This device is reported to have been used by individuals who can independently operate it, but it has not achieved widespread use or evaluation. It would be feasible in theory to operate Vincent's apparatus by attaching a pants alarm and a small powered pump. It could be tried either in conjunction with a toilet training programme or for use on special occasions such as outings.

It should be noted that there is no alarm device that reliably detects continent or incontinent defaecation alone.

GROUP VERSUS INDIVIDUAL TRAINING

One major practical difference evident in the literature is the difference between 'intensive individual' training and less intensive 'group' training (Smith 1979a). Typically, in an intensive individual training programme, one child is trained at a time by one trainer (one-to-one training situation). In a group training situation, one trainer attempts to train several children or adults at once. Thus training for the latter is less intensive. The distinction between individual and group training is a very important practical issue in mental handicap because of the scarcity of resources, particularly in settings such as hospitals and schools for the handicapped, rather than at home. There has been little investigation of the differences in effectiveness between individual and group training, although it applies to many areas other than toilet training.

As recognised in our earlier discussion on components and models of continence, full continence involves a complex set of skills, including, for example, the ability to be independent at toilet, that is going to the toilet of one's own accord, rather than having one's continence dependent upon or managed by others. Thus, Bettison (1978, 1980) distinguishes between studies that view toilet training as a unitary response or a 'simple' skill and those that view it as a 'complex' process. In group training situations, continence, through necessity, is usually viewed as a relatively simple process whereby ability to pass urine on the toilet is increased and frequency of wetting accidents is decreased. In intensive individual training situations, there is generally more appreciation of the nature of continence as a complex process and more emphasis is placed on detailed shaping of component skills such as toilet approach and dressing skills.

The first report featuring a fairly intensive, individual training approach was that of Giles and Wolff (1966). They were also the first to feature specific attempts to shape self-initiated approach to the toilet. The detailed account presented by these authors clearly provided a basis for the later studies that were to emerge. The amount of detail available to designers of behaviour modification programmes was also increased by Minge and Ball (1967), who provided a good outline of prompt and fade procedures and shaping procedures for teaching self-help skills.

Examples of studies that would appear to have used a more intensive individual approach also include Van Wagenen *et al.* (1969a and b), Azrin and Foxx (1971), Mahoney *et al.* (1971), Smith *et al.* (1975) and Bettison *et al.* (1976). Studies that have used less intensive, group-training procedures have included Blackwood (1962), Dayan (1964), Baumeister and Klosowski (1965), Miron (1966), Kimbrell *et al.* (1967), Levine and Elliot (1970), Thompson and Grabowski (1972), Fewtrell (1973), Tierney (1973), Connolly and McGoldrick (1976) and Ando (1977). Smith (1979a) reported on a small study comparing five profoundly mentally handicapped children trained using individual training methods with five being trained together as a group. It was concluded that the intensive individual training was not only clinically more effective but also more cost effective. This was a small, practical study, as opposed to a well-controlled experimental study.

OTHER STUDIES

Before attempting to discuss or integrate the preceding studies further, a few unusual and interesting studies that do not readily fit into the structure of this review should be mentioned.

The distinction noted earlier between continence as a simple skill and as a complex process leads to the question of whether specific component skills can be isolated and trained separately. For example, one component skill of simply sitting on the toilet has been described in single case studies by Hattersley (1978) and Luisselli (1977). The former instance concerned a severely handicapped boy who would not sit on the toilet long enough to benefit from any training. After determining the mean length of time he could be restrained to sit on the toilet, this was increased by using reinforcement through successively longer periods, i.e. a shaping procedure. When the child would sit on the toilet for several minutes, a toilet-training programme was successfully introduced. The latter case study involved a 15-year-old severely mentally handicapped boy who had been previously toilet trained but who had developed a toileting phobia. Ultimately he had ceased to use the toilet and was completely incontinent. Luisselli successfully treated this by using a behavioural approach that included contingent reinforcement for appropriate use of the toilet and time-out contingent upon incontinence. Another specific component skill in males is urinating into the toilet bowl from a standing position. This is one of the higher-level component skills of toileting in males and a study by Siegel (1977) deals with training this ability. With normal adult males, Siegel found that there was a preference for directing the urine stream at a target (a small object) in the toilet bowl. Additionally there was a preference for a moving target to a stationary one. Siegel then applied this finding in a study of three moderately mentally handicapped institutionalised boys who were considered to have problems with respect to their ability to direct the urine stream into the toilet and not the surrounding area — a common problem. The introduction of a black and white striped float, which acted as a target and which spun when hit by the urine stream, quickly brought misdirected urinations under control. The use of a reversal design further confirmed this finding. This would seem to provide a simple and effective method of teaching this skill.

A singularly intriguing study is that reported by Edgar *et al.* (1975). Their idea of using relaxation and tension training to teach handicapped children to 'differentiate and gain control of the toileting musculature' is an interesting one. It is presumably similar to the sensory motor training briefly alluded to by Eyman, Silversen and McLain (1975). The rationale of the procedure is as follows. A series of relaxation exercises is used to help the child's development of gross body differentiation. Following this and through the use of an 'internal kinaesthetic figure-ground mechanism', the child should be able to make use of different parts of his body more proficiently. The relaxed child can now:

> begin to attend selectively to kinaesthetic feedback from his muscles, joints and tendons as he tenses or moves various parts of his body. The child can then use his body for problem solving, since he can now feel how the parts of his body work and are related.

For the purpose of toilet training, the relaxation and exercises concentrate on the area of the lower abdomen to make the child 'aware of the feelings to which, although always present . . . he could not selectively attend . . . (so that he can) then respond to these internal cues rather than external cues'. They compared two groups each of ten profoundly mentally handicapped children. The experimental group received individual relaxation and tension training of abdominal musculature and the control group received equivalent amounts of staff time spent playing with toys. Both groups appear to have been trained for approximately two weeks and positive reinforcement was given contingent upon urination in the toilet. When wetting accidents occurred trainees were reprimanded and prompted to the toilet. Analysis of variance of data before and after training indicated that the experimental group performed significantly better for both passing urine in the toilet and reduction in wetting accidents.

Although interesting, elements of this study do seem rather incongruous. The children are described as profoundly mentally handicapped, with chronological ages ranging from four to twelve years and Gessell developmental ages ranging from 15 to 23 months, yet they were 'taught to alternate the experience of tension and relaxation in the abdomen and upper thighs'. The procedure that they outline would seem to require a high degree of co-operation and understanding on the part of the child. The techniques included massage, stretching and shaking. A degree of linguistic and cognitive involvement is also evident:

Throughout the relaxation phase of the regimen, the progress in attaining relaxation was noted by the technician who gave the child auditory cues if he was having difficulty understanding the purpose of the procedure. The technician would say 'relax your leg' or 'you're too tense' or instruct the child to 'relax', 'let go' or to 'let me do it' meaning the child should let the technician manipulate his body and should let the tension go from his body.

It seems unlikely that profoundly mentally handicapped children could understand and co-operate with these parts of the training procedures. The study certainly requires replication. However, there is more than enough in this paper to justify some interest and comment. The crucial stimuli in bladder function are interoceptive and this is the first possible approach to tackling these stimuli, apart from the rather less practical methods outlined by Soldoff and Slucki (1974), Kohlenberg (1973) and Engel et al. (1974). It may be that some parts of the procedures of Edgar et al. do have some merit and that some form of cognitive involvement and physiotherapy could be fruitfully integrated into toilet programmes.

By the late 1960s, all of the key features and issues currently involved in behaviour modification toilet training programmes in mental handicap had appeared. From the first major milestones of Blackwood (1962) and Ellis (1963), the next major milestones resulted from the work of Van Wagenen et al. (1969) and Mahoney et al. (1971), and Azrin and Foxx (1971) and Foxx and Azrin (1973a). These two groups integrated all that had been made available from previous reports and developed this into the most detailed and sophisticated training approaches produced yet. Van Wagenen and Mahoney developed theirs along a 'timing' approach, while Foxx and Azrin developed theirs using a 'regular toileting' approach. To judge by subsequent reports, Foxx and Azrin have made a greater impact than any other authors in the literature. The key features of the approach detailed in Foxx and Azrin's (1973a) manual include: intensive training close to the toilet for a prolonged period; increased fluid intake to increase the frequency of the operant behaviour; the use of pants alarms and toilet bowl alarms to aid consistent and immediate reinforcement of inappropriate and appropriate urination; positive reinforcement for passing urine on the toilet and for remaining dry; punishment procedures contingent on wetting accidents; prompts to toilet at half-hourly intervals; 'fading' of prompts to teach independent toileting; shaping of dressing skills and an emphasis on procedures to maintain progress after completion of training.

METHODOLOGICAL CONSIDERATIONS AND FURTHER RESEARCH

The fact that the acquisition of continence is a complex process involving numerous component skills means that comprehensive evaluation of training methods in order to further understanding of the process requires many different types of measurement.

One problem that confounds a comparison of the outcome of different training methods is that there is no standard method of presenting data by which to judge the effectiveness of training. Some authors present frequency of incontinence before and after training, but give no data for frequency of passing urine at toilet or independence at toilet; some combine frequency of incontinent and continent eliminations and present the percentage that were continent; some present *ad hoc* rating scales from complete incontinence through to complete independence at toilet; others present before and after ratings on standardised developmental rating scales. Sadler and Merkert's (1979) presentation and discussion of data is particularly difficult to understand. To aid a comprehensive evaluation in future studies, data should be presented on a number of variables recorded by direct observation. These should include frequency of incontinence, percentage passing continent urine of occasions seated on toilet, and frequencies of self-initiated and prompted toileting. Data should preferably be presented during the training period itself, as well as before and after. The possibility of recording other variables such as latency to passing urine and complete emptying of the bladder will be mentioned shortly.

There are two main types of methodology required in investigation of incontinence and continence. The first is the standard group comparison, with sufficiently large numbers. This is required to investigate the effects of different types of training or the effects of experimentally varying factors between groups in order to determine the effects of specific factors within a training package. The second method of study required is small-sample, longitudinal studies using continuous observation of many toileting component skills and behaviours. The aim is to understand the *process* of incontinence or the development of continence, rather than to evaluate a treatment. Using this approach, a model of continence can be determined from a small number of individuals studied over a longer period. How far the model generalises to further individuals can be tested afterwards. How far the model generalises to further individuals can be tested afterwards. Time Series Analysis (see e.g. Chatfield 1975) is particularly well suited to analysis of single-subject data but requires lengthy, uninterrupted data series of about 50 consecutive data points per phase of study. Two variables that look promising for further investigation are latency to passing urine and whether the bladder is emptied completely or not. Latency to response has been used as a measure of learning in animal studies. A brief account of the use of this measure in toilet training is included in Smith (1979b). The time taken from the child sitting on the toilet seat until the toilet bowl alarm was activated was measured for ten minutes with mentally handicapped children during training. The mean daily latency reduced from a grouped mean of around three minutes to less than twenty seconds. The initial reduction was fairly rapid and the trends are reminiscent of learning curves. It is possible that latency could be used more as a measure of training effects. It is easily measured, reliable and a study of regression of latency on other variables and vice versa would determine the validity of its use.

In future studies of bladder training, the continuity of urine flow should certainly be investigated. From experience of toilet training programmes, there is a strong suspicion that not all children completely empty the bladder on the toilet and a number of children definitely pass urine in a discontinuous stream on some occasions, i.e. they will stop and start their urine flow two or three times instead of passing all their urine at once. Fielding (1982) also raises the question of whether or not some children empty the bladder completely. Determining with certainty that the bladder is empty in mentally handicapped children is difficult to do. This emphasises one of the component skills in the process of continence — the ability to maintain the urine flow once it has been initiated. Soldoff and Slucki (1974) found that stimulus offset was discriminated poorly by rhesus monkeys learning tasks with bladder pressure as the discriminant stimulus. Maintenance and cessation of the urine flow must be linked to discrimination of stimulus offset. In theory, therefore, proper maintenance of the urine flow could be a difficult skill to teach if not acquired.

7

Fluid Intake

Another precaution to be taken with
patients who wet their beds is to restrict
the amount of liquid they take . . .. Such
patients should not be allowed access to
the water tap.

Charles Mercier 1894

The question of how much to drink is an extremely important practical issue in the management of incontinence and the promotion of continence.

Clearly there are both physiological and behavioural components to water balance (Fitzsimmons 1971). Internally, the regulation of water retention in the body is maintained by physiological homeostatic mechanisms. An individual's water requirements are related to thirst, appetite, caloric consumption, body weight, specific gravity of urine and conditions that influence fluid loss (Friedin, Borakove and Fox 1982). There is a widespread belief that incontinent people should have their fluid intake reduced to reduce their incontinence, the belief being that the bladder will be capable of holding a smaller volume of urine. However, as Morgan (1981) points out, the bladder simply adjusts to holding a smaller amount of urine and triggers at a lower level. It is not only the carers (whether staff or relatives) of incontinent people who may hold this belief about fluid restriction: some incontinent people themselves, especially the elderly, may share this belief and virtually dehydrate themselves. Furthermore, many incontinent elderly, physically disabled, severely mentally handicapped or other institutionalised people are dependent on others for access to fluids, so that the behaviour of drinking in response to the stimulus of thirst may not be fully under voluntary control. Individuals who lack the basic self-help and communication skills may, in institutional settings, be subject to the restrictions of ward routines for their drinks. Inevitable spillages and a certain amount of food-stealing on the part of a few residents may make the determination of actual fluid intake difficult. In mental handicap, amongst the many problem behaviours found, some individuals may display an abnormal avoidance of fluid consumption or lack of thirst (Friedin *et al.* 1982). Sleeplessness may also pose a problem in institutions: elderly people do not require so much sleep and the nights can seem particularly long if one does not sleep well. It can seem even longer when lying awake longing for one of the few pleasures left in life — a nice cup of tea. Worse, many institutionalised people receive medication of one sort or another, one of the commonest side effects of which is dryness of the mouth.

Clinically, there is an impression that most incontinent people have experienced fluid restriction at some time, or advice to restrict fluids has at least been given. Curiously, perhaps because of the obvious disadvantages and risks to the patient, it is difficult to actually find this reflected publicly in the literature: it seems far more widespread than the literature would suggest. The practice certainly goes back a long way. Chambers, in 1846, recommended in the treatment of bedwetting that 'No fluids are to be taken within three hours of going to bed'. The same fairly mild approach is still given currently, e.g. Isaacs (1981) 'It is sensible to restrict fluid in the late evening so as to reduce the likelihood of incontinence occurring at night'. Ouslander and Fowler (1985) studied the written bladder-training guidelines supplied by 46 nursing homes for elderly people and found that 15 per cent of them formally recommended restriction of fluids at night. Parker (1984) interviewed 73 families with an incontinent severely disabled child. Over half of the parents recalled having discussed toilet training at some point with a professional and of this 10 per cent are reported to have been advised to restrict fluids.

In contrast to this, increased fluid intake has been a feature of bladder training programmes in recent years. This was first introduced to daytime training by Van Wagenen *et al.* (1969a and b) with the rationale of increasing the frequency of the operant behaviour for work within an operant conditioning framework. Since then, many studies have utilised increased fluids as part of a training package, in particular those who have followed the training manuals provided by Foxx and Azrin (1973a) and Bettison (1982) (see also Thompson and Hanson 1983). There is now more awareness of the need to promote adequate hydration in the management of continence and Ouslander and Fowler (1985) found that 35 per cent of the nursing homes in their survey stressed the need to encourage a minimum or 'adequate' level of fluids.

Thus, there are two opposing approaches to managing the same problem: both restriction and increase of fluids are advised. The question arises as to what empirical evidence exists relating fluid intake either to incontinence or to the promotion of continence. Three studies have been carried out that shed some light on this issue, in the areas of night-time control in children, in daytime control in incontinent mentally handicapped people and in elderly people.

The earliest of these is Hagglund's (1965) study of 46 children aged 4 to 13 years who suffered from nocturnal enuresis. The children were allocated to three groups: a fluid-restriction group, a forced-drinking group and a control group. In the first group, 'children were repeatedly instructed not to drink fluids in the evening and to empty their bladder before going to bed'. In the second group the children were encouraged to drink extra fluids throughout the day. The children in the third group received no specific treatment and the attitude towards their wetting was tolerant. Hagglund reported that six of the eighteen children in the increased fluids group were cured, whereas none of the children in the fluid restriction or control groups were cured. Cystometry carried out after three months of treatment showed increases in bladder capacity of the forced drinking group over the other two groups. It also showed increases in volume before the desire to void was apparent in the forced drinking group, whereas the fluid restriction group showed a decrease.

Smith and Wong (1981) carried out a detailed study of ten severely mentally handicapped children during bladder training. Over a period of several weeks for each child, data were recorded on a daily basis for frequency of wetting accidents, frequency and volume of continent urine passed on the toilet and volume of fluid intake. They found increased fluid intake to be related to the passing of continent urine but not to the passing of incontinent urine. There was also some evidence of a relationship between daily fluid intake and bladder capacity. Thus, overall, the role of increased fluid intake was found to be a positive one.

The third study, on 16 non-ambulant patients aged 59 to 96 years, was carried out in a nursing home by Spangler, Risley and Bilyew (1984) who compared 'standard care' with a continence promotion 'package'. Standard care comprised bed checks every three hours to change linen if necessary. The experimental procedure included visiting each patient every hour and a half to help at toilet if desired and to offer extra fluids. The outcome of the study was that dehydration levels, as measured by specific gravity of urine, were reduced and that the frequency of incontinence was also reduced.

Thus, three separate studies on different populations using different methodologies all point to the same conclusions: that there is no evidence that restricting fluids has any beneficial effect on incontinence, but that there is positive evidence that increasing fluids can contribute to the promotion of continence. Anyone who advises restriction of fluids should clearly demonstrate an empirical rather than an intuitive basis for an expectation of improvement in continence. Such evidence is, in fact, completely absent. Fluid restriction is a drastic, unhelpful and ethically questionable procedure.

However, the evidence on the relationship between fluids, bladder capacity and incontinence is important and complex: for example, that nocturnal enuresis is linked to small initial bladder capacity and that improvement in enuresis is frequently associated with increase in bladder capacity is apparently well documented (Starfield and Mellits 1968; Zaleski, Gerrard and Shokeir 1973). However, the use of increased fluids along with retention-control training in the treatment of bedwetting, although it may increase bladder capacity, does not necessarily improve the enuresis (Harris and Purohit 1977).

It has been argued strongly here that fluid restriction has negative effects and that fluid increase has positive effects, but recently Thompson and Hanson (1983) have voiced some misgivings about possible harmful effects of increasing fluids. Although there are no reports of adverse effects of excess fluids during bladder-training programmes, there are a number of reports of water intoxication in the psychiatric literature (Jose and Perez-Cruet 1979; Vieweg *et al.* 1984; Zubenko *et al.* 1984; Blum and Friedland 1983). This is enough to raise the possibility that over-zealous use of increased fluids may result in either water intoxication or in compulsive polydypsia. It is clear that the use of increased fluids as a treatment procedure should be monitored during use, over and above routine medical examination beforehand to rule out complications from obvious kidney disorders, etc. Both Thompson and Hanson (1983) and Feneley and Blannin (1984) give good advice for how much and what to drink to avoid both overhydration and dehydration. The behavioural treatment of polydypsia is described by Klonoff and Moore (1984).

Specific gravity and osmolality of urine have been proposed as useful checks on fluid balance. Spangler *et al.* (1984) used specific gravity as a simple approach, arguing that an increasing score on the urinometer indicates a greater mineral concentration and a lower proportion of water. In their initial sample, they deemed four of their sixteen residents to be dehydrated. Specific gravity is a rather crude measure of hydration. The osmolality of the blood is largely determined by its sodium content and is related to thirst, the secretion of the hormone vasopressin and reabsorption of water in the kidney. Urinary osmolality is closely related to blood plasma osmolality and gives a better objective measure of hydration. Joseph (1979) used this approach to study hydration levels in sixteen profoundly mentally handicapped male hospital residents and found their urinary osmolalities to be within normal limits. This is a useful non-invasive technique and could be used more widely to monitor this aspect of well-being in handicapped people.

Finally, an extension of the rationale underlying the use of increased fluids is Thyer and Curtis' (1984) use of a diuretic in conjunction with behavioural techniques to treat 'bashful bladder' type psychogenic urinary retention. They successfully used furosemide, a short acting diuretic, in five cases to provoke an adequate supply of urine for training purposes. Mindful of some of Thompson and Hanson's (1983) cautionary notes, one can envisage instances in which careful short-term use of diuretics may help to accelerate otherwise slow training programmes where the urine flow in toileting situations is inhibited.

8

Training Guidelines

Along comes the clever harlot, namely natural
reason, looks at married life, turns up her nose
and says: Why, must I rock the baby, wash its
nappies, change its bed, smell its odour, heal
its rash, take care of this and take care of that
do this and do that? It is better to remain single
and tell my children to do the same.
But what does Christian faith say? The father
opens his eyes, looks at these lowly distasteful
and despised things and knows they are adorned
with divine approval as with the most precious
gold and silver. God with his angels and
creatures will smile — not because nappies are
washed but because it is done in faith.

Martin Luther, *Concerning Married Life*, 1522

Much of this book has been concerned with an academic review of
the available information on the achievement of daytime urinary
continence. It seems reasonable, therefore, to consider at this point
a more practical outline of guidelines for designing and implementing daytime continence-training programmes. Practical details about
training approaches to nocturnal dryness are outlined by many
including Morgan (1981), Dische (1973), Griffiths (undated), and
Taylor and Turner (1975). The literature on achieving daytime
dryness has been less prolific, but practical guidance for training
programmes can be obtained from sources such as Bettison (1982),
Foxx and Azrin (1973), Pfadt and Sullivan (1980, 1981) and Tierney
(1973).

The outline presented here is at a personal level and is presented
in this way so that it can be used with those working in client-care
situations with handicapped incontinent people and who are attempting to carry out continence-training programmes. *It is intended that
this chapter be used to contribute towards teaching of such staff or
parents*. The approach here is also behaviourally based, not because

100

manipulation of the environment, and learning theory in particular, is seen as the only determinant of continence, but because it provides the most practical framework for intervention. A good general introduction to the principles and practice of behaviour modification is provided by Yule and Carr (1980). It should also be apparent from the following that the incontinent person who is the subject of the training programme cannot be seen as the single focus of the intervention. A person cannot be considered in isolation from the social system within which he or she functions. Intervention must concern itself not only with changing that person's behaviour, but also with wider changes in the social system in which the new behaviour will be expected to flourish and consolidate, to maintain and generalise.

Finally, in this preamble, the processes outlined here have chiefly been developed with respect to developmentally disabled individuals, but workers in other fields should not be put off by this. The principles have wide application and many aspects of these training programmes can be adapted for use with people with other types of disabilities.

GUIDELINES FOR DESIGNING A DAYTIME CONTINENCE TRAINING PROGRAMME

Introduction

Incontinence is a very old and very common human problem. Most people take their own continence for granted. But just a little thought about it shows that continence is far more complex than it seems at first. Think of the number of separate skills or components involved in remaining dry and using the toilet throughout the day: there is the ability to pass urine on the toilet, with or without a full bladder; the ability to inhibit the urine stream when the bladder feels full; the ability to go to the toilet of one's own accord; to handle clothes at toilet; to sit on the toilet and so on. An incontinent person may have difficulty with all or any of these areas. Yet most people in thinking about toilet training an incontinent person think only in simple terms of stopping wetting accidents.

Assessment

No two problems of incontinence are necessarily the same. The first essential is to assess the nature of the problem. A quick and relatively easy way to do so is by using the rating scale and chart shown here (Figure 8.1). This covers a number of important areas and helps us to begin to think more clearly about what is involved.

Figure 8.1: Incontinence rating scale

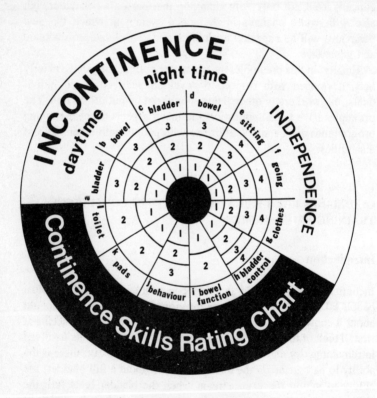

Continence skills rating chart

This rating scale is intended to give a brief overall picture of an incontinent person's continence skills for use in planning a continence training programme. It will help to demonstrate, first of all, that continence comprises a number of component skills and that an incontinent person is likely to have strengths and weaknesses in specific areas. Secondly, it will help to clarify and establish the goals of the training programme. This instrument is a rating scale with all of the problems of subjectivity inherent in rating scales. It is based on the experience and opinions of the rater. It is not intended to be a substitute for direct observation and recording.

Toileting skills are broken down into the components listed and defined below. By shading in the appropriate boxes a visual check of continence strengths and needs will emerge. The unshaded areas will show the steps of the component skills yet to be achieved.

Incontinence

(a) If daytime bladder accidents:
1. Occur frequently, i.e. once a day or more, then shade in area 1.
2. Occur occasionally, i.e. less than once a day, then shade in areas 1 and 2.
3. Never occur then shade in areas 1, 2 and 3.

(b) If daytime bowel accidents:
1. Occur frequently, i.e. once a day or more, then shade in area 1.
2. Occur occasionally, i.e. less than once a day, then shade in areas 1 and 2.
3. Never occur then shade in areas 1, 2 and 3.

(c) If night-time bladder accidents:
1. Occur frequently, i.e. once a night or more, then shade in area 1.
2. Occur occasionally, i.e. less than once a night, then shade in areas 1 and 2.
3. Never occur, then shade in areas 1, 2, and 3.

(d) If night-time bowel accidents:
1. Occur frequently, i.e. once a night or more, then shade in area 1.
2. Occur occasionally, i.e. less than once a night, then shade in areas 1 and 2.
3. Never occur, then shade in areas 1, 2 and 3.

Independence

(e) Sitting on the toilet, if
1. Afraid or refuses to sit, then shade area 1.
2. Sits with help, then shade areas 1 and 2.
3. Sit briefly without help, then shade areas 1, 2 and 3.
4. Sits without help for long enough to complete voiding, then shade areas 1, 2, 3 and 4.

(f) Going to toilet, if
1. Gives no indication of need to go to toilet, then shade area 1.
2. Gives some indication of need to go to toilet, then shade areas

1 and 2.
3. Sometimes goes to toilet of own accord then shade areas 1, 2 and 3.
4. Always goes to toilet of own accord, then shade areas 1, 2, 3 and 4.

(g) Handling clothes at toilet, if
1. Cannot handle clothes at all, then shade area 1.
2. Attempts or helps to pull pants down, then shade areas 1 and 2.
3. Pulls pants down by self, then shade areas 1, 2 and 3.
4. Pulls clothes up and down without help then shade areas 1, 2, 3 and 4.

Other components

(h) Bladder control, if
1. Never or rarely passes urine on toilet then shade area 1.
2. Passes urine on toilet sometimes, then shade areas 1 and 2.
3. Passes urine on toilet every time, then shade areas 1, 2, and 3.
4. Can stop and start urine stream at will, then shade areas 1, 2, 3 and 4.

(i) Bowel function, if
1. Does not always have normally formed bowel movements, i.e. is subject to constipation or diarrhoea, then shade area 1.
2. Has regular normally formed bowel movements, then shade areas 1 and 2.

(j) Behaviour problem, that interferes with toileting process, e.g. screams when toileted, faecal smears, if
1. Occurs frequently, i.e. once a day or more, then shade area 1.
2. Occurs occasionally, i.e. less than once a day then shade areas 1 and 2.
3. Never occurs, then shade areas 1, 2 and 3.

(k) Wears incontinence pads, plastic pants or similar, if
1. Yes, then shade area 1.
2. No, then shade areas 1 and 2.

(l) Toilet, if
1. Uses potty or commode, then shade area 1.
2. Uses normal toilet, then shade areas 1 and 2.

Some of the items may initially be difficult to rate accurately. If so, then either direct observation and recording should be carried out for a week or two (for example, on the incontinence or bladder control components), or the incontinent individual should be tested out to see what he can do on his own, e.g. for the independence components.

Completing this assessment helps in a number of ways, not the least of which is to encourage one to think of the different aspects involved. But it also shows that two incontinent people may have a completely different pattern of strengths and weaknesses concerning toileting. The last thing that this assessment does is to help to define very clearly what the problems are and, more importantly, what the precise goals, targets or objectives should be. This in turn sets up the process for beginning to devise a programme or plan of action. We shall return to this later.

SOME BASIC PRINCIPLES IN TOILET TRAINING

Although it is important to consider individual differences in the problem of incontinence, the implication being that there is not *one* type of toilet training programme that will suit every individual's needs, there are, however, certain basic principles for continence training that apply across the board and which need to be borne in mind.

Developmental sequence

First of all, it is important to remember the normal sequences in child development. Most children in our society are expected to become toilet 'trained' around the age of two years, though there is a very wide normal variation and a child who is trained early is not necessarily a 'bright' child and a child who is trained later does not necessarily have something wrong with it. On the whole, most children become bowel trained first, then acquire bladder control during the day and finally at night as well. A child in our society is generally thought to be ready for training when he can walk, can feed with a spoon, has some speech and can follow simple instructions.

Consistency: the key issue

The next basic point concerns the myth of strict toilet training. Strict toilet training is a rather unhelpful and unclear concept. It is usually taken to imply a heavy emphasis on punishment, which is neither necessary nor desirable. A good training programme can be systematic and consistent without being strict in the punitive sense: in fact, it should be a positive and enjoyable experience for the incontinent child or adult. It is, however, possible for toilet training to be strict in the punitive sense, but simultaneously very inconsistent. Many mothers handle wetting accidents inconsistently, 'exploding' from time to time when they eventually run out of patience with a child, but this is not consistent training and is of little help to the child. The key issue is the consistency with which each instance of a particular behaviour is handled (e.g. wetting) and not strictness: the same procedures for toilet training, whatever they are, should be carried out throughout the day, whenever toileting arises and whoever is with the child. Similarly, the same approach to training should be persisted with over a period of weeks and not just tried once or for a day or two.

Rewards

The issue of whether rewards should be used or not in toilet training also concerns many people. There is some concern that this may 'spoil' a child, or that it may lead to problems of some sort later. Briefly, the evidence shows that rewards used properly and consistently help an incontinent person to learn more effectively. Rewards need to be given consequent only upon those appropriate toileting behaviours targeted and not for other things. They should be given on every such occasion and not just some of the time, and they must be given immediately and not five seconds or five minutes later. We shall see some of the ways this may be done later on. The use of rewards is then gradually phased out, not just discontinued abruptly.

DEFINING OBJECTIVES

We can now turn to the next issue here, that of defining clearly and precisely what our goals, aims or objectives are. The purpose of this is to formulate clearly and unambiguously what we are aiming for. 'Toilet training' is too vague and can mean different things to different people. Are we talking about bladder or bowel and day or night? Do we expect him to be able to go of his own accord and to handle his clothes, or will we be satisfied to have him clean and dry and using the toilet, but still requiring help and supervision for this?

This must be stated in a form that can be clearly understood by whoever else may be caring for the incontinent child or adult at any time, but who will probably have different views on what incontinence and toilet training mean.

Another reason for stating the objectives clearly is that it helps immensely when writing out a plan of action. Indeed, once the objectives are properly formulated, such a programme often follows quite easily. Further, it provides a standard by which we can evaluate the effectiveness, or otherwise, of our programme.

The best way to formulate objectives is to return to the assessment chart and ask the question 'Exactly what is it that he is not able to do at the moment, that we want him to be able to do?' This puts the emphasis on the positive side, so that you have some new skill that you can begin to teach. Do not think in terms of what you want to stop him doing: for example, if one of the main problems is frequent wetting accidents during the day, then do not formulate the objective in terms of 'stopping him wetting his pants', but rather in terms of his 'having dry pants throughout the daytime'. Turn the formulation of your objective round from viewing it as a problem you want to 'stamp out', to a positive behaviour that you can begin to teach.

Short-term objectives

Next, one should begin to think about what the short-term objectives are. Think about which of the component skills you want to concentrate on initially. Is it bladder or bowel training, or both? Does it include handling clothes or going to toilet independently, or not? There are no definitive right or wrong answers to these questions: the important thing is that you specify these goals clearly. The degree of success expected and how much help, if any, the person is expected to need when they reach this level, should be included in the statement about the objectives.

Example of *badly* defined objective:

At the end of training John will stop wetting his pants and be toiled trained.

Example of a *well-defined* objective:

At the end of training John will keep his pants dry throughout the daytime, with no more than one 'accident' per week, and will pass urine on the toilet every time. He will be able to take his pants down and pull them up every time, but will still need to be taken regularly to the toilet.

The second example explains clearly what is being aimed at, provides positive skills or behaviours that can be taught, describes what degree of success he will achieve and what help he will ultimately be expected to need and provides standards by which to evaluate the programme.

DEFINING REINFORCERS

To produce an appropriate list of rewards or positive reinforcers for an individual you must ask the question 'What is it that he likes?' or 'What does he spend his time doing'.

Social reinforcement is extremely important. Suitable examples for the severely mentally handicapped person may include lavish praise, talking about how pleased other 'important figures', e.g. daddy, teacher, nurse and so on, will be; hugs, cuddles, tickles (especially good on the toilet), stroking his cheek, rubbing his back — lots of warm physical contact; play, with favourite toys or objects, which need not necessarily be 'constructive' play, with cars or puzzles or dolls, but may be 'manipulative' play — hitting things, throwing things, banging things, pulling things to pieces, tearing paper, scrumpling things and so on; music — favourite tunes or songs, simple games of anticipation involving peek-a-boo or tickle; food and sweets of various sorts are often popular rewards, but should be the sorts of things that are easily and quickly consumed, rather than chewed or sucked for a long time (e.g. various types of small sweets, pieces of chocolate, spoonfuls of ice cream or other puddings, small amounts of sherbet, honey, jams, flavoured dessert toppings, crunchy breakfast cereals, raisins, bits of banana or apple, crisps of various flavours, savoury biscuits and other small savoury items); drinks of various sorts are to be encouraged too — milk, fruit juices, brightly coloured and flavoured lemonades, tea, coffee, cocoa, Bournvita, packet soups and so on. Use as wide a variety of rewards as possible to avoid 'satiation'.

Sometimes it seems difficult to think of suitable rewards for some individuals, but don't give it up — try all sorts of things. For one mentally handicapped adult who didn't seem interested in much

apart from picking up small items of fluff and rubbish, we successfully used simple play with screwed-up pieces of paper — putting
them into boxes and so on. One child's main 'like' in life was eating
grass, so we included shredded cabbage for him, which he enjoyed
greatly. Even if he does not like social reinforcement at first, he will
gradually become more responsive, if social reinforcement is paired
with other types of reinforcers.

WRITING A PROGRAMME

Having assessed and rated the various component skills of toileting
abilities on the chart shown earlier, having determined the objectives
clearly, and having listed the reinforcers to be used, a plan of action
can now be formulated and the actual teaching methods and programme we are going to use to teach these new skills can be
considered.

The assessment shows the point at which the incontinent person
is now, the objectives show the point we want him/her to reach.
Breaking the distance between the two down into a series of small
steps, and adding the consistent use of the reinforcers we have listed,
will go a long way to determining our programme for us. The
teaching methods are exactly the same as the structured teaching
methods used to teach other skills. Two of the main methods for
teaching new skills are known as backward chaining and prompt and
fade. Basically, if the new skill can be broken down into small steps
and taught one step at a time, then this is called chaining. For example, the objective might be to teach him to pull his pants down at
toilet without help. At the moment he may need to have this done
fully for him. This can be broken into small steps. First his hands
can be held and he can be guided through the entire procedure and
rewarded solely for co-operating. Then, he can be rewarded for
pulling his pants down from below his knees the last few inches; then
for pulling down from the knees; then from above the knees and
finally from the hips. There may need to be more steps than this,
but this is an example of the idea behind chaining.

If the person can actually do something but requires some help,
guidance, cues or prompts to do it, and you have to remove this help
to get them to do it independently, then this is called 'fading'. For
example, another objective might be to teach him to go to the toilet
of his own accord without being told to go by someone else. You
may start teaching from very close to the toilet and determine, very

carefully, how much guidance, help or prompting he needs to get him to go to the toilet. You may work out a series of steps for the physical, spoken and gestural prompts separately in order to fade them out. Gestures are easiest to work with and can be faded systematically by rewarding him for responding, gradually, to successively smaller prompts. Initially, your prompts may include an elaborate pantomime of gestures from looking at him and looking at the toilet, pointing with a sweeping gesture, patting the seat and gesturing him with both hands to sit and so on. Each gesture can be broken into a series of steps and faded out thus: a sweeping arm movement can be shortened a few inches then a few more, until it is just a hand movement, then just a finger movement, then just a slight pointing with the finger. When down to very small prompts he will learn to go without prompts quite easily. Having faded prompts from close to toilet you may then have to teach him to go to the toilet from gradually further away. Often fading and chaining are combined in the same programme.

The main example we will use here is teaching daytime dryness. We will look in more detail at the use of reinforcement in designing a programme for daytime bladder training below.

GUIDELINES FOR IMPLEMENTING A CONTINENCE TRAINING PROGRAMME

We will take as our example daytime bladder training. We will assume that we are going to try to teach daytime bladder control to a severely or profoundly mentally handicapped child or adult who has never been dry during the day before. Jack is a profoundly mentally handicapped twelve-year-old boy. He can walk and is a robust and active boy. He has achieved little spoken language but he can comprehend simple instructions. He can feed with a spoon, albeit messily, and drink from a cup. His play tends to involve manipulation of objects rather than imaginative or constructive play. He has no serious behaviour problems, but not surprisingly he can have temper tantrums when frustrated. He is responsive to attention and affection.

The steps in writing the programme include as before, assessment, defining the objectives and defining the reinforcers. From our assessment we know that he is wet frequently during the daytime and soils occasionally during the day; that he is wet frequently at night but never soils at night; that he can sit without help on the toilet; that he helps to pull his pants down; that he gives no indication of the need to go to the toilet; that he passes urine on the toilet some of the time; and that he has fairly regular bowel movements. The priority that is chosen is daytime bladder control. The other aspects, such as independence at toilet, are not considered here. The objectives are therefore fairly easily defined as teaching Jack to remain dry, with no more than one daytime accident per week, with prompting to toilet every two hours, and to teach him to pass urine on the toilet every time.

We shall now try to bring together the points covered above and apply them to this problem. First of all, though, we need to consider some practical points and aids to training.

Before starting the training programme, we need to consider four things:

1. Fluids
2. Equipment
3. Clothing
4. The setting where the training is carried out.

1. *Fluids*

Increased fluid intake, by coaxing and encouraging Jack to drink more of a wide variety of fluids right throughout the day, will help to train him more easily and will speed up the training process because there should be more training 'opportunities'. We should try to increase the amount he drinks by about three times if possible. This will help him to pass urine more often and to increase his bladder capacity. Of course, it is essential to see that he has a medical examination beforehand, to ensure that it is absolutely safe to do this. In a few instances it may not be so and some caution is necessary.

2. *Equipment*

There are two types of equipment that can help toilet training — toilet bowl alarms and pants alarms. The toilet bowl alarm is a device that is attached to the toilet that signals the instant urine is passed on the toilet. The pants alarm is a device attached to the underpants, which signals the occurrence of a wetting accident. Both these pieces of equipment, properly used in conjunction with a well-designed training programme, can aid immediate and consistent detection of both appropriate and inappropriate urination and hence immediate and consistent reinforcement. Overall, the bowl alarm is more important than the pants alarm, as it puts the emphasis on the positive side. It is also more reliable and easy to use in practice, so if only one of these is to be used, then choose the bowl alarm rather than the pants alarm in isolation. For smaller children musical potties are available. You need not worry that the use of a musical pottie will condition a child to pass urine in response to a particular tune in later life. According to the learning theory involved this should not happen, and experience of using such potties over a number of years demonstrates that it does not happen.

3. *Suitable clothing*

This is very important to arrange in advance. Underpants should be close fitting and made of cotton if a pants alarm is to be used. Trousers should have elastic waists for easy handling. Dresses or skirts should not be too long.

Plastic pants, incontinence pads, tights, dungarees or anything with difficult belts, buttons, clips or zips should not be used.

4. *The training situation*

Most of the training will actually be done close to the toilet, so the toilet area should be made as pleasant and comfortable as possible. Toilets in hospitals, schools and Day Centres often have more space than at home, but they are usually less pleasant. They should be brightened up and some soft furnishings introduced to deaden echo and noise. Foam-rubber floor mattresses should be used for playing on, and there should be a good supply of toys/activities for the child/adult being trained. The trainer should have a comfortable chair, a radio, access to coffee and a clock. There is no reason why toilet training should be an unpleasant experience for anyone involved. At home it may be necessary to leave the door open if the bathroom or toilet is small and use the space on the landing or hallway outside — as long as you can still see the toilet.

The training programme itself

We know from our statement of objectives that we need a teaching procedure to teach Jack to pass urine on the toilet more consistently, and we need a teaching procedure during the day to teach him to remain dry. We will, however, also need a procedure for when he does have a wetting accident. This gives us three components for the programme for which we will need training guidelines:

i. Bladder training on the toilet
ii. Dry pants training
iii. Wetting accident procedure.

Using the principles we have already discussed, Jack's programme begins to look as follows:

Bladder training

1. Keep Jack playing happily within sight of the toilet for prolonged periods (up to several hours).
2. Every half hour, on the hour and half hour, prompt or guide him to sit on the toilet.
3. Let him sit on the toilet for up to 5–10 minutes or until he passes urine.
4. The instant he starts to pass urine and the toilet bowl alarm is triggered, reward him substantially.

Reward him actually on the toilet and when he starts to pass urine, not when he finishes. One useful tip is to keep a bedside trolley parked just round the corner or out of sight with a selection of rewards. When the bowl alarm sounds, the trolley is quickly wheeled in.

Dry pants training

Between half-hourly prompts to toilet, the dry pants check procedure is carried out. Every five minutes right throughout the day, take Jack's hand, guide him to feeling his own dry pants and praise for being dry. Do this also whenever you interact with him for any purpose. So, before a meal or drink, before speaking to him or starting another activity, make it consequent first of all upon a dry pants check. This is an extremely important part of training and one that is usually not emphasised enough.

The underlying rationale of these two training procedures is to give massive and consistent reinforcement consequent upon (a) passing urine on the toilet and (b) remaining dry. Remember that, even if Jack rarely passes urine on the toilet beforehand, if you increase fluids, and if you prompt to toilet every half hour, then the chances are high that even on a chance basis, he will pass urine on the toilet in the not too distant future and then you will have something to work with.

Wetting accident procedure

1. When Jack wets his pants and when the pants alarm is triggered, then guide his hand to feel his wet pants immediately and at the same time reprimand sharply by saying 'No, you're wet.'
2. Switch alarm off, do *not* prompt him to the toilet and do not change his wet clothes.
3. Use 'time-out from reward' for five to ten minutes. That is, ignore him for that period and withdraw all other attention and activities as well. Remove any toys or objects he is playing with, drinks, etc.
4. At the end of this period, change him into dry clothes in a neutral manner without any fuss. Then carry out a dry pants check and praise him for being dry again. Recommence the bladder training procedure at the point you left off.

The reason behind this procedure is not to seek retribution for the wetting accidents, but simply to make the difference between being dry and being wet as clear as possible, in order to help him learn to discriminate the difference as effectively as possible. The balance of any programme, overall, must be very heavily on the positive side.

Organisation

One can design the best training programme in the world but if it is badly organised or inconsistently implemented, it will have little effect. Almost everybody must have seen examples of this at some time. Many, many programmes do not work because of poor organisation. A little thought beforehand about planning and organisation can anticipate many of the common problems that often arise and cut across training programmes. The steps we have considered so far designing the programme are as follows:

> assessment
> behavioural objectives
> defining reinforcers
> teaching methods

In implementing the programme we have also considered:

fluid intake
training aids or equipment
clothing
the training situation

We now have to consider:

the length of baseline
the length of training
the evaluation of training
the responsible staff
maintenance
generalisation

The length of baseline

How long should the baseline period be? The standard answer is that it should be long enough to ensure that the behaviour with which one is dealing is stable. In other words, if during the baseline period there is evidence that the behaviour is changing already, i.e. increasing or decreasing in frequency, then one should consider the matter carefully. If it is already improving then introducing a new training programme could change this and make matters worse, rather than better. In practical terms, a baseline period of at least two weeks duration is normal.

Length of training

A bladder-training programme for a client such as Jack may be expected to last for several weeks. This, of course, will vary according to whether the client is developmentally disabled or not and if so, by how much. If the client is handicapped or disabled, it is best to assume six weeks or so will be needed. There may be little point in starting in a week when you know that the trainee is going away for a lengthy holiday the next week. Thus, a reasonably uninterrupted period should be chosen. It is important also to specify achievable objectives. If progress appears to be too slow, then make sure that the steps and objectives are small enough to make some measurable progress within a short period.

Evaluation

Evaluating the effects of any training programme is now widely accepted as being extremely important. You need, first of all, a baseline or pre-treatment measure of the behaviour or skill you are trying to train. Keeping simple but accurate records before and during training, of how often Jack passes urine on the toilet or how often a wetting accident occurs will aid decision-making about whether to continue the programme unchanged or whether the programme needs to be changed in some way.

Responsibility for training

The training programme is far more likely to be implemented consistently if one key person is identified as having the responsibility for it. This means co-ordinating the programme across different situations. Whether Jack lives at home or elsewhere, he will also attend a school. Incontinent adults may be attending a Day Centre. It is essential that training is carried out consistently in these different situations and that *everyone* who comes into contact with him has full information about the programme. Those who are actually carrying out the training may need training themselves in the procedures being used. It is useful to act out the training procedures on each other using a simulated training situation and role playing. Morale is very important. Clear feedback on progress should be provided to all concerned.

Maintenance and generalisation

Maintenance means maintaining progress once the objectives have been achieved. Generalisation means generalising a new behaviour to situations other than the one in which the training was carried out originally. If you teach a normal child a new skill, it is not usually necessary to worry about these issues, as the child will maintain and generalise the skill or ability spontaneously. This is not always the case with a mentally handicapped or otherwise disabled person. It is best to assume that this will not happen and plan accordingly.

There are a number of points that help to maintain a new skill at the end of training:

1. Do not cut the programme off suddenly, but phase it out gradually. Reduce the amount of extra attention he gets during the training period as gradually as possible. Carry on reinforcing the appropriate behaviour with all the extra reinforcers for some time after the objective is reached. It is quite reasonable to expect that social reinforcement (usually praise) should continue indefinitely, but reduce the other reinforcers by dropping them intermittently at first. For example, from using these reinforcers on every occasion, try reducing them to four out of five occasions then three, two and one out of five occasions and so on.
2. Ensure that all in contact with the trainee know how to reinforce the new behaviour and that they do not revert to former or other habits of handling or managing toileting. Ensure that occasional occurrences of the old behaviour are not inadvertently rewarded, e.g. attention contingent upon a wetting accident.
3. If a relapse occurs, briefly reimplement the original training procedures as quickly as possible. Define a relapse in advance. For example, a relapse may be considered as three wetting accidents within any two-day period.
4. Consider carefully the situation or placement where the new skills or abilities are to be maintained indefinitely.

This brings us on to generalisation. Training must be generalised both to different places and to different people:

1. Start, if possible, by carrying out training sessions in one location and with one person training him, for example at home. Then when some progress has been made there, extend training to other locations where he spends time and will have to use the toilet. Then extend training to include toilets that he will use less frequently, such as on trips or outings. Go on some trips specifically for the purpose of toilet training in these situations.
2. Similarly, having started with one person carrying out most of the training, when some progress is made, introduce other people to carry out the programme. It may be necessary to have the first person still present initially, until the trainee learns to perform equally for different people.

If these steps are followed in designing a programme and planning ahead is carried out to take into account these practical issues in organising the programme, then the chances of the incontinent person becoming bladder trained and of maintaining the results of training long-term will be greatly improved.

OTHER CONTINENCE TRAINING ISSUES

Training independent toileting

Thus far we have considered teaching Jack to remain dry and to pass urine consistently on the toilet. If one of the aims of training had been to teach him to initiate going to the toilet himself, then a separate training procedure would have been required for this. This is quite feasible, but would require more intensive training and the teaching procedure is more complex.

If it has been established that Jack cannot adequately follow or understand spoken instructions or explanations, then teaching him to go independently to the toilet can be done as outlined below.

The basic approach to training is first, to establish clearly the types of prompts or cues that are used in taking him to the toilet and then to very systematically fade or phase these out; second, to start training first of all from very close to the toilet and when he can go without prompting from close to the toilet, to then gradually train from further away from the toilet.

When prompting to the toilet there are three main types of prompts:

1. Physical prompts
2. Verbal prompts
3. Gestural prompts

A physical prompt consists of any prompt involving touching Jack. A very major physical prompt might consist of walking along-side him with one arm round his shoulder and physically guiding him to the toilet, turning him round at the toilet, pushing his body forward into a slightly bent position, bending his knees and physically guiding him into sitting on the toilet. Physical prompts may range from this extreme through to holding his hand lightly as he goes to the toilet, or lightly touching or shadowing his back or elbow with your hand.

A verbal prompt consists of any spoken prompt to the child such as 'Jack, go to the toilet'.

A gestural prompt effectively consists of any other form of prompt or communication to him where you use your body non-verbally, or without touching him. Thus, at one extreme, a gestural prompt can involve an elaborate mime whereby you look at him and then look at the toilet, point to him and then, with a sweeping wave of the arm, point to the toilet, hold out both arms and hands and dramatically gesture to Jack to move to the toilet, then pat the toilet seat with both hands and gesture to him to sit on the toilet. Towards the other extreme, a gestural prompt can consist of a very minor point with one finger, or a small head nod. Ultimately, establishing eye contact with him and using simply a movement of the eyes towards the toilet is a very minor gestural prompt.

At the beginning, it is necessary to establish exactly what sort of prompts are necessary to get him to go *from a few feet away from the toilet*. The prompts are then broken down into their physical, verbal and gestural components, and a series of small steps is determined to systematically fade out the prompts. *Prompts to toilet are always faded in order from physical to verbal to gestural.*

Physical prompts are deemed the major type of prompt related to dependence on others for toileting, so they are faded first. Verbal prompts are faded next simply because in practice they can be the most difficult type of prompt to fade. If left to the last, you can become easily stuck with a verbal prompt: once down to a minimal verbal prompt of just one word spoken softly — 'toilet' — this is very difficult to fade further. There is far more scope for fading gestural prompts, so these are faded last. There can be a great richness, variety and subtlety in the use of gestural prompts, as you can use the whole range of body, limb, head and eye movements, as well as such things as facial expression.

In order to facilitate the correct sequence for fading prompts, the prompts are given in the reverse order, this is gestural first, verbal second, physical last. The different types of prompt are given first with a gap of a few seconds in between, and then if necessary in combination. In this way, when Jack is able to respond to a lower category of prompt or a lower level of prompt, he has the full opportunity to do so. *When he responds to a lower level of prompt within one category, then subsequent prompts never go back up beyond that category or level.* Every time a prompt is given, it is reduced first of all to one small step below the previous level. A series of small steps is worked out for each category of prompt. For example, gestural prompts can gradually be faded down from a sweeping head and arm movement to a small finger and eye movement, and finally to a small eye movement alone.

Fading whole categories of prompts can be 'set up' by using the correct sequence of prompts described above, but procedures for aiding this further have developed from experience of these programmes. It is often possible to fade directly from physical to gestural prompts without the intervening step of fading verbal prompts. This can be done by first fading the physical prompt down to holding him lightly by the hand. He is then prompted from in front, rather than beside him by lightly holding or touching his hand and then this is faded by reaching out to hold his hand, but moving your hand away just as he touches it and pointing to the toilet. If the hand is moved away, he is likely to step forward to try and hold your hand and this can be paired with, or briefly preceded by, pointing dramatically and quickly to the toilet. In this way, fading to gestural prompts can be achieved more rapidly. Overall, the use of gestural prompts is achieved as quickly as possible, or additional gestures introduced to replace other categories of prompt, as they are easiest to work with in toilet training.

With Jack seated close to the toilet and going back and forward to the toilet every half hour, with substantial reinforcement for using the toilet and for having dry pants, and with a reprimand and time out for wetting accidents, *a self-initiated toileting* (i.e. going without a prompt) is a relatively easy step for him to make. When prompts have been faded down to the lowest possible gestural prompt and he has not self-initiated to toilet, then the following procedure is useful. A few minutes before a prompt is due, he should be casually manoeuvred to stand next to the toilet without any overt prompting. If made to stand next to the toilet, the chances are that after about five minutes or so he will sit down on the toilet simply to 'take the weight off his feet'. When this happens he should be rewarded and training should then work back from there.

Prompts to toilet should be discontinued completely when Jack can self-initiate reasonably consistently to the toilet. The frequency of prompts can be reduced to once an hour or less when self-initiations appear. After an initial minor prompt to toilet in the morning at the start of training, two or three self-initiations during the day should be sufficient to warrant the complete termination of prompts thereafter. Because of variations between individuals, it is not possible to set an exact criterion for terminating prompts. Unless he starts to self-initiate very frequently, it is unwise to stop all prompts after the first self-initiated toileting. When prompts to toilet have been stopped, and when he has been self-initiating successfully for a few days from close to the toilet, he can then be moved gradually away from the toilet and back towards the regular living area. He should only be moved a few feet at a time and often may stay at each point for a few days to ensure that he can self-initiate consistently from that point. The important places to train from are corners, doors or any point where he may have a choice of direction on his way to the toilet.

Relapses in independent toileting

A clear definition of a relapse needs to be established beforehand. Such a definition may be, for example, two full days without a self-initiated toileting, when either a person just sits and has wetting accidents, or in institutional settings follows others when they are prompted to the toilet. In any retraining, it is extremely important to reintroduce prompts to toilet at fixed regular intervals of time and not at the time of wetting accidents or when the trainee is fidgeting shortly before an accident.

FURTHER COMMON BLADDER-TRAINING PROBLEMS

'He wets as soon as he comes off the toilet'

This is a common complaint and the first thing to do is to record toiletings and wetting accidents for about two weeks. This often puts the problem in perspective and may demonstrate clearly that this only happens occasionally: it only has to happen once or twice for it to seem as if it happens every time. If it is, in fact, less frequent than was thought, then training can proceed as normal. However, it does occasionally happen that an incontinent person wets regularly very shortly after coming off the toilet. If this is established clearly by recording then the remedy can be relatively simple. Often, in fact, the child or adult knows what is expected of him on the toilet and tries hard but is tensing the wrong muscles. The answer is to forget about the sort of training programme outlined before and to concentrate on relaxing him on the toilet. This can be done by playing with the trainee on or close to the toilet for longer periods, rather than sitting him on the toilet for ten minutes and coming back later to see if he has performed. The trainee can be played with, read or sung to, occupied with a favourite activity or even given a meal to enjoy. When he relaxes he will pass urine, and once this happens progress will be rapid.

Messy toileting

The final problem of messy toileting is a common one in institutional settings and concerns male residents who are able to stand at the toilet but who cannot, or will not, direct the urine stream accurately. With more able residents a structured incentive scheme may be appropriate. Otherwise, the best solution is to float a target in the toilet. A table tennis ball painted half red, which spins when it is hit, is ideal and will not be flushed away. You will find that, whether the problem is due to poor motor control or to poor motivation, this device will greatly improve accuracy.

Good luck with your training programmes.

9

Nocturnal Enuresis

> Many times . . . as well old men as children are
> often times annoied, wha their urine issueth out
> either in their slepe or waking against their
> willes, having no power to reteine it when it
> cometh . . .
>
> Thomas Phaire, 1553

That nocturnal enuresis is one of the commonest reasons for families seeking advice from family doctors and child specialists is well known. The distress caused to the bedwetting client and his family by this problem is also attested to by the very great number of publications on every aspect of this topic. Indeed, the problem has been recognised as such as far back as the Egyptians (Glicklich 1951), and was mentioned later in a chapter entitled 'Of Pyssying in the Bedde' in Thomas Phaire's 'Boke of Children' in 1553. Glicklich's (1951) account reviews the wide-ranging treatments, many of them punitive, that desperate families have resorted to through the course of history. Despite this, most authors, like Fritz and Armbrust (1982), conclude that 'Enuresis remains a common problem which continues to defy medical understanding'.

Theories abound as to the cause of nocturnal enuresis, including urological and medical causes, deep sleep, small functional bladder capacity, genetics, maturation and development disorders, psychological disorders, learning disorders, etc., but the most that can be said is that its origin seems likely to be multi-factorial (Essen and Peckham 1976; Kolvin 1975; Benjamin *et al*. 1971; Fritz and Armbrust 1982).

Of course, since all but one or two per cent of children will grow out of this problem by approximately the mid-teens and since it is not a problem that in itself is harmful to the child's physical well-being, with the exception that urinary tract infections are found to be commoner in enuretic children (Zaleski *et al*. 1972), the question might be asked as to why such an apparently disproportionate amount of time and effort has gone into attempting to find a cause of and solution to the problem. Anyone who has ever suffered from nocturnal enuresis can testify to the severe social and emotional consequences of the problem for the enuretic child; while on the parent's part, a range of reactions can be found from those who are sympathetic to and understanding of the problem, to those who show intolerance.

As an exhaustive literature review would be beyond the scope of this chapter, the aim here will be to present the reader with an overview of current perspectives of the problem of nocturnal enuresis.

DEFINITION

Definitions such as 'persistent wetting of the bed in the absence of neurological or urological pathology' (Doleys 1977) and '. . . the involuntary discharge of urine after the age when bladder control is usually attained' (Fritz and Armbrust 1982) serve to underline the vagueness surrounding definitions of nocturnal enuresis. In fact, the only point on which most authors seem to agree is that there exists considerable disagreement in the literature as to the age at which a child can be regarded as nocturnally enuretic and the frequency with which he must wet the bed to be regarded so.

For example, Weir (1982) states that enuresis exists when 'any child over age two years has more than an occasional daytime or nighttime event that suggest loss of control'. Some authors (Muellner 1960; Campbell 1970) suggest that that the physiological maturation necessary for night-time control is present by age three and therefore define nocturnal enuresis as bedwetting in individuals over the age of three. Azrin, Sneed and Foxx (1974) offer bed-wetting treatment to children over three years of age. Other authors (McKendry and Stewart 1974; Schaeffer 1979) define nocturnal enuresis as beginning after the age of five. Following Brazelton's (1962) study, which found that 98.5 per cent of children were dry at night by the age of five, it would certainly seem that the necessary maturation must have occurred at least by five years.

Definition using statistical prevalence by age would be a more objective way of defining 'normality' but neither is this wholly satisfactory, since the behaviour would still be regarded as statistically normal long after it becomes a problem for most bedwetters.

Kolvin (1975) accepts an earlier definition of 'night wetting in the school age period' as being a practical solution to the problem, as the prevalence and spontaneous remission rates are relatively low at this age and because it is around this time that many children begin to become worried about the problem. With regard to frequency of bedwetting, rates from one to twenty-two wets per month have been regarded as constituting nocturnal enuresis (Doleys, Schwartz and Ciminero 1981). In view of the wide range of opinions as to how frequently a child must wet to be regarded as nocturnally enuretic, Doleys *et al.* (1981) propose a very detailed guide to classification.

PREVALENCE

It is a well-established fact that the incidence of nocturnal enuresis declines with age. In the first year, about seven to eight per cent of infants become dry at night; in the second, Oppel, Harper and Ryder (1968a) report that 36 per cent of those still wet become dry; in the third, 42 per cent become dry; after age five years, approximately 15 to 16 per cent of those stll wet will become dry each year (de Jonge 1973; Schaeffer 1979). Thus, a five-year-old child has only about a 50 per cent chance of outgrowing this problem by age ten and it may take several years for this to happen (Schaeffer 1979).

As the peak age range for the emergence of dryness is between one-and-a-half and four-and-a-half years, McKeith *et al.* (1973) therefore propose the existence of a 'sensitive' period (though not, they point out, a 'critical' one) for the spontaneous emergence of night-time dryness. A sensitive period is usually typified by a high rate of the behaviour during the proposed period and is preceded and followed by a lower rate of the behaviour concerned. Figures of 8 per cent in the first year and 15 per cent in the following years would support this view. Prevalence rates reported in the literature for each age vary according to the definition of nocturnal enuresis used, the population sampled, and whether the data were gathered retrospectively or with regard to the current status of the behaviour (Weir 1982). Miller (1973) also believes that prevalence rates for nocturnal enuresis are frequently underestimated, no doubt due to the nature of the problem. De Jonge (1973) lists four reasons for the substantial differences in the quality of reports on the prevalence of enuresis at various ages: different definitions of nocturnal enuresis; different methods of investigation; selection of subjects; statistical reliability, dependent on number of subjects. Thus, between 43 and 83 per cent of two-year-olds, 13 to 49 per cent of three-year-olds, 6 to 40 per cent of four-year-olds and 6 to 28 per cent of five-year-olds are said

125

to be still wet at night.

Some constant features do nevertheless emerge from these studies. First, more boys than girls suffer from nocturnal enuresis, though again the frequency is variously reported as being twice as high in boys, to slightly higher for boys and Verhulst *et al.* (1985) found this sex difference to decline with age. Second, there do seem to be cross-cultural differences in the age at which children become dry at night. Thus, it seems likely that both inherent and environmental factors play a part (McKeith *et al.* 1973).

TYPES OF ENURESIS

Previously, no distinction was made between different types of enuretics, but many attempts are now made to do so with regard to different causes, courses, prognoses and types of treatment required (Kolvin and Taunch 1973).

The main widely accepted distinction nowadays is between 'primary' or 'continuous' nocturnal enuresis, when the child has never been consistently dry, and 'secondary', 'acquired' or 'onset' nocturnal enuresis, when the child has relapsed after a period of dryness. There is some disagreement as to the length of the dry period required before a child is regarded as suffering from secondary enuresis, ranging from one month (Oppel *et al.* 1968) up to at least one year (Kolvin 1975). Kolvin (1975) sees primary enuresis in terms of a 'disorder of neurophysiological maturation of structures subserving bladder control', i.e. biological in origin, whilst proposing secondary enuresis to be mainly psychogenic in origin. Kolvin *et al.* (1973) found this distinction to have some validity in terms of outcome of different treatments: using 'buzzer' and imipramine treatments, primary enuretics tended to respond slightly better to buzzer treatment than to imipramine, though not significantly so, and primary enuretics tended to respond better to buzzer treatment than did secondary enuretics; but secondary enuretics responded significantly better to imipramine than to the buzzer. However, Kolvin and Taunch (1973) admit that there is only limited evidence to support the hypothesis of two types of nocturnal enuretics and conclude by proposing at least two types. Sacks and De Leon (1973), on the other hand, can see little usefulness in this distinction in terms of treatment outcome. Using a conditioning method of treatment, still regarded by many clinicians as inappropriate in the treatment of secondary enuresis, which is seen as symptomatic of psychological conflict and not modifiable by conditioning, they found no difference between primary and secondary enuretics with regard to initial success rate, percentage relapse, days to cure, or severity of wetting on relapse.

Fielding (1982) distinguishes between those nocturnal enuretics who are only wet at night and those who wet both by day and night, over the age of five years. She found differences in percentage initial success in response to alarm treatment, speed of response to treatment and time to relapse, with day-and-night wetting children showing a poorer response on each measure.

Weir (1982), distinguishes no less than five or six subgroups of nocturnal enuretics: heavy sleeper, school problems, immature pre-schooler, erratic stool patterns, infection and enuresis, and enuretic females, although he does not make explicit the basis for these groupings. Each type of enuretic responds to a different type of treatment, although again he offers no objective evidence to support the validity of this. Trombini, Rossi and Umilta (1982) distinguish purely between nocturnal enuresis caused by emotional disturbance and that caused by organic pathology and claim to be able to distinguish between these two groups on the basis of a rather doubtful performance test that the enuretics are required to solve: attempts to solve these tests are said to result in changes in the level of pressure inside the bladder as a consequence of emotional tenseness and thus can distinguish between enuretics of psychogenic origin and those of organic origin. Most other authors (e.g. Schaeffer 1979) seem to accept the primary and secondary distinction. However this may be, Schaeffer (1979), Gardner and Hedge (1984), in a recent study of 126 enuretic children, have found that classifications based on factors such as primary vs secondary and familial vs non-familial are of little practical importance in predicting outcome of treatment.

CAUSES OF ENURESIS

Urological/medical causes

Fritz and Armbrust (1982) report that 'uropathies of all types probably account for 2 to 4 per cent of the enuretics in a general paediatric setting'. Estimates for nocturnal enuresis caused by organic factors range between one and ten per cent, depending on the sample and diagnostic differentiation (Sorotzkin 1984). Essen and Peckham (1976), in a study of 12,000 children from the National Child Development Study, found that 'underlying abnormalities of the urinary tract clearly did not play a major role in the aetiology of enuresis'.

Most authors, with the exception of some like Trombini *et al.* (1982), do not now regard organic pathology of the urinary tract as being a significant factor in the causation of nocturnal enuresis (Morgan 1981; Kolvin 1975; Sorotzkin 1984). According to Scott (1973), there has been a '. . . tendency to ascribe somewhat nebulous and ill-defined conditions to the urinary tracts of children with enuresis'. While some enuretic children have abnormalities of the urinary tract, this does not infer causation; indeed, children with demonstrable organic pathology of the urinary tract frequently do not suffer from nocturnal enuresis (Sorotzkin 1984). Many studies, like that of Trombini *et al.* (1982), who have demonstrated organic pathology in their samples of bedwetters, have not included normal control groups and those who have have usually found as many non-enuretics with such abnormalities. Scott (1973) goes as far as to say that 'There are no well-defined organic lesions responsible for primary enuresis.'

Thus, there seems to be general agreement that organic pathology is unlikely to be a major factor, especially when the enuretic child is wet only at night and where the enuresis is primary. Such factors may hamper rather than prevent learning (Kolvin and Taunch 1973).

Urinary tract infection

There are several reasons why urinary tract infections have been regarded as a cause of nocturnal enuresis. First, nocturnal enuretics have a higher rate of such infections than non-enuretics (Zaleski *et al.* 1972). This is especially true of girls; as many as one in twenty bedwetting girls will have a urinary tract infection, increasing to one in ten when bedwetting occurs every night (Stansfeld 1973). Thus, urinary tract infection is relatively common amongst nocturnal enuretics. Secondly, a proportion of children presenting with such infections will also suffer from nocturnal enuresis, which may clear up with successful treatment of the infection.

However, the exact relationships between enuresis and urinary tract infection is not clear. Although about 16 per cent of children presenting with an infection will also suffer from enuresis, treatment of the infection will only cure the enuresis in about one-third of cases. Treatment is more likely to be successful in cases in whom the enuresis is secondary (Stansfeld 1973). Thus, in most cases it seems more likely to be the wetting that causes the infection (Zaleski, Gerrard and Shokeir 1973). In all cases of persistent wetting, though, screening and if necessary, treatment, should be carried out.

Sleep

Parents of bedwetting children are still advised in the popular press that many bedwetters are unusually heavy sleepers (e.g. *Woman and Home* 1973; National Association for Maternal and Child Welfare 1975). If true, this would explain the child's unresponsiveness to the signals indicating a full bladder. However, evidence on this view has been contradictory. Broughton (1968), for example, found that enuresis usually occurs during the transition from deeper, non-REM, stage three and four sleep, to stage one sleep and usually at the end of the first sleep cycle. Some authors believe that enuresis may occur in stages three and four in the young child, as young children spend proportionately more time in stages three and four sleep.

Later EEG studies have failed to support either the belief that the sleep patterns of enuretics are deeper than those of non-enuretics, or that enuresis always occurs in the deepest stages of sleep (Gillin *et al.* 1982). In a comparison of enuretic and non-enuretic boys, Gillin *et al.* (1982) found that severely enuretic boys actually had more shallow sleep. Furthermore, when the sleep of enuretic boys was compared on wet and dry nights, no differences were found. They concluded that the enuretic act seemed to depend on time since going to sleep rather than the stage of the sleep cycle: on nights when only one episode occurred, peak wetting time was approximately four to five hours after going to sleep; on nights with two or more episodes, peak wetting time was during the second hour, with the second enuretic act most likely to occur four hours after the first. Overall, the evidence would now seem to indicate that enuresis can occur in any sleep stage, except during REM sleep (Norgaard *et al.* 1984; Graham 1973; Gillin *et al.* 1982).

Other authors have attempted to explain nocturnal enuresis in terms of a disorder of arousability. Although some authors previously used arousability as a measure of depth of sleep, Doleys *et al.* (1981) believe we should now distinguish between the two, depth

129

of sleep being based on EEG patterns and arousability being a behavioural measure. A child who is difficult to arouse would be relatively unresponsive to both internal (bladder distension) and external (bell or buzzer) cues (Finley and Wansley 1977). It is true that the problem of the enuretic child sleeping on through the bell or buzzer, whilst everyone else in the home may be rudely awakened, is still one of the biggest problems besetting this method of treatment (Young and Morgan 1973a). However, the few studies that have looked at the problems of whether enuretic subjects are more difficult to arouse than non-enuretics have produced conflicting results, as have studies comparing louder bells or buzzers. Finley and Wansley (1977) recommend using a 105 dB alarm in order to overcome the problem of arousability in slow responders; Young and Morgan (1973a), on the other hand, found no clear difference in overall effectiveness of louder buzzers. However, the types of subjects studied were different, which makes comparison of the results difficult. Doleys, Schwartz and Ciminero (1981) conclude that 'some enuretic children may indeed have an arousal problem that would benefit from the use of a louder stimulus . . .'.

Finally, successful treatment of nocturnal enuresis using drugs has often been thought to have its effect by lightening sleep. Indeed there is some EEG evidence that imipramine, for example, does alter sleep patterns (Graham 1973). But it is equally likely that these drugs have their effect in some other way, such as by causing the muscles in the bladder to relax and the sphincter to contract (Graham 1973).

Functional bladder capacity

Functional bladder capacity (FBC) refers to the volume of urine retained before voiding occurs and is not a measure of the structural size of the bladder. It is now a well-established fact that nocturnal enuretics tend to have smaller functional bladder capacities than non-enuretics.

Zaleski et al. (1973) and Berg, Fielding and Meadow (1977) found no difference between the enuretic and non-enuretic for the total volume of urine passed at night or during a 24-hour period, the enuretic child simply passing urine more frequently. Zaleski et al. (1973) found children with diurnal enuresis to have even smaller FBC than nocturnally enuretic children, although Berg et al. (1977) found no significant differences in maximum bladder capacity between day-and-night wetting children and children who wet only at night.

An increase in FBC has often been found in children who cease being nocturnally enuretic (Starfield and Mellits 1968), hence some authors have assumed that nocturnal enuresis is caused by a small functional bladder capacity. However, there are several problems with this explanation. First, children with smaller bladder capacities do not necessarily wet the bed (Kolvin 1975). Secondly, although some authors have claimed that a bladder capacity over a certain amount will enable a child to remain dry (Hagglund 1965), other authors have not been able to find a capacity beyond which nocturnal continence is guaranteed (Starfield and Mellits 1968): a bedwetting seven-year-old may have a larger functional bladder capacity than a dry five-year-old. Thirdly, although an increase in FBC often seems to coincide with cessation of wetting, this is by no means always the case; children who become dry may show no increase, whilst the bladders of some who remain wet may show substantial increases (Starfield and Mellits 1968; Fielding 1980).

The results of studies aiming to increase FBC by training the child to withhold urine for increasingly long periods (retention-control training or RCT) have shown equivocal results: for example, Kimmel and Kimmel (1970) and Miller (1973) obtained very good results using RCT; Starfield and Mellits (1968) found mixed results; and Fielding (1980) and Mahoney (1973) found poor results. Fielding's (1980) study is of particular interest here, as FBC was carefully measured before, during and after treatment. She found no significant changes in FBC for children wetting only at night who became dry compared with those who did not; and whilst increases in FBC did occur for those day-and-night wetting children who became dry, the evidence suggested that the changes occurred *after* dryness was achieved. She concludes that low FBC is probably a consequence of being nocturnally enuretic, not a cause of it, and Miller's (1973) hypothesis may be worth considering as an explanation of how the FBC remains or becomes low in enuretic children. He suggests that mothers of enuretics are oversensitive to cues indicating the child's need to void, resulting in frequent prompting to urinate in response to very weak bladder distension cues and a consequent failure of the child to learn to tolerate increases in bladder pressure. He, however, goes on to deduce that the small bladder capacity causes the enuresis and that the RCT cures the enuresis by causing the bladder capacity to increase. However, it is possible that the mother's behaviour was a response to the child's frequent need to urinate in the first place but that in handling the problem in this way the FBC becomes or stays low. It seems fair to conclude that the relation between FBC and nocturnal enuresis is not a simple one, as may have been previously supposed.

Abnormal EEG, epilepsy and subclinical epilepsy

Salmon, Taylor and Lee (1973), in a review of the literature on EEG and enuresis, confirm the findings of previous authors that a proportion of nocturnally enuretic children show an abnormal EEG despite never having suffered from epilepsy. They are, however, critical of previous authors who have assumed this to be indicative of epilepsy and who have attempted to link it with nocturnal enuresis. They are strongly opposed to regarding nocturnally enuretic children with abnormal EEGs as epileptic in the absence of any observable epileptic behaviour. Nor can they see any logical reason why epilepsy and nocturnal enuresis should be regarded as manifestations of the same thing simply because of similarities in the EEG pattern in a proportion of both. Before any conclusion can be reached regarding a hypothesised link between abnormal EEG and nocturnal enuresis, a longitudinal study of EEG patterns in children is required.

Allergy

Zaleski et al. (1972) found an increased incidence of hay fever, urticaria, food and drug allergies and an antipathy to milk in enuretic boys; in enuretic girls there was a significant increase in eczema. Simmonds and Parraga (1982) also found that significantly more subjects with ENT allergies were nocturnally enuretic compared with those without such allergies. Zaleski et al. (1972) suggest that the link between nocturnal enuresis and allergies might lie in the similar muscle components of the systems involved, which may react in a similar adverse manner to certain foods.

In a discussion of the possible effects of food in nocturnal enuresis, it is appropriate to consider the effect of caffeine. Excessive intake of caffeine is characterised, among other things, by frequent urination. In a small but interesting study in a group of residents in a psychiatric institution, deemed to have a large daily caffeine intake, Edelstein, Keaton-Brasted and Burg (1984) found a marked reduction in number of enuretic nights following withdrawal of caffeine. However, there were some limitations of this study.

Genetics

It is now a well-established fact that nocturnal enuresis runs in families. Bakwin (1973) found 77 per cent of children to be enuretic when both parents had been enuretic, 43 to 44 per cent when one parent was, and 15 per cent when neither parent was enuretic. Similar findings of a positive family history have been reported by others (e.g. Simmonds and Parraga 1982; Zaleski *et al*. 1972). Family history is said to be higher for primary rather than secondary nocturnal enuretics (Schaeffer 1979).

Dispute exists as to whether these findings support a genetic or environmental explanation. Bakwin (1973), in a study of monozygotic (MZ) and dizygotic (DZ) twins, found the concordance rate for MZ twins to be about twice that of DZ twins, a result reinforcing the importance of genetic factors. The 30 per cent discordance rate in MZ twins shows that environmental factors nevertheless do play a part in nocturnal enuresis.

It can be argued, though, that concordance rates would be expected to be higher in MZ twins as MZ twins tend to be treated alike by others, whereas DZ twins are treated no more alike than ordinary siblings. There are no studies of nocturnal enuresis in MZ twins reared apart to resolve this issue. However, the frequency of bedwetting would appear to be directly related to the closeness of the genetic relationship.

Despite evidence such as that from twin studies, some authors nevertheless conclude that 'there are obviously many alternative explanations and speculations regarding these data' (Doleys *et al*. 1981). A family history of enuresis has not, according to Schaeffer (1979), been found to affect treatment.

Maturation and development

Woman and Home magazine (1973) advises mothers that '. . . we presume that bedwetting results from a simple deficiency in nervous or muscular control'.

Many authors use the terms 'maturation' and 'development' synonymously. However, McKeith *et al*. (1973) urge us to distinguish between the two as follows: '. . . maturation, an inherited, inherent, predestined process in the nervous system, and development, the sequence of appearance of behaviours'. Development depends on the maturation of the nervous system and the existence of a behaviour is, of course, evidence that maturation of the underlying CNS structures has taken place.

Some authors (e.g. Campbell 1970) believe that the necessary physiological maturation for nocturnal dryness has taken place by about age three. The work of Brazelton (1962) is generally accepted as showing that, in 98.5 per cent of children, it must have taken place by five years. Furthermore, many children suffering from prolonged primary nocturnal enuresis do nevertheless have dry nights, indicating that the basic necessary maturation must have taken place: Miller (1973) found that 20 per cent of bedwetting five-year-olds had intermittent dryness, 29 per cent had dry periods of three to nine months and 50 per cent had the odd dry night. Many bedwetters also become dry for periods when away from home, e.g. on holiday or in hospital. Therefore, a delay in CNS maturation seems unlikely to account for the 20 per cent or so of bedwetting children over the age of five years (McKeith et al. 1973). McKeith et al. (1973) conclude that delayed maturation is unlikely to be responsible for more than a very small proportion of failures to be dry, and prefer to describe such a child as having a 'behavioural delay', thus avoiding the term 'developmental delay', which, they feel, implies a delay in maturation of the CNS for which evidence is lacking.

Other researchers in the field have, on the other hand, made great attempts to show that nocturnally enuretic children do show other signs of a maturational lag. Unfortunately, it is difficult to compare findings here as most of these studies have adopted rather different measures of the hypothesised developmental or maturational delay.

For example, Weir (1982), in a study of three-year-olds, found an association, for boys only, between nocturnal enuresis and 'delayed development' using scores on the Vineland Social Maturity Scale 'plus a few other developmental items'. The Vineland Social Maturity Scale would seem a rather crude measure for such a purpose, as does their method of assessing language. There was, however, no association for other factors that might be considered to be relevant to the issue of general immaturity and which others have found significant, such as height, weight or low birth weight (Oppel et al. 1968). He concluded that 'Among children who are wet at three, there is an excess of boys, of children . . . showing other delays in development and language'. Essen and Peckham (1976) found that more early bedwetters (at five to seven years) than dry children showed other signs of delayed development, e.g. not walking by eighteen months and not joining two words by two years. This did not apply to those still wetting at eleven years. But bedwetting at eleven years was significantly associated with shorter stature, poor speech and poorer physical co-ordination (girls only). They conclude that factors suggesting delayed development were associated only with bedwetting at an early stage. The information gathered in this study was retrospective, and should rightly be regarded as of suspect reliability.

Mikkelsen *et al*. (1982) in a search for signs of a maturational lag in neurological development, compared neurological status in various groups of boys, including primary enuretics and normals. Using the 'Physical and Neurological Examination for Soft Signs' (PANESS), considered to be a valid measure of developmental neural maturity, they found no significant differences between the scores of normal and enuretic boys between five and thirteen years, although differences were found between encopretic and non-encopretic enuretics and psychiatrically disturbed and non-disturbed enuretics. The authors conclude that some children with behaviour disorders, e.g. encopretic enuretics, do show signs of a lag in neuro-developmental maturity.

In an attempt to test the hypothesis that primary enuretics, when compared with acquired enuretics, would show a closer association with neurological measures and a less close association with social and psychological factors, Oppel *et al*. (1968) followed 859 children from birth to two years and compared permanently dry, relapsing and never-dry children. Children who showed some abnormality on clinical neurological examination at six years were more likely to be in the 'never-dry' category; also low-birth-weight children had a tendency to wet more frequently than full-term children. The authors conclude that bedwetting is associated with the types of neurological impairment that occur in low-birth-weight children. Unfortunately, despite the large sample size, there are various questionable features in this study. First, they defined 'relapsers' as children who had initially been dry for one month or longer but who subsequently wet at some time. This may be regarded by some as a somewhat over-inclusive definition of 'relapse' compared with the definitions used by others. Secondly, the categories of 'normal', 'questionable', or 'definite long-term defect' used to define neurological status did not seem to be very reliable: a second examination confirmed the first finding in about one-third of 'questionable' cases and three-quarters of 'definite' ones.

Kolvin (1975) proposes a subgroup of nocturnal enuretics suffering from an 'isolated milestone delay' due to neurological immaturity of structures subserving bladder control. Support for this hypothesis is claimed by the tendency to spontaneous improvement and the well-established family history of nocturnal enuresis, which argues for a genetic determination of the maturational delay.

McKeith *et al.* (1973), having said that delayed maturation is only rarely responsible for delayed dryness over five years, propose that if maturation has occurred relatively late, say in the fourth as opposed to the second and third years, other 'negative' factors may upset or inhibit the emergence of dryness. Such 'negative' factors could be, for example, high anxiety due to chronic family stresses in the early years, or prolonged illness. Thus, a slight maturational delay could interact with adverse environmental factors.

Psychological factors

Psychodynamic approaches hypothesise that nocturnal enuresis is a symptom of psychological disturbances caused by an underlying intra-psychic conflict.

This evidence is supported by evidence that enuretic children, particularly girls, display a higher rate of various types of behaviour disturbances (Rutter, Yule and Graham 1973; Srivastava, Nigam and Singh 1982; Benjamin, Serdahely and Geppert 1971; Essen and Peckham 1976; Oppel *et al.* 1968). However, first, on closer inspection, there emerges no particular pattern of emotional disturbances consistently associated with enuresis. For example, some authors find 'nervousness', e.g. tics, mannerisms, thumb sucking, withdrawal, fearfulness, etc., related to bedwetting (Oppel *et al.* 1968), whereas others do not (Weir 1982).

Second, although enuretic children may show signs of disturbed behaviour, these may still be within normal limits (Couchells *et al.* 1981).

Third, by no means all nocturnal enuretics do show signs of emotional disturbance. Kolvin (1975) quotes 71 per cent as being psychiatrically normal and Schaeffer (1979) quotes a rate of one in five as having emotional disorders. Other authors find evidence of psychiatric disturbance only in particular subgroups of enuretics such as girls with day-and-night wetting and not in those that wet only at night (Rutter *et al.* 1973; Berg *et al.* 1977).

Fourth, it is not clear that the emotional disturbance is the cause of the enuresis. There is evidence to suggest that the reverse may be true, namely that the embarrassing and sensitive nature of the problem of nocturnal enuresis cause the emotional disturbance and that emotional problems frequently disappear when the enuresis is cured (Baker 1969).

In the absence of any real evidence that *primary* nocturnal enuresis is caused by psychological factors, it is frequently hypothesised that *secondary* nocturnal enuresis has its origins in psychological disturbances due to stresses such as hospital admissions, break up of the family, moving house, starting school, or birth of a sibling. Figures as high as 81 per cent have been reported for secondary enuretics experiencing such a stress in the month preceding onset of the enuresis (Fritz and Armbrust 1982). However, other authors do not believe that specific stresses have been identified in secondary enuresis either (Kolvin 1975).

Anxiety has been proposed as playing a substantial part, both in primary and secondary enuresis. Since it is established that fear can produce a voiding reaction and anxiety can increase the frequency of micturition, it is proposed that high levels of anxiety can cause a recurrence of bedwetting as well as hindering the emergence of nocturnal continence in children around the age when this normally develops. Certain stressful events may cause high levels of anxiety and fear. For example, Benjamin *et al.* (1971) found that bedwetting is greater in children who had been separated from the primary caretaker in the years two-and-a-half to five and that such children show greater fear of abandonment. He also found that bedwetters show greater fear of abandonment than children dry at night. By contrast, Couchells *et al.* (1981) found that stressful events in early life did not relate significantly to enuresis, nor did Weir (1982) find any relation between admissions to hospital, separations, or family life stresses and day-and-night wetting in a population of three-year-olds.

However, the same stresses will not necessarily result in bed-wetting in all children — only those particularly sensitive to that form of stress or for whom the achievement of continence has been somewhat precarious anyway (Morgan 1981). McKeith *et al.* (1973) propose a sensitive period for the emergence of night-time dryness, during which time anxieties and stresses can have an inhibiting effect. Night-time dryness having failed to emerge because of such stresses present around the expected time, other anxiety producing factors, such as negative parental attitudes, may then come into play, causing current stresses that perpetuate the problem.

Finally, Rutter *et al.* (1973) have proposed the existence of two types of enuretics, the first type wetting only at night which is commoner in boys, runs in families and is not associated with psychiatric disorder; and the second type, which is commoner in girls, and is characterised by wetting in the day as well as night and psychiatric disturbance. Berg *et al.* (1977) found some evidence to support the existence of two independent groups, but found that enuretic children did not tend to fall neatly into one or other group.

To summarise, the vast majority of bedwetters show no sign of psychiatric disturbance. However, for a minority of bedwetters anxieties and stresses may hinder the emergence of nocturnal continence, or may cause a recurrence of bedwetting. There is some evidence that girls who are wet by day as well as by night are more likely to show psychiatric disturbances.

Learning factors

Because conditioning treatment of nocturnal enuresis has to date proved the single most successful form of treatment in terms of initial arrest of bedwetting, some authors have inferred that nocturnal continence normally develops via a conditioning process and that nocturnal enuresis is therefore caused by faulty learning. In discussing this, various writers quote Mowrer and Mowrer (1938), Lovibond (1963) and Azrin, Sneed and Foxx (1973, 1974) as proposing nocturnal continence to be learned by way of a classical conditioning, instrumental avoidance conditioning, or operant conditioning paradigm, respectively (Doleys *et al.* 1981; Sorotzkin 1984; Schaeffer 1979). However, the fact that a conditioning procedure can result in nocturnal continence does not logically imply that nocturnal continence always develops due to a conditioning process.

Mowrer and Mowrer (1938) proposed nocturnal continence to be a learned habit, most commonly learned through the practice of 'lifting' the sleeping child at times when it is supposed that his bladder will be partially filled, so that the attendant bladder distension cues eventually become associated with the response of waking. Thus, presumably,

Bladder distension ⟶ lifting ⟶ waking
CS ⟶ UCS ⟶ (U)CR

Whether the practice of 'lifting' achieves any training in itself apart from helping to achieve dry beds seems to be a matter of some dispute. Some authors feel it does not and may even do harm by making the child dependent on being wakened (Morgan 1981). Other authors have found that children can become dry by using systematic waking schedules (Rolider, Van Houten and Chlebowski 1984), although not so effectively as when bell and pad are included. Mowrer and Mowrer (1938) themselves admit that most parents do not bother with this practice anyway. Second, this explanation for the development of nocturnal continence assumes that parents who 'lift' their child are doing so at a time when bladder distension cues are sufficiently strong so as to become associated with the response of waking up. But as has been pointed out, the practice of 'timing' in toilet training is a highly dubious one. Third, although there are no good observational data on what happens as children are developing dryness at night, it seems that many, if not most children do not go through an interim stage of waking up and going to the toilet prior to being able to sleep the night through without the need to urinate; most probably simply stop wetting and sleep through. Fourth, many of the examples given by Mowrer and Mowrer (1938) of training practices used in primitive societies can equally easily be explained in operant terms. Finally, they admit that most children, if left to themselves, would almost certainly develop night-time continence of their own accord.

Thus, although Mowrer and Mowrer (1938) explicitly propose a classical conditioning model to account both for what they refer to as 'the most common method of training bladder control during sleep' (i.e. lifting), and for the mode of operation of bell and pad treatment, it is not at all clear that they are proposing a classical conditioning model to account generally for normal development of nocturnal continence.

Azrin *et al.* (1973, 1974) view toileting as 'an operant process in which social and motivational factors play as great a role as does sensitivity to bladder and bowel stimuli'. Bedwetting is viewed as a complex problem involving factors such as ease of arousability from sleep, ability to inhibit urination, social motivation to become dry and the strength of alternative responses to bedwetting. Accordingly, they have developed a training 'package' for nocturnal continence that, along with bell and pad for immediate detection of wetting accidents, uses increased fluid intake to increase the frequency of the operant behaviour and other features such as positive reinforcement for appropriate urination and punishment for wetting accidents. Results are claimed to be substantially improved over those obtained using standard bell and pad, a finding supported by others to a greater or lesser extent (Bollard and Nettlebeck 1981). A previous study by Azrin *et al.* (1973) had found no reduction in bedwetting using the alarm alone, unless social and motivational events were associated with the buzzer. Furthermore, in order to test whether the conditioning function of the alarm was classical or operant in nature, they omitted the buzzer for the enuretic child and found the enuresis to be eliminated just as effectively. Thus, they claim that Pavlovian conditioning did not contribute to the effectiveness of their procedure.

Against an operant learning explanation, McKeith *et al.* (1973) believe it unlikely that bladder control is normally thus learned, since rewards and punishments must be linked closely in time with the behaviour concerned and obvious difficulties are presented in a sleeping child learning in this way. Nor could one argue that dryness at night is a carry-over from conditioned dryness by day, as a sizeable percentage of children become dry at night first (McKeith 1973). Thus, although McKeith *et al.* (1973) accept that training is an important factor in the development of daytime control, they believe that night-time dryness emerges spontaneously without teaching.

Treatment by bell and pad method does, on the other hand, suggest a learning component (Turner 1973) as do any cultural differences in rates of wetting (e.g. Weir 1982). Kolvin (1975) proposes that maturation and learning are complementary components in achieving bladder control.

Toilet training practices

Related to any discussion of the role of learning factors in nocturnal enuresis is the issue of toilet training practices. Early, strict, or inconsistent training have been proposed as factors in nocturnal enuresis, but findings here have been contradictory (e.g. Christmanson and Lisper 1982; Couchells *et al.* 1981; Benjamin *et al.* 1971).

Environmental factors

Social class. Nocturnal enuresis is reported as being higher in lower social classes (Miller 1973; Essen and Peckham 1976). Oppel *et al.* (1968) found this relationship with 'relapsing' children (i.e. children dry for at least one month) but not for 'never dry' children.

Family size. A number of studies have found enuresis to be associated with larger families (e.g. Miller 1973).

Birth order. Likewise, a number of studies have found enuretics to be second or middle children (Miller 1973; Oppel *et al.* 1968). Essen and Peckham (1976) found such a relation between enuresis and fourth or later born children.

Overcrowding. Enuresis tends to be associated with overcrowding and measures of overcrowding, such as sharing a bed (Miller 1973; Essen and Peckham 1976). Essen and Peckham (1976) found no relationship between bedwetting and lack of an indoor toilet.

Parental skills and characteristics

As might be expected, studies here have shown less clear results, but do tend to support the idea that parents of enuretics are generally less competent and more socially inadequate (Miller 1976; Oppel *et al.* 1968). To summarise, enuretics do seem to come from families showing a greater general degree of social handicap. Kolvin (1975) proposes that social factors have their effect through poor training experiences.

MEDICAL SCREENING AND HISTORY

Kolvin (1975) and Doleys *et al.* (1981) recommend a full examination and history prior to embarking on treatment. This should involve history and description of the problem, family medical history, other problems, home and family environment and previous treatments. This serves to highlight the likely cause or causes of the enuresis and to determine whether the enuresis is primary or secondary. Although extensive urological invesigation is generally considered both unnecessary and undesirable at the outset (Doleys *et al.* 1981), urinary tract infection and other related disorders should always be excluded at the beginning as possible causes. On examination, the vast majority of children will be found to be normal, healthy children.

141

TREATMENT

There is some disagreement in the literature as to when treatment for nocturnal enuresis should be considered. Azrin *et al.* (1974), for example, offer 'Dry Bed' treatment as early as three years of age. Weir (1982), although defining enuresis as more than the occasional accident after age two, would not recommend 'treatment' at this age, but does recommend physical and urine examination, as well as the taking of a history to ensure development is progressing normally. Mowrer and Mowrer (1938) do not recommend enuresis alarm treatment under three years of age. Treatment for nocturnal enuresis is generally not recommended below five years (Kolvin 1975).

SIMPLE MEASURES FOR DEALING WITH NOCTURNAL ENURESIS

Many authors recommend beginning with 'supportive treatment' or 'simple measures', particularly in the pre-school age range (Fritz and Armbrust 1982; Kolvin 1975; Morgan 1981; Schaeffer 1979; Brazelton 1973). These generally involve neither risk nor expense, although there is little hard evidence to show that they do much good either. However, they may be useful, used alone or in combination.

Anxiety reduction

The importance of stress during the 'sensitive' period when maturation occurs and dryness normally emerges is frequently emphasised (Kolvin 1975; Schaeffer 1979; McKeith, Meadow and Turner 1973). Brazelton (1973), in whose clinical practice 98.5 per cent of children achieved dryness by age five, goes so far as to recommend that parents be counselled and guided from the birth of the child through the pre-school years, with regard to the issue of urinary control. The aim here is to reduce conflict between parent and child, first, by teaching them the importance of waiting until the child shows readiness to become dry, then by handling the 'training' gently and sympathetically. Similarly, Benjamin *et al.* (1971) who recommend (in contrast to Brazelton) beginning night training at no later than two-and-a-half years, emphasise the need to encourage maturation and mastery without arousing fears of abandonment in the child and without turning training into a power struggle.

Night-time awakening

Waking or lifting the sleeping child during the night, especially just before the parents' bedtime, is one of the most common methods of 'training' used by parents (Mowrer and Mowrer 1938). However, although this can result in a reduction in bedwetting, just whether or not this procedure actually results in any training is a matter for some debate; when lifting is stopped, the number permanently cured is much lower than any other method and is probably explicable in terms of spontaneous remission.

Kolvin (1975) believes lifting is most successful with children already on the verge of dryness, but has little effect on others. Benjamin, Serdahely and Geppert (1971) found no statistically significant evidence that night lifting helps bedwetting. Morgan (1981) concludes that not only it is not an effective procedure, but it may even be harmful by causing the child to become dependent on being awakened. However, he recommends trying a staggered-timing programme of lifting, for at most six months, where the time between going to bed and being lifted is gradually increased, but not in a fixed interval fashion (thus one hour, three hours, one and a half hours, four hours, two hours, three-and-a-half hours, etc.).

Other authors have claimed improved cure rates using nightly awakening in conjunction with other training procedures (Azrin *et al*. 1973, 1974; Rolider *et al*. 1984; Bollard and Nettlebeck 1981). For example, Azrin *et al*. (1974) combine the use of an enuresis alarm with procedures that include increased fluid intake and hourly awakening (with practice in going quickly to the toilet) during one night of intensive training on the 'Dry Bed' programme. By contrast, though, rather than being asked to urinate each time, the child is asked each time if he can hold back his urine for a further hour, if not, he is asked to hold back for at least a few minutes. After the intensive training night, the child is awakened for toileting just before the parents' bedtime and thereafter half an hour earlier each night, provided he has been dry the previous night, until the time of awakening would follow the child's bedtime by only one hour, at which point the procedure is discontinued. Rolider *et al*. (1984), in a comparison of a modified 'Dry Bed' procedure and the awakening procedure on its own, found their particular awakening procedure to be the effective component. The 'stringently faded' awakening procedure involved waking the child, on the first night of training, five hours before his usual time of waking up in the morning; then, if dry for six consecutive mornings, awakening the child one hour earlier and so on, until the awakening time was eight hours before his normal waking up time in the morning. On the other hand Bollard and Nettlebeck (1982), in an attempt to analyse the effectiveness of the various 'Dry Bed' components, including the waking procedure in the 'Dry Bed' programme, found no component to be significantly effective on its own. If waking schedules are effective, it is not clear why: Bollard and Nettlebeck (1982) suggest it may improve ease of arousability (see section on 'sleep' as a factor in nocturnal enuresis) from sleep, and results in positive reinforcement for maintaining a dry bed.

Whether a lifting procedure 'trains' nocturnal continence or not, it can be useful in boosting morale all round if it results in a dry bed. Parents who try this approach might usefully consider the findings of Gillin et al. (1982), whose EEG studies on enuresis found enuresis to be time dependent, rather than dependent on the stage of sleep, with the peak frequency of wetting approximately four to five hours after onset of sleep on nights with one enuretic episode; on nights with two or more episodes, peak frequency (although less clear) occurred during the second hour, and again durng the fourth hour after the first episode.

Finally, there is some debate about whether or not it is necessary for the child to be fully awake when lifted for toileting. Christmanson and Lisper (1984) believe lifting the child while sleeping to be counter productive. They found, first, that significantly more enuretic children had been 'lifted' during the night than non-enuretic children, and second, that all had been sleeping or almost sleeping when urinating. Some authors go so far as to establish wakefulness by questioning the child as to the day of the week, etc. (Rolider et al. 1984). Young and Morgan (1972a) also emphasise the importance of the child being fully awake. Mowrer and Mowrer (1938) state the importance of arousing the child as quickly as possible while the bell is still ringing. Failure to achieve dryness by using the enuresis alarm has often been attributed to failure of some children to awaken to the alarm (Young and Morgan 1973a). On the other hand, Lovibond (1963) believes it is not essential for the child to be completely awake during the training process.

Fluid restriction

Fluid restriction is perhaps the procedure most commonly recommended to parents of bedwetting children. For example, the popular woman's magazine *Woman and Home* recommended fluid restriction to parents in both 1973 and 1977. Restriction usually takes place in the hour or so before bedtime, or sometimes even from teatime onwards.

Kolvin (1975) suggests that 'sensible fluid limits' are often successful with some children if used in conjunction with lifting. The problem is that what seems 'sensible' limits to some parents would probably be, in effect, quite drastic: for example the middle-class parents of two pre-school children who recently permitted no fluids from (and including) teatime onwards. These parents were thus obliged to conceal their own teatime drink under the table, while taking surreptitious sips from time to time, a practice of which the children cannot have been unaware. One can hardly imagine a situation more likely to cause thirst and consequent bad temper and resentment on the part of bedwetting children. Situations like this are encountered regularly by workers in this field. Morgan (1981) believes that fluid restriction as a method of controlling bedwetting is based on a misconception, namely that if the child drinks less, the volume of urine will be smaller, and the bladder will be capable of holding a smaller volume for the entire night. Although this may seem to help initially, it is ultimately likely to do more harm than good by reducing the functional bladder capacity, since the bladder simply adjusts to holding a smaller amount of urine and triggers at a lower level. Certainly, Benjamin, Serdahely and Geppert (1971) found no evidence that restricting fluid intake after evening meal or stopping the night bottle helped bedwetting. Some clinicians, however, still recommend it (Olness 1975; Stanton 1979).

Other clinicians not only do not recommend fluid restriction, but actually recommend increasing fluid intake by one or two cups just before going to bed when seven consecutive dry nights have been achieved by children over five years, until a further seven consecutive dry nights are achieved.

Young and Morgan (1972b), Morgan (1978) and Taylor and Turner (1975) recommend the use of an 'overlearning' procedure in enuresis alarm treatment, in which after achieving the initial arrest criterion, the trainee is required to learn to tolerate the additional stress imposed on the bladder by drinking one to two pints of liquid immediately before retiring. There is evidence that such a procedure reduces the relapse rate. Azrin *et al.* (1973, 1974) use increased fluid intake to increase the frequency of the operant behaviour as part of their 'Dry Bed' programme. In all these treatment programmes, there is evidence that, far from aggravating the problems of nocturnal enuresis, increased fluid intake is, in the long term, helpful.

In summary, the consensus now seems to be that restricting fluids is not helpful, and may even the make the problem worse by resulting in reduced functional bladder capacity. On the other hand, there is no evidence that increasing fluids is in any way harmful, but there is some evidence that it may speed up training and reduce relapse rates.

Star charts and other rewards

Star charts are frequently recommended as helpful as a reward system, especially for younger children (Morgan 1981; Weir 1982; Sorotzkin 1984). Other clinicians give qualified support to their use, provided it does not increase anxiety or sense of failure when it does not work (Kolvin 1975; National Association for Maternal and Child Welfare 'Enuresis' leaflet 1975). This, of course, could be said for any attempt at treatment, whatever the method. A concrete reward as a back-up reinforcer in conjunction with star chars is sometimes recommended (Morgan 1981). For example, one could offer a special treat of some description for, say, three consecutive dry nights. Others feel this is not beneficial (Benjamin *et al.* 1971). Benjamin *et al.* (1971) found that positive interpersonal interactions, especially hugging and kissing, were the most effective reinforcers in night training. Their study showed that parents implicitly use an operant conditioning approach to the training of night-time continence. If this is so, then it is clearly crucial that parents reward the appropriate (dryness) and not the inappropriate (wetness) behaviour: for example, Christmanson and Lisper (1982) found that significantly more enuretic children had been taken into bed with their parents (i.e. rewarded) contingent upon wetting the bed. It is understandable that tired parents may find this the easier option than getting up to change a wet bed.

Punishments

It is an established fact that learning occurs more rapidly under conditions of reward than punishment. That parents, faced with a child waking them perhaps every night for a change of sheets, sometimes lose their patience is also understandable — the middle of the night, when one is tired, is not the best time to be faced with problems that require sympathetic handling. Many parents resort to shaming, spanking, scolding, threats, etc., under these circumstances, but this may only serve to increase anxiety and further aggravate the problem (Kolvin 1975). Benjamin *et al.* (1971) found that night training was hampered by the use of punishments such as shaming, spanking, rejecting and name calling. Weir (1982) phrases it thus, when explaining the problem to parents: 'If I tell you not to think about the Golden Gate Bridge, you cannot eliminate it from your mind. Now imagine your child trudging to bed with the admonition not to wet his bed. Perhaps he hears his mind say "Don't wet the bed, don't wet the bed, don't wet the bed . . ." ' Wetting accidents are best ignored or minimised by saying 'Never mind, we'll do better next time'.

Reactions to food

Allergies could be a causal factor in nocturnal enuresis, since there is some evidence that nocturnal enuresis in boys is significantly associated with various allergic conditions. Zaleski *et al.* (1972) found nocturnal enuresis to be significantly associated with food and drug allergies and an antipathy to milk, as well as hay fever and urticaria, in boys but not girls. They suggest that other systems with a smooth muscle component, as well as respiratory and gastrointestinal, might also react to certain foods.

Excessive caffeine intake is known to result, amongst other things, in frequent urination. Edelstein *et al.* (1984) carried out an interesting study on the effect of caffeine withdrawal on nocturnal enuresis, insomnia and severely disturbed behaviour, on ten residents of a psychiatric institution deemed to have excessive caffeine intake. The most interesting finding concerned the reduction in enuretic episodes, fairly dramatic in some cases, that occurred. Shortcomings of this study, highlighted by the authors themselves, included the lack of a double-blind procedure during withdrawal of caffeinated beverages and the lack of accurate monitoring of fluid intake over the various phases. Also, the criterion for 'excessive' caffeine intake was set at three cups of coffee per day or more. Nevertheless, the results of this study are certainly worth considering.

MAJOR TREATMENT APPROACHES

A review of the literature indicates that a variety of treatment approaches are available for nocturnal enuresis. Fritz and Armbrust (1981) conclude, somewhat pessimistically, that permanent success rates are frustratingly low, due probably to the fact that there is no objective basis for deciding which type of treatment to use with which enuretic child. Weir (1982) differentiates six subgroups of nocturnal enuretics with different treatment methods proposed for each group. Unfortunately, he fails to make explicit the basis for these subgroups, and provides no data on the validity of the different treatments proposed for each subgroup. It is interesting to note that he suggests the enuresis alarm for use with only one group, the lifelong enuretic or heavy sleeper (see p. 127), with the almost dismissive comment that some patients in this group will respond to alarms. It is, though, generally agreed that there may be different types of nocturnal enuretics who may respond differently to various methods of treatment (e.g. Fielding 1982).

Enuresis alarm

The enuresis alarm is still the most widely used method of treatment for nocturnal enuresis. Some clinicians regard it as the treatment of choice in the case of primary enuresis (Kolvin 1975), but others do not differentiate between primary and secondary enuresis as far as use of alarm in treatment is concerned, since they find no differences in outcome with the two groups (Sacks and De Leon 1973).

A battery-operated alarm which sounds a bell, or more commonly a buzzer, or shakes a vibrator box beneath the pillow (for deaf trainees or for use in communal sleeping settings), is connected to an electrode in the form of a pad of some sort, placed under a draw sheet. When the child urinates, the urine passes through the draw sheet to the electrode, completing the electrical circuit and activating the alarm. The alarm continues until the child wakes or is wakened, switches it off and changes the bed. The alarm is then ready to be reset for use. As training progresses, the child learns to inhibit urination increasingly quickly upon activation of the alarm (the diameter of the wet patch is said to decrease), until he finally learns to inhibit micturition and wake up before the alarm is activated.

Although first devised by Pfaundler in 1904 (Mowrer and

Mowrer 1938) as a method of indicating when an infant required changing, it was discovered during its use to be a successful method of treatment for nocturnal enuresis. It was reintroduced by Mowrer and Mowrer in 1938 to 'excellent effect' with thirty children between three and thirteen years, all of whom became dry within four to eight weeks. They hypothesise that the alarm works via a classical conditioning paradigm thus:

$$\text{bladder distension} \longrightarrow \text{alarm} \longrightarrow \text{waking}$$
$$\text{CS} \longrightarrow \text{UCS} \longrightarrow \text{(U)CR}$$

where bladder distension cues eventually become conditioned to the response of waking up.

Effectiveness

Initial success rates for standard bell and pad treatment are reported as high, although success rates such as those claimed by Mowrer and Mowrer (1938, 100 per cent cured), have given way to more modest, but still impressive claims of around 80 per cent. Sloop (1970), for example, reports a mean initial success rate of 84 per cent for twenty studies. High initial success rates have even been reported under training conditions that one might regard as potentially more difficult: Jehu *et al.* (1977) achieved dryness with eighteen out of nineteen children in residential children's homes and Sacks and De Leon (1978) found 81.8 per cent of disturbed enuretic children to reach their initial success criterion.

Bell and pad treatment is more effective than retention control training (Fielding 1980), drugs (Blackwell and Currah 1973), psychotherapy (Werry and Cohrssen 1965), contingent but delayed alarm (Collins 1973; Peterson, Wright and Hanlon 1969), nonspecific factors such as professional attention, impressive apparatus (Collins 1973), and spontaneous remission (Collins 1973). No study has shown any evidence of symptom substitution. Several report improvement in behaviour problems (e.g. Jehu *et al.* 1977).

There is, however, some difficulty in evaluating results obtained in different studies, as data for a number of crucial factors may either not be presented at all or may vary considerably across studies making comparison difficult. These factors are as follows:

Criterion for success

Deacon (1939) used a criterion for success of seven consecutive dry nights, whereas Dische *et al.* (1983) used 42 consecutive dry nights. Others have used criteria of ten (Collins 1973), thirteen (Sacks and De Leon 1978) or fourteen consecutive dry nights (Sloop and Kennedy 1973; Young and Morgan 1972a), or one wetting incident in 28 consecutive nights (Taylor and Turner 1975). The most popular has been fourteen consecutive dry nights.

Definition of relapse

Criteria such as more than one wet night per week for two weeks (Collins 1973), at least once a week for four consecutive weeks (Dische *et al.* 1983; Sacks and De Leon 1978) or two wet nights in any week (Fielding 1980) have been used. Others have defined a 'relapse' as being a 'recurrence of wetting sufficient to cause the parents to request a further appointment at the clinic' (Young and Morgan 1973b). Others do not define relapse at all (Mowrer and Mowrer 1938). Jehu *et al.* (1977) describe the definition of relapse as 'completely arbitrary'. Definition is made difficult by the fact that there are unfortunately no normative data on wetting accident rates after development of nocturnal continence in non-enuretic children. However, Dische *et al.* (1983) found that as many as 71 per cent of their long-term successes had occasional wet beds after successful training, approximately half of them within the first year and the remainder between one and two years. Jehu *et al.* (1977) found isolated cases of wetting two or three times a month among non-relapsers over a 20-month period. Dische *et al.* (1983) found that most of these occasional wettings were related to physical illness or transient environmental stress and remitted spontaneously. It would thus seem important that a relapse should be defined as occurring over a period of several consecutive weeks (Dische *et al.* 1983), since according to Fielding's (1980) definition, a child who wet twice during a week of illness would be said to have relapsed.

Length of follow-up

Relapse rates will clearly depend on length of follow-up, the shorter the follow-up period, the lower the relapse rate will generally be (Doleys 1977).

Some studies state only that trainees were followed up, but not for how long (Sacks and De Leon 1973). Follow-up periods of three months (Finley *et al.* 1973), nine months (Collins 1973), twelve months (Sacks and De Leon 1978), twenty months minimum (Jehu *et al.* 1977), to over three or four years (Dische *et al.* 1983) have been reported. Even within a study, follow-up of individual children may vary from three months to over two years, depending on date of discharge (Young and Morgan 1973b). Dische *et al.* (1983) argue for follow-up of at least two years. Many studies do not present data for what percentage of trainees were followed up successfully or the manner in which follow-up was carried out (e.g. home visit, by telephone, etc.).

Presentation of results

Comparison of results is frequently difficult as some reports express results in terms of percentage improvement (Kolvin *et al.* 1973), others in terms of mean number of wetting accidents per week (e.g. Finley *et al.* 1973) or medians (Azrin *et al.* 1974). Duration of treatment may be expressed in terms of days, weeks, trials (i.e. alarm activations), or may not be given at all.

Dropouts

Dropouts before and during treatment are difficult to deal with, since one cannot really know whether these cases would have been successfully treated or not. Some exclude dropouts from the results altogether; others group dropouts before and during treatment together, but treat failures separately; and yet others group dropouts during treatment along with failures and ignore dropouts before treatment. The practice of excluding from the results those who dropout before or during treatment has been argued as resulting in artificially high initial success rates (Taylor and Turner 1975). Young and Morgan (1972b) feel that termination must to some extent be equated with failure: they found that, in a comparable period of time, those who terminated had made significantly less progress than those subsequently discharged.

Criterion for inclusion of subjects

Severity of wetting may vary considerably across studies. Criteria have included: at least one wet night per week (Fielding 1980), at least three times per week (Dische *et al.* 1983) and 'if the parents saw the enuresis as a problem' (Taylor and Turner 1975).

Baseline data

Duration of baseline data may vary considerably from one week (Peterson *et al.* 1969) to nine weeks (Dische *et al.* 1983) or may be based on a mother's estimates of frequency. However, Taylor and

Turner (1975) found a correlation of 0.845 between mother's estimates and actual frequency, indicating mother's reports to be quite accurate.

In an attempt to overcome some of those problems, Doleys (1977) used his own criteria to evaluate the result of twelve studies and found a success rate of 75 per cent.

Duration of treatment

Doleys (1977) reports on twelve studies in which the mean duration of treatment ranged from 5 to 12 weeks. Some studies use a criterion to failure: for example, Kennedy and Sloop (1968) terminated treatment after 7 weeks. Mean duration of treatment can hide a very wide range of treatment durations: Jehu *et al*. (1977) found a range of 5 to 28 weeks in residential childrens homes; Sacks and De Leon (1978) report a range of less than 2 to 53 weeks for training non-disturbed children.

Relapse rate

Mowrer and Mowrer (1938) report relapses following this method of treatment to be relatively rare, occurring a few weeks or months after treatment. They present no data, nor do they specify length of follow-up period. Since then, relapse rates have been reported to be high, usually between 35 and 50 per cent at follow-up after three to six months (Turner 1973; Lovibond 1964). Doleys (1977) found that 41 per cent of the relapsers in the twelve studies he evaluated did so within six months of treatment. Dische *et al*. (1983) found 88 per cent of relapses did so within one year, two-thirds of these relapsing within the first six months. Retraining of relapsed trainees has been found to result in 40 to 50 per cent of these becoming and remaining dry, though more than one retraining is sometimes necessary (Sacks and De Leon 1983; Dische *et al*. 1983). Doleys (1977) reports a mean success rate of 68 per cent for retraining of relapsed trainees.

Great efforts have been made to find factors predictive of outcome, for both initial and long-term success and also for dropout from treatment.

Factors affecting initial success

Kolvin *et al*. (1973), Collins (1973), Sacks and De Leon (1973) and Fielding (1985) have not found *frequency of bedwetting* to be a factor in initial outcome. However, Finley, Rainwater and Johnson (1982) found that multiple wetting (more than one wet bed per night) beyond the third week of treatment was associated with longer treatment time to dryness criterion. Evidence as to whether *problems of daytime control* are a factor in successful treatment with bell and pad is contradictory: Fielding (1980, 1982, 1985) found that children wet by day as well as night, and those with problems of daytime frequency and urgency were less likely to become dry, and when they did, took significantly longer. Taylor and Turner (1975) and Dische *et al.* (1983), on the other hand, have found no such relationship. Berg *et al.* (1977) and Fielding (1985) have found no relationship between *low functional bladder capacity* and failure in enuresis alarm treatment. A number of authors have found no significant difference in treatment outcome for *primary and secondary enuretics* (Sacks and De Leon 1973; Collins 1973; Morgan and Young 1975; Taylor and Turner 1975; Dische *et al.* 1983), although Kolvin *et al.* (1973) found that primary nocturnal enuretics responded better to the enuresis alarm than did secondary enuretics. There is no evidence for any relation between *sex and age* and initial treatment outcome (Collins 1973; Taylor and Turner 1975; Dische *et al.* 1983; Finley *et al.* 1982; Fielding 1985). Thus, whatever the reasons are for more boys than girls being bedwetters, given a group of enuretic girls and boys, sex seems no longer to be a factor of importance (Young and Morgan 1973b). Although Mowrer and Mowrer (1938) claim that excellent results may be achieved when enuresis is not complicated by serious personality difficulties, the findings of other authors have not shown *deviant behaviour* to be a factor in treatment outcome (Collins 1973; Taylor and Turner 1975; Sacks and De Leon 1978; Dische *et al.* 1983; Fielding 1985).

Family history of enuresis has not been found to be associated with treatment outcome (Taylor and Turner 1975; Dische *et al.* 1983; Fielding 1985). Evidence for a relationship between factors indicative of *unsatisfactory housing* (e.g. shared sleeping arrangements, lack of bathroom/indoor toilet) and initial success is contradictory (Jehu *et al.* 1977; Dische *et al.* 1983; Fielding 1985), as is evidence for the effect of *family difficulties* (e.g. marital discord, mental illness (Dische *et al.* 1983; Fielding 1985)). *Social class* has not been found to be predictive of initial success (Collins 1973; Taylor and Turner 1975; Dische *et al.* 1983). Fielding (1985) found treatment failure to be significantly associated with *previous alarm treatment*, whereas Dische *et al.* (1983) did not. *Non-response or poor response* to the auditory stimulus of the alarm has been found to be associated with poor therapeutic outcome (Young and Morgan 1973a). They compared alarms of different loudness, but concluded that louder buzzers are not necessarily more effective.

Finley and Wansley (1977), on the other hand, using a very much louder alarm, found it to be effective in increasing acquisition rate for slow responders. They used mains-operated equipment to avoid fluctuation due to drained batteries, and positioned the alarm in the bedroom so as to result in the required loudness at the pillow, as the loudness in the pillow will normally vary according to furniture and furnishings in the bedroom, a factor not adequately controlled for by Young and Morgan (1973a).

Factors associated with withdrawal from treatment

Parental attitudes have been found to affect likelihood of withdrawal from treatment (Morgan and Young 1975; Fielding 1985), with less-tolerant parents being more likely to drop out of treatment. These authors found parental intolerance to be greater in lower socioeconomic groups, where incidence of enuresis is greatest and thus may be related to the practical problems presented by enuresis in unsatisfactory housing conditions. A study by Butler, Brewin and Forsythe (1986) confirmed that greater intolerance was related to greater perceived burden on the mother. Perhaps related to this, Young and Morgan (1972c) found *family history of enuresis* to be significantly associated with likelihood of withdrawal from treatment. In a study specifically of factors related to withdrawal from treatment, Young and Morgan (1972b) also found that *difficulty in awakening to the alarm* was associated with withdrawal from treatment but Fielding (1985) did not. Other factors such as severity and irregularity of enuresis, poor daytime control, soiling, presence of psychological symptoms, various family variables such as social class, family size, birth order, family difficulties, unsatisfactory housing and treatment variables such as previous attempts, referral source, etc., time on waiting list, were not associated with dropout from treatment (Young and Morgan 1972b).

Factors related to relapse

Evidence as to the relation between *frequency of wetting* and relapse rate is contradictory: Sacks and De Leon (1973) found greater resistance to extinction of the conditioned response in trainees whose wetting rate rose in week one compared with those whose wetting rate fell. Those whose wetting rate increased were found to have had a lower initial severity of wetting. Finley *et al.* (1982) found children who were multiple wetters beyond the third week of treatment were twice as likely to relapse after acquisition of continence. No mention is made of whether multiple wetters had a higher or lower initial frequency. It is not clear how Sacks and De Leon's 'risers' relate to the 'multiwetters' of Finley *et al*. Others have found no relation whatever between severity of wetting and relapse (Young and Morgan 1973b; Bollard and Nettlebeck 1982; Fielding 1985). A number of authors have found no relationship between relapse and *accompanying eliminative disorders* (Young and Morgan 1973b; Dische *et al*. 1983; Fielding 1985). But Fielding (1980) found that children wet by day and night relapsed significantly earlier than those wet at night only, and Bollard and Nettlebeck (1982) found that day wetters beyond age four were more likely to relapse. Fielding (1985) did not find *low functional bladder capacity* to be related to relapse. A number of authors have found no differences in relapse for *primary and secondary enuretics* (Sacks and De Leon 1973; Young and Morgan 1973b; Bollard and Nettlebeck 1982; Dische *et al*. 1983; Fielding 1985). Young and Morgan (1973b), Fielding (1980, 1985), Bollard and Nettlebeck (1982) and Dische *et al*. (1983) failed to find any relationship between relapse and either *sex or age*. However, Finley *et al*. (1982) found nine- to ten-year-old children more likely to relapse than three- to six-year-olds. Turner and Taylor (1974) conditioned nine out of ten adults and found that only one trainee relapsed, although follow-up periods ranged from only 3 months to 22 months. There is conflicting evidence for the existence of a relationship between relapse and *behavioural deviance* (Sacks and De Leon 1978; Dische *et al*. 1983; Young and Morgan 1973b; Fielding 1985). No relationship has been found to exist between relapse and *failure to awaken to alarm* or *sleep characteristics* (Young and Morgan 1973b; Finley and Wansley 1977; Fielding 1985). *Family history of enuresis* has been found not to be a factor in relapse (Young and Morgan 1973b; Dische *et al*. 1983), nor is *unsatisfactory housing* a factor (Young and Morgan 1973b; Dische *et al*. 1983; Fielding 1985). Dische *et al*. (1983) did however, find *family difficulties* (marital discord, parental mental illness) to be a significant factor in long-term success, but Young and Morgan (1973b) and Fielding (1985) did not. Jehu *et al*. (1977) did not find a higher relapse rate in children trained in residential childrens homes, although for those who did relapse, family difficulties did seem to be a factor. Finley *et al*. (1982) found that children who became dry within eight wetting episodes rarely relapsed, although they comment that this figure (13 per cent) approaches the spontaneous remission rate; Dische *et al*. (1983) likewise found that relapsers had required a *greater number of conditioning trials* to initial arrest criterion. On the other hand,

Bollard and Nettlebeck (1982) found no relation between number of trials and relapse, and Sacks and De Leon (1973) found a greater number of conditioning trials to result in greater resistance to extinction.

Methods of improving relapse rates

Twin signal alarm

Lovibond (1963) has criticised the classical conditioning explanation of enuresis alarm treatment on the grounds that repeated presentation of the CS (bladder distension) in the absence of the UCS (buzzer) would eventually lead to extinction of the CR. He proposes conditioned avoidance learning as providing a more likely explanation, since conditioned avoidance responses are more resistant to extinction. Thus, in operant terms, the buzzer is an aversive stimulus and the responses of waking and contracting the sphincter are conditioned avoidance responses. Development of a conditioned avoidance response should be facilitated when the response (sphincter contraction) permits escape from the noxious stimulus (buzzer). Thus Lovibond developed his twin signal alarm; sphincter contraction in response to the first auditory warning signal permitted escape from a second, louder and more aversive auditory stimulus, which alarm, he hypothesised, should be more effective than the standard enuresis alarm. However, although he found a difference in the predicted direction for speed of response to treatment, initial success rates were little different and relapse rates were the same. Failure to find a difference in the rate of extinction between the alarms clearly contradicts the hypothesis. Hansen (1979) used a twin signal device with two enuretic children, one of whom had previously been treated unsuccessfully with standard enuresis alarm and both of whom were wet every night, usually several times per night. Both were successfully trained, subsequently relapsed, were successfully retrained and were dry in the long term. Turner, Young and Rachman (1970) failed to confirm Lovibond's hypothesis. They criticise Lovibond's findings on the grounds that differences between the alarms might be due to differences in stimulus intensity and not escape training, a point made by Lovibond himself. Lovibond (1972), in return, is critical of Turner et al.'s (1970) evaluation of his hypothesis on the grounds that their study fell far short of acceptable methodological standards. Both Turner et al. (1970) and Lovibond (1972) conclude that there is little practical reason for opting for the twin signal alarm over the standard enuresis alarm. Morgan (1978) suggests that passive avoidance learning may nevertheless be an important factor in conditioning treatment of enuresis. If so, a stronger aversive stimulus would be expected to be more effective, as indeed the work of Azrin *et al.* (1973, 1974) seems to have shown.

Auditory intensity of the alarm

Although Lovibond (1963) believes it is not essential that the trainee awaken to the noise of the alarm in order for conditioning to occur, non-response or poor response to the alarm has been associated with poor therapeutic outcome (Young and Morgan 1973a). Young and Morgan (1973a) compared three alarms of 80, 86 and 90 dB but found no difference in treatment efficiency and relapse rate, and concluded that louder buzzers are not necessarily more effective. Finley and Wansley (1977), however, found that an auditory stimulus of 105 dB affected rate of acquisition of dryness, particularly with regard to slow responders to treatment, but not relapse rate. It is likely that the increased rate of acquisition found by Lovibond (1963) using his twin signal alarm was due not to escape training, as hypothesised, but to the increased auditory intensity of the alarm (Lovibond 1963; Turner *et al.* 1970; Morgan 1978). Morgan (1978) concludes that there may be a case for using considerably louder alarms where treatment response is poor, but training conditions in the home would have to be carefully assessed to ensure that the alarm was, in practice, louder, as location, furniture and furnishings in the bedroom are all factors affecting the operation of the alarm. Stimulus intensity has been a largely uncontrolled factor in most studies and may well account for different acquisition rates found.

Overlearning

Successful treatment with the standard enuresis alarm procedure will have resulted in the bladder having learned to tolerate volumes and pressures related to normal fluid intake. Increased fluid intake immediately before bedtime will result in additional strain which, if not tolerated, will result in further conditioning trials and overlearning. Mowrer and Mowrer (1938) recommended increasing fluid intake by one or two cups after the child has achieved seven consecutive dry nights and until a further seven consecutive dry nights were achieved, but only for older children. Young and Morgan (1972a and b) have reported a significant reduction in relapse rate by increasing fluid intake by up to two pints before

157

bedtime, after achieving a criterion of fourteen consecutive dry nights, and until a further fourteen consecutive dry nights are achieved, but nine per cent of these allocated to overlearning had to be withdrawn due to the severity of the relapse (Young and Morgan 1972a). Taylor and Turner (1975) increased fluid intake by one to two pints after seven consecutive dry nights. Although both these studies found that overlearning significantly reduced the relapse rate, the results of the latter were not quite so promising as those of the former. However, as Taylor and Turner (1975) point out, the amount by which fluid is increased is no doubt a major factor, as may be the criterion for dryness upon which overlearning is introduced, that of Taylor and Turner's being only seven dry nights. Morgan (1978) reports most children to be capable of increasing fluids by one to one-and-a-half pints without discomfort, but recommends stopping the procedure when renewed wetting exceeds 50 per cent or wetting fails to reduce.

Finley *et al.* (1982) are critical of the above three studies on methodological grounds: Taylor and Turner's (1975) because follow-up for overlearning was only eight-and-a-half months compared with 15.5 for the standard enuresis alarm group and relapse rate is known to increase with length of follow-up; and Young and Morgan's (1972a and b) two studies, since the nine per cent of trainees withdrawn from overlearning due to severity of relapse were then excluded from the results of the overlearning group: thus 'they screened out those children who were likely to relapse . . . from ever being followed up for relapse assessment'. Finley *et al.* (1982) do not, however, question the theoretical basis of overlearning nor its likely beneficial effects in terms of reduction of relapse rates, but claim that treatment time is increased and the procedure may not be suitable for all trainees.

Intermittent reinforcement schedules

It is known that intermittent reinforcement provides a greater resistance to extinction of the learned response than continuous reinforcement. Viewing relapse as the extinction of a response, Finley *et al.* (1973) hypothesised that the use of an intermittent reinforcement schedule would reduce relapse rate. Comparing continuous, intermittent and 'placebo' reinforcement schedules, they found rate of acquisition of dryness not to be significantly different for continuous and intermittent groups, but relapse rate to be significantly greater in the former. Viewing each wetting accident as a trial, Finley *et al.* (1973) used a 70 per cent variable ratio reinforcement schedule after the first seven wettings, which received continuous reinforcement. Maximum treatment time was six weeks, and a criterion for success of seven consecutive dry nights was used to encourage a high relapse rate in a short time. Follow-up was only three months, a shortcoming they recognise: clearly, since extinction should occur more slowly in the intermittent group, relapses in this group might continue to occur over a longer period of time than for the continuous reinforcement group and a considerably longer follow-up period would thus be required to reliably compare relapse rates. Taylor and Turner (1975) are critical of the shortness of Finley *et al.*'s six-week treatment period and three-month follow-up period. But, in view of the initial success rate of 90 per cent for the continuous reinforcement group and 80 per cent for the intermittent reinforcement group within this six-week period, results that seem comparable with those generally obtained, this criticism would seem unimportant, and Finley *et al.* had already recognised the shortness of the follow-up period as limiting conclusions. Using each night and not each wetting accident as a trial, Taylor and Turner (1975) used a continuous reinforcement schedule for the first two weeks of training followed by a 50 per cent variable reinforcement schedule. They found no differences between continuous and intermittent groups with respect to initial success or relapse rates. Finley *et al.* (1982) criticise this study for using each night and not each wetting accident as a trial, a factor that could affect children who wet more than once a night. Whereas Taylor and Turner (1975) state that such children only make up a small proportion of bedwetting children and that multiple wetting usually only occurs in the early stages of treatment, Finley *et al.* (1982) found that 80 per cent of their sample were multiple wetters during the first week of treatment and 30 per cent continued to be so beyond the third week. They claim multiple wetting beyond the third week of treatment to be the single most important variable determining the outcome of treatment, and feel that treating each night as a trial is likely to prejudice the chances of initial success of multiple wetters in the intermittent reinforcement group. Finley *et al.* (1982) found different alarm schedules to be effective with different groups of wetters: non-multiple wetting children fared best on a 70 to 79 per cent variable reinforcement schedule and multiple wetters on a 60 to 69 per cent schedule.

Comparison of intermittent reinforcement and overlearning

Only one study, that of Taylor and Turner (1975), has compared the effectiveness of continuous reinforcement, intermittent reinforcement and overlearning treatment in nocturnal enuresis. They found no significant differences between initial success rates for all three, nor between relapse rates for continuous and intermittent schedules, but did find overlearning to be significantly superior to both with regard to relapse rate. As mentioned above, Finley *et al.* (1982) have been heavily critical of this study. Morgan (1978) has reviewed recent findings on intermittent reinforcement and overlearning and has concluded overall that overlearning is superior in reducing relapse rates. Finley *et al.* (1982) criticise cross-study comparisons as revealing, at best, possible trends, due to methodological and sampling differences. Finley *et al.* (1982) and Morgan (1978) both conclude that both procedures appear to reduce relapse rate and that the success of both may interact with patient variables. Finley *et al.* (1982) conclude by proposing the use of increased fluid together with intermittent schedules for non-multiple wetters.

Enuresis alarm and drugs

Young and Turner (1965) and Turner and Young (1966) have used CNS stimulants in conjunction with enuresis alarm in the treatment of nocturnal enuresis. However, although the use of drugs may facilitate conditioning, especially in extraverts, they seem to do so at the expense of a higher relapse rate.

Retention control training and enuresis alarms

Fielding (1980) compared nocturnal enuretics treated with enuresis alarm only and alarm preceded by four weeks' retention control training. Within the first four weeks of training, alarm treatment was significantly superior to RCT. There was a slight but non-significant tendency for relapse rates to be lower at twelve-month follow-up for these children treated with RCT prior to enuresis alarm.

Enuresis alarm, type of therapist and therapist contact

James and Foreman (1973) suggest that personality factors of the trainer may affect results. He found evidence to support his hypothesis that personality type affects the reduction in bedwetting achieved, though no mention is made of relapse rates. Bollard and Nettlebeck (1981) compared standard enuresis alarm treatment under closely supervised and not supervised conditions. Significant differences between the two groups were found for dropout rate and speed of response to treatment although initial success and relapse rates were not different.

Dry bed training

Reinterpreting the treatment of nocturnal enuresis in terms of operant as opposed to classical conditioning, Azrin *et al.* (1973) outlined an intensive 'Dry Bed' training programme for mentally handicapped institutionalised residents, similar to that devised for daytime continence training (Foxx and Azrin 1973a and b). Along with the use of an enuresis alarm (for immediate detection and immediate reinforcement of wetting accidents) and increased fluid intake (to increase the frequency of the operant behaviour), the programme uses hourly toiletings, positive reinforcement for appropriate urination and dry beds, and punishment and positive practice for wetting accidents. This programme comprises three phases: *intensive training period* (all the above features), until no more than one accident per night and 50 per cent appropriate urinations; *monitored post-training period* (urine alarm and accident procedure, but no increased fluid intake, hourly awakenings or positive reinforcement) for seven nights after the last accident; *normal ward procedure period* (bed inspection in morning — if wet on two days, monitored phase reinstated). They compared the Dry Bed programme to the use of urine alarm apparatus alone, when a wetting accident was followed by the buzzer but the resident was not awakened as is usual in the standard urine alarm procedure, in order that social consequences contingent upon wetting be cut out altogether. A mean of 1.4 nights' intensive training was required to reach criterion with twelve trainees. One relapse of two wet nights occurred in the three-month follow-up period. The control procedure of buzzer alarm alone did not reduce enuresis, thus demonstrating that the function of the urine alarm in training is to produce social and motivational consequences, rather than direct conditioning of the bladder. Azrin *et al.* (1974) modified the programme for use with normal children over three years old. Modifications included one night of intensive training, greater use of verbal instructions and explanations, minimum supervision during toilet practice and training to delay urination. The Dry Bed procedure was compared with and without the alarm for the child in order to test the importance of the UCS buzzer, and with standard urine alarm procedure. One night of intensive Dry Bed training reduced accidents from every night to a median of one accident during each of the first and second weeks and one after the third week and for the six months of follow-up. A median of three weeks to fourteen consecutive dry nights was required. Standard urine alarm procedure for two weeks had reduced enuresis to a median of six and five accidents per week. Number of accidents for Dry Bed with the alarm in both the child's and parents' room and without the alarm in the child's room were not significantly different, a result indicating association of the buzzer with enuresis to be unimportant. Various further modifications of the Dry Bed programme have included training using a parents' manual only (Besalel *et al*. 1980) and Dry Bed training dispensing with the enuresis alarm completely (Azrin and Theines 1978; Azrin, Thienes-Hontos and Besalel-Azrin 1979).

Griffiths, Meldrum and McWilliam (1982) carried out the Dry Bed training programme with twelve trainees who had previously been unsuccessfully trained. Although their median of four weeks to fourteen nights of dryness compares favourably with Azrin *et al*.'s (1974) three-week median to criterion, they found a wide range from 2 to 20 weeks. In Griffiths *et al*.'s study, though, only four trainees were visited by the specialist trainer at the home for the one night of intensive training, while four received one night of specialist training in hospital and four received the one night of intensive training carried out by the parents. Statistical comparison between these three groups was not possible because of the small numbers, but results did not seem to differ. Bollard and Nettlebeck (1981) carried out a comparison of standard enuresis alarm training and Dry Bed training. The Dry Bed training was administered under four conditions: by the child's parents at home; by a professional trainer at home; by a professional trainer in hospital; or by the parents at home but without the use of an enuresis alarm. Although both Dry Bed training and standard enuresis alarm training were effective in reducing enuresis, the former was superior in terms of percentage successfully treated and speed of training. Dry Bed training was equally effective irrespective of mode of delivery, a finding that supports those of Griffiths *et al*. (1982). The Dry Bed training administered by parents did not receive any more professional time than did the standard enuresis alarm training, thus the superior effects of the former must have been due to the added operant features. Follow up after two years showed no different in relapse rates of Dry Bed and standard conditioning and no differences in numbers successfully retrained. Where Dry Bed training was carried out without the enuresis alarm, Bollard and Nettlebeck (1981) found it was only slightly better than no treatment at all, and 60 per cent of the Dry Bed — no alarm group dropped out of training during the 20-week experimental period. Bollard, Nettlebeck and Roxbee

(1982) found similar results for Dry Bed with and without an alarm where parents administered the training, as had Nettlebeck and Langeluddecke (1979). Bollard and Woodroffe (1977), in a similar comparison, had previously found a significant decrease in their Dry Bed–No Alarm treatment group, although no child reached the criterion of fourteen consecutive dry nights. Fincham and Spettell (1984), in a comparison of standard enuresis alarm treatment and Dry Bed–No Alarm treatment, found that 75 per cent of the former reached the criterion of fourteen consecutive dry nights compared with 41 per cent of the latter. However, Keating et al. (1983) using Dry Bed with no alarm, and comparing home- or office-based training of parents only or parents and child, found 78 per cent of the children reached the criterion of fourteen dry nights. Thirty-three per cent of those relapsed. There were no differences according to place of training, etc. No comparisons were made with Dry Bed with alarm or standard conditioning in this study, but cure, relapse and success rates were reported to be comparable to those reported in Doleys (1977) review of standard enuresis alarm treatment. Thus, claims by Azrin and Theines (1978) and Azrin et al. (1979) as to the effectiveness of Dry Bed training without an alarm must be tempered by findings from replications that have shown Dry Bed with alarm to be far superior. Fincham and Spettell (1984) compared the acceptability to parents of Dry Bed training without an alarm and standard conditioning. Using both an unstructured and structured technique of evaluating the acceptability of treatment, they found that parents who had used the standard conditioning approach rated it more favourably than did those who had used Dry Bed–No Alarm training. Parents commonly reported difficulty in implementing positive practice procedures, a finding supported by Griffiths et al. (1982).

Besalel et al. (1980) described the use of Dry Bed training using a parents' manual and not professional assistance. Results were reported to closely approximate those obtained previously with direct training. However, Fincham and Spettell (1984) found that acceptability of a treatment was affected by its source: a clinic programme was considered more acceptable than that presented in a self-help manual. It is actually rather difficult to compare results obtained for the various variations of Dry Bed training as presented by its originators, as results are presented in different ways, data sometimes being presented in terms of means (Azrin et al. 1973) and sometimes medians (Azrin et al. 1974). Other writers most commonly present data in terms of mean wetting accidents per week.

Finally, Bollard and Nettlebeck (1982) carried out a component analysis of Dry Bed training. They identified the major components as the enuresis alarm, the waking schedule, retention control training and positive practice and cleanliness training. Urine alarm plus either positive practice or retention-control training reduced bedwetting frequency by only slightly more than did urine alarm treatment alone. Urine alarm plus the waking schedule was somewhat more effective, though the addition of none of these three singly made a significant difference compared with urine alarm treatment alone. But the combination of urine alarm, waking and positive practice did result in a significant reduction in bedwetting compared with alarm alone, as did the complete programme. However, the combination of waking schedule plus alarm was almost as effective as these, so clearly one could dispense with retention control training and positive practice and cleanliness training and achieve almost as effective results. Rolider *et al*. (1984) had similarly found the use of a nightly awakening schedule, although more stringently faded out than that of Azrin's, in combination with urine alarm to be more effective than Dry Bed training with no alarm.

Drugs

Blackwell and Currah (1973) have thoroughly reviewed the literature in this area. An exhaustive review of the one hundred or so publications found by them on the subject of drug treatment in nocturnal enuresis would be beyond the scope of this chapter. Prior to 1960, research reports on the use of drugs in the treatment of enuresis were largely uncontrolled, with conflicting results. An increasing interest in this area and a greater regard for the importance of methodological issues has been apparent since then. Blackwell and Currah report that more than 80 per cent of the research since then has concerned the tricyclic antidepressants, mainly imipramine. Studies of imipramine have mainly reported significant results, compared with placebo when used with children, but not with adult hard-core enuretics, institutionalised neurotically disordered children, or the mentally handicapped. Similar results are reported for other tricyclic antidepressants. Total remission rates are usually below 50 per cent and generally between 20 and 30 per cent. Beneficial effects usually occur within the first week of treatment and on withdrawal the immediate relapse rate is high, only 10 to 30 per cent of those successfully treated remaining dry. Blackwell and

Currah are critical of the often confused and inadequate long-term follow-up data. Just how the tricyclic antidepressants have their effect is not clear (Fritz and Armbrust 1982). Although they were previously believed to lighten sleep, it now seems more likely that they act on the bladder muscles themselves, permitting an increased volume of urine in the bladder before bladder contractions and voiding occur. Blackwell and Currah conclude that results of treatment by the tricyclic antidepressants have been less promising than standard enuresis alarm treatment. They report little evidence for the effectiveness of any other type of drug, including stimulants, MAO inhibitors, sedative-hypnotics, major tranquillisers, anticonvulsants, diuretics, anticholinergics and pituitary snuff. Fritz and Armbrust (1982) believe it to be inappropriate as a first approach to treatment of enuresis, due to the small but significant incidence of serious side effects and accidental poisoning. Morgan (1981), however, believes them to be useful for occasions when quick relief is important, e.g. holidays, or when parents can cope no longer. Drug treatment is also easier to administer and not so demanding as alarm treatment.

Retention control training

Because nocturnal enuretics tend to have smaller functional bladder capacities than non-enuretics, it has been assumed that nocturnal enuresis could be cured by increasing the bladder capacity to the point where it could hold the night's urine. Attempts have been made to do this by training the child to withhold urine for increasingly long periods of time, starting for example with five minutes after the urge to urinate is initially felt. This is called 'retention control training' (RCT). Holding time is increased by a few minutes each day, so that the bladder muscles gradually learn to tolerate increasing volumes and pressures. Programmed exercise (Starfield and Mellits 1968) and rewards (e.g. Kimmel and Kimmel 1970) are sometimes used. Treatment programmes using this approach have produced mixed results.

Using unrestricted fluids and programmed exercises, Starfield and Mellits (1968) found 19 per cent of subjects cured and 66 per cent improved. Children who did not improve showed significantly smaller increases in functional bladder capacity. They conclude that an increase in FBC is associated with improvement in enuresis. There was no no-treatment control group in this study and the figure of 19 per cent cured approximates to the spontaneous remission rate.

Finley *et al.* (1982) comment that a percentage of children may be on the verge of spontaneous remission whatever treatment is used. Miller (1973), using an ABAB research design with two secondary enuretics, found reductions in the frequency of daytime urination and bedwetting during RCT phases but not baseline phases, both trainees becoming dry within 16 weeks. He concludes that RCT can effect rapid cure of nocturnal enuresis. However, since social reinforcement and increased fluids were combined with RCT only in the experimental phases, it is difficult to disentangle the effects of these. Furthermore, follow-up was only of 7 and 4 months duration. Kimmel and Kimmel (1970), likewise using RCT in conjunction with increased fluids and rewards for holding, also found rapid cessation of bedwetting in three enuretic children. Unfortunately, baseline data (not reported) were obtained over only two days and two of the subjects were 'approximately four years of age', an age at which spontaneous remission is still high. Controlled studies show less promising results. Mahoney (1973) found that training in withholding urine did not result in trainees voiding larger quantities less frequently, nor did it cause an increase in the time between sleep onset and micturition. This study included a no-training control group. Harris and Purohit (1977) studied the effectiveness of 35 days of bladder training using increased fluids and rewards. They found a significant increase in the bladder capacity of the experimental group compared with control, but no significant reduction in bedwetting frequency. Fielding (1980), in a comparison of enuresis alarm treatment and RCT, found the alarm to be far superior in reducing nocturnal enuresis. Some changes in FBC did occur, but only for children wet by day as well as night, the changes notably occurring after dryness was achieved. Fielding concludes that low FBC is probably a consequence and not a cause of bedwetting.

Doleys (1977) concludes that the above studies do not provide strong support for RCT as a treatment for nocturnal enuresis and is critical of the varying methodologies used, small numbers of subjects and absence of substantial follow-up data. Sorotzkin (1984) believes there are, however, some advantages to this treatment, namely low cost and convenience. But Fritz and Armbrust (1982) disagree, as the family must devote considerable energy to encourage holding, and the feeling of urgency is uncomfortable for the child. Finally, Starfield and Mellits (1968) admit that there does not seem to be a bladder capacity that, when exceeded, guarantees nocturnal continence.

Psychotherapy

According to the psychodynamic approach, nocturnal enuresis is merely a symptom of some intra-psychic conflict. Therefore, in order to cure the symptom, one must first seek and cure the cause of the problem, or symptom substitution will occur, i.e. the symptom of enuresis will be replaced by some other maladaptive behaviour.

Studies comparing brief psychotherapy with enuresis alarm treatment and no-treatment controls have found psychotherapy to be no better than no treatment at all, and significantly inferior to standard enuresis alarm treatment (Werry and Cohrssen 1965; De Leon and Mandell 1966).

Scientific methodologies have not been applied to long-term psychotherapy in the treatment of nocturnal enuresis. Indeed, whether or not it is effective, there seems little to recommend it as a choice over enuresis alarm treatment in terms of speed and cost, particularly as there is no evidence of symptom substitution (Doleys 1977), the reverse more usually being the case (Baker 1969).

There seems little evidence that psychotherapy is effective, short or long term. Doleys (1977) is critical of the vagueness of psychotherapy 'studies', in terms of specifying the procedures used and providing follow-up information. Certainly, studies such as those of Daniels (1971) and Rister (1983), which seem typical, are not impressive in terms of the quality of logical reasoning and argument.

Clearly, general supportive counselling is an essential feature of many treatment programmes for nocturnal enuresis and, where evidence exists of any psychological disturbance, psychotherapy together with specific treatment for nocturnal enuresis may be recommended (Morgan 1981).

Hypnotherapy

Olness (1975) used self-hypnosis with 40 primary and secondary enuretic children between 4 and 16 years of age, most of whom were wet between five and seven nights per week; 77½ per cent were cured to a criterion of one or fewer wet beds per month, 15 per cent improved and the remainder did not improve. Follow-up ranged from 6 to 28 months. Stanton (1979) reports an approximately 70 per cent success rate with 28 patients between 7 and 18 years.

167

Follow-up at 12 months showed 75 per cent of these to be still dry. Interestingly, failures were amongst the youngest trainees. Improvement occurred largely within the first two or three sessions.

Although hypnotherapy is not a widely used treatment, results of the above studies seem to indicate that it merits closer inspection. It is clearly a less disruptive method of treatment than the various conditioning methods, less risky than drugs and probably cheaper in terms of professional time. However, as Stanton (1979) found, a great deal of trial and error and failure may be involved before the therapist comes up with a formula that seems to work for him. He tried replicating Olness's approach with little success. Furthermore, hypnosis must have a very high 'placebo' effect on patients, so controlled studies would be important.

Family therapy

Family therapists view as inappropriate attempts to treat nocturnal enuresis as a problem concerning solely the child. In the context of a family, parents and child are always interacting with one another and this model would therefore perceive family dynamics to be a substantial cause of the enuretic problem. Thus, the family must be viewed and treated as a system (Wright, Wilkinson and Proud 1983).

Wright *et al.* (1983) describe a single case study of a treatment programme embodying elements from psychoanalytical theory, family therapy and behaviour therapy. The authors conclude that their approach succeeded where others had failed, although they fail to specify the nature of previous approaches to treatment and imply that success was due to their integrated treatment approach. As a modified Dry Bed treatment programme was used, which approach seems to justifiably claim higher initial success rates, it seems at least possible that success was due to this and not the other treatment elements. No follow-up data are given. Protinsky and Dillard (1983) report on eight families presenting with an enuretic child. Initial success rate was 100 per cent. Treatment time is expressed as mean length of time in therapy, eight one-hour sessions. At six-month follow-up, two had relapsed (25 per cent). No baseline data are given. Selig (1982) also reports a single case study where a six-and-a-half-year-old boy with secondary enuresis became dry in the two weeks between first and second therapy sessions. Although the abstract of the articles states that 'Follow up at one year indicated no recurrence of the symptoms . . .', the text of the article actually states that 'One year after the second family interview, Brian continued to be dry most of the time'. No data are given indicating what 'most of the time' specifically means. Furthermore, the fact that, at follow-up, 'Mother also reported that she was much less worried about his bedwetting', seems to indicate that the trainee might have relapsed but that therapy had effected changes in the family's perception of the enuresis as a problem, rather than significantly altering the enuresis itself. Without actual follow-up data, it is impossible to say whether the child would have been regarded as 'relapsed' in terms of the commonly used criteria.

The main criticisms that family therapists (e.g. Protinsky and Dillard 1983) level at other therapeutic approaches seem to be as follows: that most current techniques focus on the child as the source of the problem, whereas according to family therapists the cause lies substantially in family dynamics, hence the high relapse rates; no current technique is very successful anyway; there are many unsatisfactory aspects to the treatment of nocturnal enuresis currently; current techniques have not been evaluated in controlled studies.

Whilst agreeing completely with the necessity of obtaining the wholehearted support and co-operation of the family when treating a disruptive problem such as nocturnal enuresis, and whilst accepting that such a problem must have had a profound effect on family life over the years, it seems something of a logical leap to assume that family dynamics are a substantial cause of nocturnal enuresis. Much work has been carried out into possible aetiological factors in nocturnal enuresis and little has emerged. Hard data, as opposed to armchair theorising, have as yet been conspicuously absent on the part of the family therapy movement. Since nocturnal enuresis is probably caused by a number of different factors, it is, though, likely that family dynamics may be a contributing factor in some cases. But since a substantial proportion of bedwetters are successfully treated by using various conditioning techniques, family dynamics seem unlikely to be a major cause of nocturnal enuresis. With regard to the high relapse rates of other treatment techniques, it remains to be seen whether family therapy is any more successful in the long term, when adequate follow-up data are provided for more substantial numbers of subjects.

Statements to the effect that 'no current technique is very successful' are both unhelpful to the clinician seeking information on treatment approaches and misleading. Conditioning techniques, especially the 'Dry Bed' technique, can rightly claim considerable success. Although it is true that there are many unsatisfactory aspects to current treatments, mostly regarding unanswered questions as to why some children fail and why the relapse rate is high, much work of a high scientific standard is being carried out in a continuing attempt to answer these questions, despite the obvious difficulties in field work of this type. One is more than a little surprised to see the fourth criticism, that current techniques have not been evaluated in controlled studies, in articles published in the 1980s. There are many controlled studies of the major forms of treatment, i.e. conditioning treatment and drugs.

Family therapy may prove to be a promising technique for some, or many, nocturnal enuretics. However, while the evidence is limited to poorly described case studies, with no control groups, little or no baseline data and either poor or no follow-up, a proper evaluation of family therapy is not currently possible.

TREATMENT OF NON-CHILD POPULATIONS

Most of the studies of the above treatment methods have been carried out on children. There are, however, other groups whose problems as nocturnal enuretics may be even greater.

Adults

Turner and Taylor (1974) have reviewed the scanty literature in this area. Most data on adults with enuresis have been obtained from conscripts to the armed forces. Reliability of data becomes an issue in such a situation where motivation to evade conscription is high. Between 1 and 3 per cent of adults are estimated to be enuretic. Most are male and have a lifelong history of enuresis. Familial incidence seems to be a feature and emotional disturbance is suggested, although there is no agreement as to the exact nature of this. Most of the same aetiological factors proposed for children have also been proposed for adults: sleep abnormality, epilepsy, developmental defect and CNS abnormality, small FBC, abnormalities of the urinary tract. However, few of the studies include control groups of non-enuretic adults so the value of studies of the above is unclear. Turner and Taylor (1974) are critical of the contradictory results contained in the small amount of research on treatment of enuretic adults because of methodological shortcomings. In a study of bell-

and-pad treatment with ten adults, nine were successfully treated within 16 weeks and only one relapsed, although follow-up varied from 3 to 22 months. Turner and Taylor stress the need for caution in interpreting the results due to the nature of the sample and the absence of a control group but suggest that, in view of the practical difficulties in treating adults, the results are encouraging.

Mental handicap

Little work has been published on the treatment of nocturnal enuresis in mentally handicapped people. Protinsky and Dillard (1983) suggest that with regard to enuresis, one question that should be asked is 'Is the child old enough, sane enough and intelligent enough to be capable of dryness?' This suggests that there is some sort of cut-off beyond which one should not expect nocturnal continence of the mentally handicapped. Indeed, many studies exclude children known to be mentally handicapped. The problem is, how is the clinician to know just how intelligent/sane a child must be to be capable of being trained? 'Clinical intuition' might well lead the majority of clinicians to believe that there is little hope of training a moderately or severely mentally handicapped person, whilst holding out some hope for the more mildly handicapped.

The treatment of nocturnal enuresis in the institutionalised mentally handicapped by standard bell-and-pad treatment has certainly proved less successful, though by no means unsuccessful, both initially and at follow-up. Although Deacon (1939) reported an 85 per cent success rate with trainees of IQ 40–70 (i.e. moderate and mild degrees of mental handicap), he used a criterion to success of only seven consecutive dry nights. Kennedy and Sloop (1968) achieved 50 per cent success after 7 weeks' training with trainees of IQ 26–65 (severe to mild mental handicap). Sloop and Kennedy (1973) report approximately 50 per cent initial success after 11 weeks' training with 21 trainees of IQ 28–65, but only 33 per cent overall success at follow-up seven to twelve months later.

Azrin et al. (1973) developed their intensive 'Dry Bed' training programme for the treatment of nocturnal enuresis in the institutionalised profoundly mentally handicapped. They report a mean of 1.4 nights' training need to reach the criteria of seven consecutive dry nights with twelve trainees of mean age 37 and mean IQ 12. Follow up at 3 months showed a 97 per cent reduction in wetting accidents. However, there are many practical problems to be found

171

in running night-time training programmes in large institutions, as one night nurse may be responsible for 25 residents, some of whom will also require time during the night for other problems. Smith (1981) describes a less intensive, operant base, night-time continence training programme using an enuresis alarm, with five trainees ranging from 15 to 22 years of age, social quotient or IQ between 16 and 30 (profound to severe mental handicap), and a mean of six wetting accidents per week over each of the two weeks' baseline. The between-subject variance in time taken to reach the eight dry weeks criterion to dryness was immense, ranging from 18 to 92 weeks, although all did become dry. Furthermore, periods of five or so dry weeks followed by a few wet weeks were not uncommon. According to usual criteria, these would have been regarded as 'relapses', yet viewed in the context of the overall learning curves they did not look like relapses. Two of the five trainees (the two males) relapsed some 2 and 11 months after being considered completely dry. Both relapses occurred at times of some upheaval, indicating just how unstable new learning can be. Both were subsequently successfully retrained. Three were dry at follow-up at over two years, one at 18 months and one at nine months.

Barker (1979) compared two methods of training night-time continence not using bell and pad in 24 mentally handicapped, institutionalised adults with a mean age of 38 years and whose level of intelligence was unspecified as some of their problems made assessment impossible. They had a wide range of other handicaps and behaviour problems over and above their mental handicap. Using an ABAB design, he showed that a programme using a procedure to train and reinforce appropriate urination was considerably less effective than a programme that reinforced appropriate urination as well as using a corrective/positive practice procedure for inappropriate urination. He concluded that identification of peak periods of urination at night and the use of reinforcement for appropriate toilet use is of limited effect, better results being obtained in conjunction with a 'corrective procedure'. It is not clear how many, if any, residents became completely dry and no follow-up data are given.

Phibbs and Wells (1982) report on six institutionalised mentally handicapped adult women, of IQ 20–60, mean age 23.8 years and mean baseline wetting rate of 1.6 wetting accidents per week. They used a procedure essentially the same as Barker's appropriate urination procedure, whereby trainees were wakened and toileted and rewarded for appropriate toilet use just before peak wetting accident times, wetting accidents being largely ignored, although wet sheets were changed. Treatment was successfully completed for all six trainees after nine months, with durations ranging from three months two days to nine months six days. Although two of the six did have post-treatment wettings, these were not sufficient to require further treatment and they did not constitute a return to regular weekly wettings. At one-year follow-up, all were accident free.

These results are very consistent with those found by Barker (1979). Phibbs and Wells (1982) draw attention to the low relapse rate and low cost of treatment, despite the lengthy training period.

It seems clear from the few studies carried out that it is possible to successfully train mentally handicapped institutionalised trainees even in the moderately to profoundly mentally handicapped range of intelligence. Procedures such as 'Dry Bed', which are considered more labour-intensive at the outset, are likely to considerably reduce training time and may be cheaper in the long run. What is needed now are studies similar to those described with children and which separate out components for evaluation, e.g. Bollard and Nettlebeck (1982).

10

Encopresis

O Cloacina,[1] Goddess of this place,
Look on thy suppliants with a smiling face,
Soft, yet cohesive let their offerings flow
Neither too swift not yet unduly slow.

Sir John Harington (1596)

Encopresis is one of the most humiliating problems a person can experience. Whereas it is possible, though often difficult, for a nocturnally enuretic person to conceal his enuresis from others, it is rarely possible for an encopretic person to hide his problem with the result that he is likely to become a virtual social outcast. Small wonder then that encopretic children are often found to show signs of emotional disturbance. As well as the effect on normal peer relationships, some authors also cite persistent encopresis as a cause of child abuse by parents (Schaeffer 1979), disgusted by the problem and angered that various approaches to handling the problem (spanking, shaming, scolding, rewarding) do not seem to work. Encopresis may also be a major factor in the decision to institutionalise an elderly relative or handicapped person, who otherwise may have been kept at home. However, despite the socially and potentially physically serious nature of the problem, as well as the enormous cost of caring for institutionalised encopretic people, there has been remarkably little serious study of it, compared with say the problem of nocturnal enuresis. Published reports on treatment methods are virtually limited to single case studies, mainly psychoanalytical or behavioural in approach. There is little on prevalence and aetiology, and what there is regarded as of questionable reliability, due to the sensitive nature of the problem. Some authors cite the reason for this as being the taboo nature of the subject, which results in a tendency to hide the problem rather than seek help. Because of all this, clinicians tend to lack expertise in handling the treatment of encopresis.

---

[1]Cloacina, Roman goddess of sewers.

174

DEFINITION

The same problems besetting the study of nocturnal enuresis also apply to the study of encopresis, namely, differences in definition of the term 'encopresis' and variations in the criteria for diagnosing a child encopretic, i.e. age of child, duration of the problem, frequency of the problem, etc. To add to the confusion there also exists a problem over terminology: terms such as faecal incontinence, faecal soiling and encopresis may be used to mean the same or different things (Gabel 1981; Fritz and Armbrust 1982).

There are several features that recur in the various definitions of encopresis found in the literature. Some or all of the following features may be regarded by each author as central to his definition: organic or functional nature of the problem (Doleys *et al.* 1981; Gabel 1981; Fritz and Armbrust 1982); inappropriate place of defaecation (Doleys *et al.* 1981; Gabel 1981; Schaeffer 1979; Fritz and Armbrust 1982); voluntary or involuntary nature of defaecation (Gabel 1981; Schaeffer 1979; Fritz and Armbrust 1981); constipated or normal/near normal consistency (Doleys *et al.* 1981; Gabel 1981; Fritz and Armbrust 1982); age (Doleys *et al.* 1981; Gabel 1981; Schaeffer 1979); frequency and/or duration (Schaeffer 1979). Some authors also further distinguish between 'persistent' (never trained) and 'acquired' (soiling beginning after a period of continence ranging from six months to one year) encopresis, although others find no validity in this distinction with regard to aetiology or treatment outcome (Margolies and Gilstein 1983).

The following definitions highlight the differences found in terminology and the way in which different features are emphasised as central to the definition.

Doleys *et al.* (1981) define *functional encopresis* as 'the passage of faecal material of *any amount or consistency*[2] into the clothing or other generally *unacceptable areas* in the absence of any organic pathology beyond the age of *three years*'. Schaeffer (1979) defines *psychogenic encopresis* as '. . . repeated *involuntary* defaecation into clothing (or other *unusual receptacle*), occurring in children *four years* or older and of at least one month's duration'. Gabel's (1981) definition of *faecal soiling* is the same as Doleys *et al.*'s (1981) functional encopresis, but also includes the idea of either voluntary or involuntary nature of the event. However, by contrast Gabel uses the term *encopresis* to refer to stools of normal

---

[2]All italics are the authors'.

consistency (cf. Doley's 'any consistency'), passed either *voluntarily or involuntarily* in inappropriate places in children *without organic pathology*. DSM-3 (Diagnostic and Statistical Manual of the American Psychiatric Association 1980) defines encopresis as '. . . repeated *voluntary or involuntary* passage of faeces of *normal or near normal consistency* into *places not appropriate* for that purpose in the individual's own sociocultural setting. It is *functional when not due to any organic disorder*.'

Other authors (Davis, Mitchell and Marks 1976, 1977; Webster and Gore 1980) seem to give greater emphasis to the *place* in which soiling occurs as being the abnormal aspect of the problem, rather than the defaecation process itself. Thus, cases involving constipation due to retention would be essentially excluded.

PHYSIOLOGY OF BOWEL CONTROL

The rectum, in normal healthy individuals, is usually empty. On leaving the stomach, food is shunted along the digestive tract by a series of progressive, co-ordinated contractions and relaxations of the muscles along the tract, called peristaltic contractions. The ingestion of food or drink causes a peristaltic 'rush' to begin, which, at the end of the sequence, results in the faeces in the bowel being passed into the rectum. The walls of the rectum, then stretched, give rise to the sensation of the urge to defaecate. The strong peristaltic rush and consequent urge to defaecate occurs daily in most people, usually in the morning, approximately 20 to 40 minutes after breakfast, although substantial individual differences are found, with some people experiencing it after each meal, whilst others only experience it every other day. If the urge to defaecate is ignored, for whatever reason, the faecal mass normally moves back into the lower end of the colon. However, if this situation continues and the walls of the rectum become stretched for too long, the signals indicating a feeling of urgency in the rectum break down. The faeces remain in the rectum and a feeling of urgency is not felt. New waste arriving from above builds up an increasing blockage of faeces. As the colon continually absorbs water from its contents, the longer the faeces remain, the harder and drier they become, making them difficult and painful to pass. Because of the pain in passing hard faeces, the child/adult may retain them further, causing the blockage to increase. A hard mass of faeces may then be felt along the length of the colon. Liquid waste then finds its way around the mass of hard faeces, seeping out and causing continual soiling, which may be mistaken for diarrhoea. If the basic constipation problem does not have some organic cause, such as Hirschsprung's disease (neurogenic megacolon) or obstructing lesions or tumours of the bowel (anatomic megacolon), then it is regarded as 'psychogenic' in origin and may be variously referred to as 'psychogenic megacolon' or 'functional megacolon'.

DEVELOPMENT OF NORMAL BOWEL CONTROL

In the normal sequence of development of bladder and bowel control, bowel control usually emerges first, initially by night and then by day. Largo and Stutzle (1977a), in a longitudinal study of 413 Swiss children up to six years, found that by one year approximately 35 per cent of children had complete bowel control, increasing to around 78 per cent at two years and 97 per cent at three years, control emerging consistently earlier for girls at all ages.

As far as encopresis is concerned, they report that 'Complete bladder control by day and at night without bowel control was seen only in exceptional cases.' Before the stage of reliable voluntary control of muscles preventing evacuation, there occurs a period of partial control. Prior to this, bowel action is still under reflex control, despite the beliefs of many mothers of eight- to nine-month-old children who are able to predict the occurrence of, and 'catch' bowel movements, by seating the infant on the pot, thus believing their infants to be 'trained'. The number of bowel movements per day gradually decreases in infancy from after each feed in the neonatal period and first weeks, to one or two per day by the toddler stage. According to Schaeffer (1979), a child is ready for daytime bowel training when there is regularity in bowel movements and control of the bowels during sleep. As with bladder training, there is some evidence that the earlier training is begun, the longer it takes to complete.

Diet is very much a factor, differences being found between breast and bottle-fed babies. Certain foods have a constipating effect, as does low fluid intake, and certain foods a laxative effect. Many parents become concerned quite early on about 'regularity' of bowel movements, even though bowel movements less frequent than once a day should only give rise to concern if they are hard and difficult to pass. As we shall see later, parental over-anxiety over 'performance' has frequently been thought to result in later

177

problems of encopresis, particularly where toileting battles develop around a time a child develops the ability to voluntarily retain faeces.

PREVALENCE

However common parental anxieties may be over such issues as regularity of the bowels and toilet training thereof, it seems clear that by the age of four, the vast majority of children are continent of faeces, possibly despite rather than because of their parents, and that encopresis continues to decline with age. Some have suggested it becomes rare in the mid-teens, with the exception of severely mentally handicapped and psychotic people (Schaeffer 1979). Others (Webster and Gore 1980) suggest that there is no hard evidence to support this and that older soilers simply become more effective at hiding their problem. Reviews generally quote up to 3 per cent of four-year-olds and up to 2 per cent of five-year-olds as still soiling, reducing to less than 1 per cent by ten to twelve years (Doleys *et al*. 1981; Gabel 1981; Fritz and Armbrust 1982; Webster and Gore 1980; Schaeffer 1979). Encopresis is thus much less common a problem than nocturnal enuresis, but where it does occur, there is general agreement that incontinence of urine both by day and by night is frequently also present (Doleys *et al*. 1981; Morgan 1981). In the elderly population, Whitehead, Burgio and Engel (1985) report bowel incontinence to occur in 30 per cent of nursing home residents and in 1 per cent of the elderly living in the community.

As with the problem of nocturnal enuresis, encopresis is commoner in boys than girls, but in contrast to nocturnal enuresis, secondary encopresis is commoner than primary encopresis.

Available evidence indicates that constipation and retention are also found in the vast majority of cases of encopresis (Gabel 1981). Faecal smearing is generally found to be rare. As has been previously noted, however, figures vary according to definitions used and populations sampled and are likely to be something of an underestimate due to the nature of the problem.

AETIOLOGY

Factors such as strict toilet training patterns and related parent–child social interaction factors, social class factors involving poor or lax training and low expectations, stress, family conflicts, personality factors, learning factors, genetic factors and developmental immaturity have been variously hypothesised as being causal factors in the development of encopresis, as well as medical/physiological factors. Protinsky and Kersey (1983) make the point that these are based on clinical observations not on experimentally controlled studies.

EARLY OR STRICT TRAINING

Early or strict training has long been regarded as a cause of encopresis, particularly secondary encopresis (Fritz and Armbrust 1982).

As with the problem of enuresis, the psychoanalytical approach would view encopresis as a symptom of an underlying, unconscious conflict, the resolution of which must first be achieved before the encopresis can be cured.

Doleys *et al.* (1981) sum up the value of this approach to encopresis as follows — 'Such a theoretical approach has been most non-productive when applied clinically'. However, the age when voluntary control of the bowels is emerging usually coincides with the age at which the child is developing increasing independence and mastery over his environment generally. The child may feel some degree of inconsistency in his parents' handling of him at this stage, on the one hand urging him towards independence 'like a big boy', whilst on the other hand refusing to allow him to do just as he wants all the time. Small wonder, then, that this stage is often referred to as 'the terrible two's'. In the midst of all this, toilet-training issues can become a battleground between parent and child, as part of the more general issue as to who controls the child, and with his newly developed control over bowel function, the child can refuse to perform where and when the parent wishes him to and constipation and encopresis can be the result. Parental attitudes to toilet training and to problems encountered during training and general handling patterns can thus affect the child's behaviour, depending on whether the parents are anxious or relaxed, approving or disapproving, rewarding or punishing.

Doleys *et al.* (1981) concede that harsh training techniques may be a *contributory* factor in the development of encopresis in this way, but encopresis as the result of some unconscious conflict is denied by them. Similarly, Gabel (1981) does not accept that abnormal training inevitably leads to bowel dysfunction and draws attention to the fact that few children develop bowel problems despite everything that occurs in these early years. Schaeffer (1979), on the other hand, seems to accept the relationship between bowel and bladder dysfunction and early and/or strict training. Unfortunately, such claims are mainly based on uncontrolled studies in which groups of encopretic children have been found retrospectively to have experienced such training. There seem to be no studies in the literature that report on what percentage of matched, non-encopretic children experienced similarly harsh or early training.

LAX OR INCONSISTENT TRAINING

Conversely, *lax or inconsistent toilet training* has also been regarded as a cause of encopresis, though here primary encopresis is thought more likely to occur. Lax or inconsistent training and a general undervaluing of 'cleanliness' in this respect, tends to be associated with lower social class (Gabel 1981). Doleys *et al.* (1981) explain this in terms of such factors as:

1. Cues from rectal distension and internal and sphincter relaxation have not become discriminative cues for temporary retention and bowel movement on the toilet.
2. Sufficient reinforcement has not been applied to strengthen proper toileting behaviour as in (1) above.
3. Prerequisite skills, such as undressing, may not have been learned, though some such children will be mentally handicapped.

STRESS

Some authors have related the onset of encopresis to *stressful experiences* such as starting school, loss of or separation from parent, or birth of a sibling. Schaeffer (1979) points out that the colon is one of the organs in the body most affected by nervous tension, frequently resulting either in diarrhoea or constipation. Prolonged nervous tension could thus presumably have more serious, long-term effects.

PSYCHOLOGICAL OR PERSONALITY CHARACTERISTICS

As with nocturnal enuresis, various *psychological or personality characteristics* have been reported in encopretic children, including excessive shyness and obedience, unassertiveness, immaturity, depression and various supposedly anxiety-related behaviours such as nail biting, tics, headaches, etc. (Schaeffer 1979; Fritz and Armbrust 1982). Behaviour disorders such as truancy, stealing, tantrums, etc., have been noted. However, Fritz and Armbrust (1979) conclude that 'The degree to which the symptom of encopresis can itself lead to psychopathology, rather than result from it, is at present poorly understood', and Doleys *et al.* (1981) dismiss behavioural pathology as not being a major contributing factor.

LEARNING FACTORS

As was mentioned with regard to lax or inconsistent training leading to primary encopresis, Doleys *et al.* (1981) account for this in terms of a lack of appropriate reinforcement failing to establish and strengthen the necessary S–R links in the toileting chain of events, including: learning to discriminate the cues indicating the need to evacuate the bowels; temporarily retaining the faeces until appropriate facilities can be found; together with the necessary undressing and dressing skills needed to complete the chain.

They explain secondary encopresis in terms of either avoidance conditioning principles (where pain or fear results in holding back faeces, which causes them to become harder and hence more painful to pass, which in turn causes them to be withheld), or parental reinforcement of the inappropriate behaviour (e.g. attention, etc., given contingent upon encopretic behaviour).

NEURODEVELOPMENTAL PROBLEMS

Factors indicative of *neurodevelopmental learning and behaviour problems*, such as distractability, decreased attention span, hyperactivity, poor muscular co-ordination, have been associated with encopresis, but Fritz and Armbrust (1982) believe children with these features are likely to form only a small subgroup of encopretics, most encopretics being developmentally normal. Gabel

(1981) has also found a small number of children with regular encopresis but not factors of constipation, emotional problems, retention or social disadvantage and who may have a developmental physiological immaturity of the bowel, as well as those of the attention deficit type of disorder described by Fritz and Armbrust (1982).

GENETIC FACTORS

Genetic factors may also be implicated in encopresis, as an increased history of soiling in parents and other relatives has been found. Furthermore, a proportion of encopretic children have regular and longstanding problems with constipation (Schaeffer 1979) indicating a constitutional predisposition to constipation. However, Doleys *et al.* (1981) conclude that familial factors are not major contributors to the problem.

OTHER FACTORS

Illness, anal fissures during infancy or later, overuse of laxatives and enemas, cold school toilets, toilets with a lack of privacy, fear of toilets, or simply being too busy to stop and go to the toilet when appropriate can be initial reasons why the child becomes constipated and the passing of bowel movements becomes painful. A faulty diet (lack of fibre or insufficient fluid intake) may also result in constipation and pain on passing faeces.

GENERAL GUIDELINES FOR TOILET TRAINING

In order to avoid later problems of encopresis, Schaeffer (1979) provides general guidelines for toilet training of children:

Attitude — parents should be calm, patient, gentle and encouraging, avoiding scolding and disapproval,
Relationship — the context of training must be a warm, nurturing relationship, so that the child has a desire to please the parent,
Equipment — suitable potty with good support for the feet,
Routine — get into routine of visiting toilet, especially after breakfast,
Discriminative stimulus — take child out of nappies,

Cueing and prompting — use visual and physical prompts to remind the child,

Rewards — use rewards rather than punishments,

Imitation — take the child with you and elder siblings to the toilet,

Individual differences — accept that all children are different and some may be 'ready' earlier than others,

Rebellion — accept the idea that children may sometimes assert independence by rebelling. If so, take the pressure off for a few days.

Woodmansey (1972) also subscribes to this sort of approach in an attempt to ensure that parents do not worry about bowel training, and hence pressure the child. To this list we may plausibly add from other literature fluid intake, diet and posture as important factors in the training process.

DETERMINATION OF ENCOPRESIS

As has been previously mentioned, there is considerable disagreement as to the age at which a child can be regarded as encopretic. Most authors emphasise the need for a very thorough history taking (Fritz and Armbrust 1982; Doleys *et al*. 1981; Gabel 1981) as well as a physical examination of the child to rule out organic causes of the disorder. There is some disagreement as to just how thorough the latter need be, with some authors (e.g. Fritz and Armbrust 1982) questioning the need for the more invasive and less pleasant techniques that may prove traumatic to the child.

Classification

Encopresis is initially subdivided according to whether it is *organic* or *functional* in origin. Although a relatively small percentage of cases will have an organic cause, such causes should always be excluded first. These include Hirschsprung's disease (neurogenic megacolon) and lesions and tumours of the bowel (anatomic megacolon). Schaeffer (1979) presents a table of important differentiating features that enable discrimination between encopresis of functional and of organic origin. Differences are found in the nature of the admitting complaint, age at onset, history of the disorder, physical examination, neurological investigations and course of the disorder

(Schaeffer 1979; Gabel 1981).

Encopresis is further subdivided according to whether it is *continuous* (or primary encopresis, where child has never been toilet trained for bowel movement) or *discontinuous* (or secondary, where encopresis began after a period of successful toilet training — there is, as with nocturnal enuresis, some disagreement as to how long this period should be); and *retentive* or *non-retentive* encopresis (Morgan 1981). Other categories include fear of defaecation; refusal to defaecate on the pot; smearing; stress incontinence (Doleys, Schwartz and Ciminero 1981), and constipated and non-constipated. Doleys *et al*. (1981) outline what they consider to be a better method of classifying encopretics based on the severity and degree of constipation present, and the severity and degree of faecal incontinence. For example, where straining and hard stools are present and bowel movements are every two days or less, then soiling is infrequent — usually less than weekly — and amounts are small; where the faecal mass can be felt throughout the abdomen, is visible on X-ray, and bowel movements are every 3–5 days, then occasional large accidents — less than weekly — are likely; where stools are large with bowel movements every 7–14 days, and where the faecal mass is visible throughout the colon on X-ray, then light to moderate soiling once or more per week, or one large accident per week is likely, possibly with an absence of sensation before accidents; finally, where bowel movements are occurring every 14–21 days, the colon is enlarged on X-ray and faeces are impacted, then soiling is almost daily (Doleys *et al*. 1981).

CONSTIPATION

It has been agreed that the vast majority of encopretic people suffer to some extent from constipation. Other features frequently reported include colicky abdominal pain, poor appetite, lethargy and failure to detect the urge to defaecate.

However, the definition of constipation is another issue over which there is some disagreement, with some authors defining it purely in terms of infrequent bowel movements with no reference to consistency, and others considering the hard, dry, difficult to pass nature as an essential element. Schaeffer (1979) distinguishes three types of constipation not due to physical factors, as follows.

Rectal constipation

This is due to the continued failure to obey the call to defaecate. The urge to defaecate passes and stools become harder and drier, causing pain on passing bowel movements. Watery stools may leak out, but the child is really constipated.

Atonic constipation

Here hard, dry stools are passed but there is no abdominal pain. It is mainly caused by excessive and chronic use of laxatives and enemas, resulting in the colon losing some of its ability to move faeces to the rectum.

Spastic constipation

This is constipation with abdominal pain, caused by involuntary contraction of the muscles. It is due to emotional factors and very common under periods of stress.

Factors that can result in chronic constipation include the following: illness and fissures during infancy or later life; overzealous use of laxatives and enemas by over-concerned parents; avoidance of cold, unclean school toilets or those lacking in privacy; fear of toilets; being too busy to obey the call to defaecate; faulty diet and insufficient fluid intake. These are among the commonest reasons why a child may initially become constipated and find difficulty in passing bowel movements. Whatever the reason for the constipation, stools may be withheld due to discomfort in passing them. Small amounts may frequently be passed into the pants or very large amounts less often or continuous seepage may occur round the impacted faeces until a very large bowel movement is passed.

Webster and Gore (1980) distinguish four types of encopresis on the basis of symptoms: bowel control never achieved, bowel control achieved then lost due to some stress factor, soiling related to constipation or retention with overflow, soiling mainly intermittent deposits of small amounts of faeces. Doleys *et al.* (1981) likewise distinguish between primary and secondary, retentive and non-retentive.

Gabel (1981) distinguishes between encopretic (where bowel movements are of normal consistency), chronic constipation and overflow soiling (small amounts of loose stools associated with chronic constipation and retention).

TREATMENT

Two points are clear from the literature. First, studies of the treatment of encopresis tend to be limited to single case studies or uncontrolled group studies, with few attempts at controlled comparisons of various treatments and no-treatment controls. In order to offset the lack of controlled comparisons between groups of trainees, many authors employ other methodologies, such as ABAB reversal designs, to demonstrate the effectiveness of their procedures. Secondly, operant conditioning techniques are, thus far, emerging as providing the most successful framework for the treatment of encopresis.

Several authors recommend different treatments according to the nature of the presenting complaint (Gabel 1981; Fritz and Armbrust 1982).

MEDICAL/PHYSICAL APPROACHES TO TREATMENT

Use of enemas and laxatives

Although chronic misuse of enemas and laxatives by parents is frequently a contributory factor in the development of encopresis, their short-term, carefully monitored use is supported by many authors, both for maintaining an empty rectum and thus giving it the chance to regain its original shape in severe cases of faecal impaction, and helping to promote regular bowel habits in less severe cases of constipation and soiling (Gabel 1981; Fritz and Armbrust 1982; Doleys *et al*. 1981; Schaeffer 1979). However, Doleys *et al*. (1981) emphasise that normal muscle tone and control over toileting behaviour will not return simply by removing the impaction and toileting skills may require to be retrained.

Various types of enemas and laxatives may be used (Schaeffer 1979). Enemas include *cleansing enemas*, in which the enema imitates the normal stimulus for defaecation by distending the rectum with the fluid, and *lubricating enemas*, in which mineral or olive oil is inserted into the rectum to soften the faeces and lubricate the anal passage. Laxatives include *bulk products*, which are indigestible substances which soften the stool by adding bulk; *mineral oils and emulsions; chemical irritants*, such as senna and cascara; and *saline products*, such as milk of magnesia, which cause more fluids to reach the colon and rectum (Schaeffer 1979). The use of the above laxatives is not, however, without danger and they are therefore not recommended by some for treating encopresis: bulk products, for example, must always be taken with large amounts of water in cases of constipation, and care must be taken as blockages can build up quickly; use of mineral oils can overstimulate tense muscles and worsen some conditions; saline products can disturb normal digestive processes (Schaeffer 1979).

Other authors, however, whilst stressing the need for care (Gabel 1981) do recommend the use, for example, of mineral oil to keep the rectum clear and help promote regular, loose stools, after first using enemas to clear the blockage in severe cases of constipation with overflow. Use of mineral oil should be maintained, according to Gabel, for three to four months until a regular pattern of bowel movements has been re-established, whereupon the use of mineral oil may be gradually phased out. No mention is made by Gabel of any other techniques to retrain normal bowel habits, the assumption being that such use of laxatives over a period of time will (a) enable the rectum to regain its shape and sensation, and (b) will thus re-establish regular bowel habits. However, such a regime, he points out, would be unnecessary for less severe cases of constipation, in which changes in diet and some use of laxatives should be sufficient. Gabel further suggests that children either failing under such a 'medical management' or relapsing require further medical investigation. He thus makes the assumption that in such cases the encopresis may not be 'functional' in nature, rather than that this form of 'medical management' has failed to 'retrain' the bowel, as Doleys *et al.* (1981) would believe.

There would, however, seem to be some support for Doleys *et al.*'s (1981) belief in the need for retraining over and above the case of cathartics: many of the case studies reporting success after training by using operant conditioning techniques reported previous, unsuccessful treatment with enemas and/or laxatives along (e.g. Rovetto 1979). There would, on the face of it, therefore, seem to be little support for Gabel's concern that failure to improve with, or relapse after, the use of cathartics alone is likely to indicate organic involvement.

Diet

Increasing attention is being paid to diet as a major factor in a number of diseases and disorders of the bowel, ranging from constipation to cancer of the colon. Although Schaeffer (1979) dismisses as a proven myth the notion that poisons are absorbed into the body from faeces retained in the bowel for extended periods, bacteria in the colon can act on the contents of the colon, resulting into potential cancer-causing agents (Burkitt 1976, 1979). Potential carcinogens will be diluted and passed quickly through the colon where the volume of faeces is large. However, where constipation is a regular problem, faecal transit time is increased and potential carcinogens are left 'hanging around', as Burkitt puts it, with the ability to do more damage.

All authors are, however, agreed that the Western, highly refined diet is a major contributory factor in the problem of constipation, and that changes should be made in the diet to include foods high in fibre such as fruit, vegetables and, most especially, unrefined grain, and to reduce foods with a high fat content. Milk, which tends to have a binding effect, may have to be reduced to one pint per day. One simple method of increasing fibre in the diet is to add miller's bran to the food consumed each day. Bran can be mixed in with soups, stews, etc., without any noticeable effect on taste. Studies of bran added to the diet of populations traditionally most seriously affected by the problem of constipation, such as the elderly and the mentally and physically handicapped, have shown beneficial results (Lupson and Walton 1981), although there is disagreement as to whether increased fibre does reduce intestinal transit time (Schaeffer 1979; Burkitt 1976, 1979) or not (Eastwood *et al.* 1973; Harris 1980).

Posture

Posture is one factor that seems little studied or recognised as a factor in constipation and encopresis. The normal posture for defaecation is that of the squat position. Kira (1976) reports that 'In this way the capacity of the abdominal cavity is greatly diminished and intra-abdominal pressure increased thus encouraging the expulsion of the faecal mass.' He points out that Western-style toilets are frequently too high for adults, and that the practice of children using adult toilets is to be deplored, since 'Unless the toilet seat is low enough that the feet may rest firmly on the floor and some flexion of the thighs is possible, the accessory muscles, which aid in defaecation, normally have little opportunity to fulfil their function.'

Though some authors stress the need for the child's feet to be firmly placed on the floor during the toilet-training period (Schaeffer 1979), only a few give reasons for this (Gabel 1981). Consequently, the Western practice seems to be to wean the child off the potty and on to the adult Western toilet by means of toilet-seat inserts, as quickly as possible.

Some Western-type cultures, such as Japan, still use the squat posture while combining this with modern sanitation. Squat toilets in Japan have no seats and 'The pan is sunk into the floor, and in some places a shoe is fixed to the ground on each side of it so that a firmer foothold may be obtained.' But one of the problems nowadays is that although children in more 'advanced' societies adopt the squat posture with great ease during, for example, play, most Western adults find this posture difficult to assume and maintain for any length of time. This is primarily, according to Kira, due to lack of exercise, but no doubt also because we are not in the habit of using the (undignified and immodest) squat position when we sit, as most primitive cultures still do.

Thus, it seems that it is not only diet that has changed for the worse in the Western world, but posture during the elimination process as well.

Kira concludes that toilet designers could do a great deal of good for people if they would but pay attention to the physiology of defaecation. Encopretic people, especially those suffering from constipation, should be encouraged where possible to use the squat posture. Children should not be encouraged to sit on the toilet until they are of an age when toilet training is reliably established and feet should always be firmly positioned on a foot rest.

Gastrocolic reflex

Most authors recommend taking advantage of the gastrocolic reflex in order to establish a regular cycle of rectal filling and defaecation (Morgan 1981; Schaeffer 1979; Gabel 1981). For most people, this will probably occur in the morning, approximately 20 to 30 minutes after breakfast, although for others this will not be the case. Doleys *et al.* (1981) recommend keeping accurate baseline records of soiling and toilet use, to try to establish patterns. A warm drink on rising in the morning is often recommended (Schaeffer 1979; Morgan 1981). This serves to set the peristaltic waves in motion, and the child should be allowed to sit on the toilet for a sufficient length of time, say ten minutes. The child may also be toileted similarly after each meal. Laxatives or suppositories may initially be given so as to have their effect at the time the gastrocolic reflex would be expected to occur, in order both to increase the sensation of the need to defaecate and to ensure success in visiting the toilet. Their use can then be gradually phased out.

Exercise

Regular exercise helps promote bowel movements. Populations typically leading particularly sedentary lives, such as the elderly and handicapped, suffer particularly from lack of exercise. Housewives may also frequently be included in this category.

Abdominal massage

Abdominal massage was in fashion at one time as a treatment for various abdominal disorders, including constipation (Tidy 1952). Some clinicians still recommend it, although there are no empirical studies of its effectiveness in the literature, what reference there is to it tending to be somewhat dated.

Biofeedback

Biofeedback is a behaviourally based technique. It involves the measurement of physiological responses and the feedback of these responses to the patient, together with the use of operant procedures, so that he or she can control physical responses.

Kohlenberg (1973) used biofeedback to treat continuous encopresis in a 13-year-old boy with inadequate external anal sphincter tone. A fluid-filled balloon was inserted into the rectum to continuously measure pressure in the anal sphincter area. Treatment was conducted in 15 one-hour sessions over five days, divided into three phases. Phase one consisted of giving the trainee visual feedback of measurements, but this had little apparent effect on anal sphincter pressure; phase two used rewards of money for increases in sphincter pressure, but although this resulted in an increase in anal sphincter pressure, the response tended to fluctuate with the time of delivery of the reward and to be of relatively short duration; phase three successfully used reinforcement for increasing duration of pressure. Treatment resulted in a marked reduction of soiling, as reported by both nursing staff and parents. However, Kohlenberg urges caution in interpreting the outcome of treatment due to a lack of objective data on soiling and a lack of formal follow-up. Engel (1981) and Engel *et al.* (1974) report on the use of biofeedback in training control of sphincter pressure in seven encopretic individuals, all of whom had weak or absent external sphincter responses. These patients had daily incontinence of solid stool — retention was not a factor. One additional child trainee did have a history of severe faecal impaction and an absence of both internal and external sphincter responses. Training was carried out in three phases. First, objective measures of sphincter pressure were obtained. Second, trainees observed their sphincter responses following rectal distention, were instructed on the difference between their responses and normal responses, and were reinforced for making normal responses. Third, these responses were refined to approximate normal responses, so that relaxation of the internal sphincter and contraction of the external sphincter were synchronised. Dependence on direct visual feedback was then gradually reduced. Training was conducted successfully in no more than four training sessions of two hours each, with three to four weeks between each session. Engel found that, for these patients, learning to control their own responses was highly reinforcing and that learning was also highly specific to the response being trained. Follow-up ranging from six months to five years found four out of seven trainees had become completely continent; one had occasional staining; one did achieve bowel control at night but not by day; one withdrew due to pain from an anal fissure. The six-year-old child not only became fully continent but also passed regular normal bowel movements.

Whitehead *et al.* (1985) studied eighteen elderly hospital patients with faecal incontinence. All trainees were first treated for constipation in order to assess the effect of this on encopresis. Two became continent and three were excluded because of other problems. The remaining thirteen were given biofeedback training. Baseline measures were obtained of the patients' abilities to perceive rectal distention and the amplitude of their sphincter responses. Half were then given sphincter exercises to perform each day for four weeks prior to biofeedback training. Biofeedback training consisted of giving immediate visual feedback of pressure readings and verbal reinforcement and feedback was given for appropriate responses.

The volume of rectal distention required to produce consistent, appropriate responses was gradually reduced. Training continued until a criterion was achieved of less than one incontinent episode per month and no further improvement on two successive sessions. Records were kept of appropriate and inappropriate bowel movements. Results showed that sphincter exercises alone did not reduce incontinence. Biofeedback training resulted in a significant increase in external sphincter pressure response. Six patients reached the criterion for continence and encopresis was reduced by more than 75 per cent in four more, a total of 77 per cent. Three showed less than 75 per cent decrease in encopresis. Treatment time averaged just over four clinic visits. Poor response was not related to depression (those with very severe dementia had already been excluded). At twelve-month follow-up, five were still continent. Relapse was associated with progressive physical illness.

Biofeedback studies have shown quite clearly that it is possible, by using operant conditioning techniques, to modify and bring under voluntary control those physiological functions normally under control of the autonomic nervous system, such as heart rate, blood pressure and abnormal anal sphincter responses. Biofeedback training has been found to improve faecal incontinence even in elderly trainees, in whom encopresis has traditionally been regarded as a natural or incurable part of growing old.

OTHER BEHAVIOURAL APPROACHES TO THE TREATMENT OF ENCOPRESIS

As has been mentioned previously, the quality of the studies of encopresis differs enormously from those of diurnal incontinence and nocturnal enuresis, being mainly single case studies or uncontrolled group studies. A number of authors have, however, used various types of reversal designs in an attempt to overcome the limitations inherent in single case studies and thus improve the quality (Rolider and Van Houten 1985; Sanavio 1981) and control group studies can be found (Berg *et al.* 1983; Rovetto 1979). Behavioural approaches have involved reinforcement techniques in three areas, alone or in combination: reward for bowel movements passed into the toilet, reward for clean pants, punishment for soiling accidents.

A number of studies reward bowel movements passed appropriately into the toilet and use neither rewards for clean pants nor punishment for soiling accidents (Neale 1963; Keehn 1965; Lal and Lindsley 1968; Young 1973; Bach and Moylan 1975; Ferrell-Wright and Bunch 1977). Some clinicians feel that punishments for soiling and rewards for clean pants may teach the child to withhold faeces.

Other studies also lay the emphasis completely on the reward side, but reward both bowel movements into the toilet and clean pants (Berg *et al.* 1983; Bornstein *et al.* 1983). Yet others use all three procedures (Gelber and Meyer 1965; Plachetta 1976; Davis *et al.* 1976, 1977; Wright and Walker 1978; Sanavio 1981; Schabel 1984).

Some authors who use 'correction' procedures for soiling accidents (i.e. insisting the child washes soiled clothes and cleans himself up) claim that this is not a punishment procedure, but merely requires the child to accept responsibility for his own actions (Plachetta 1976; Webster and Gore 1980). There is some controversy as to whether 'correction' and 'overcorrection' procedures are educative (as is frequently claimed) or have their effect simply through punishment and fatigue. A number of authors have voiced serious misgivings over the ethics of using such procedures and over their supposed theoretical basis (see Chapter 6).

Finally, yet other studies employ rewards for clean pants and punishments for soiling but make no mention of specifically rewarding bowel movements passed appropriately into the toilet (Allyon, Simon and Wildman 1975; Rolider and Van Houten 1985; Webster and Gore 1980). Webster and Gore (1980) seem to lay an unduly heavy emphasis on the use of punishment procedures: punishment (staff disapproval), time out (removal from teaching group or activity) and correction procedures were applied immediately and contingently upon soiled pants, whilst rewards were administered 'once a clean day is recorded'. Rolider and Van Houten (1985) also give considerable emphasis to punishment procedures in a case study involving the successful use of negative reinforcement.

Such an emphasis on punishment in papers published in the 1980s is somewhat worrying, as the ethics of using behavioural techniques demand that greater emphasis always be given to the reward side of training. Even given successful treatment by using punishment techniques, ethical considerations demand that a hierarchy of least drastic alternatives be tried first. Furthermore, it is established that organisms learn faster under reward conditions than punishment conditions.

Effectiveness

Some papers do not present adequate data on soiling accidents and bowel movements in the toilet throughout training (Gelber and Meyer 1965; Webster and Gore 1980; Keehn 1965; Davis *et al.* 1976) but for those that do, soiling is reported to have ceased from one week (Davis *et al.* 1976, 1977) up to 14 weeks (Neale 1963). The vast majority of cases reported are said to have been successfully treated.

CONDITIONING TECHNIQUES AND THE USE OF MEDICATION

A number of studies combine the use of conditioning techniques with medication (Rovetto 1979; Wright and Walker 1978; Bornstein *et al.* 1983; Berg *et al.* 1983; Ferrell-Wright and Bunch 1977; Rolider and Van Houten 1985; Young 1973).

In an interesting study using glycerine suppositories in the treatment of eight encopretic housewives, Rovetto (1979) used a classical conditioning paradigm where the glycerine suppository was the UCS and the CS was a cup of coffee and the reading of a newspaper or book. At the end of twelve days of conditioning trials, evacuation (R) resulted from the CS (coffee and newspaper). 'Booster' conditioning sessions were carried out four and seven months after initial conditioning. At twelve-month follow-up, seven out of eight subjects met the training criterion of seven or more spontaneous evacuations in a 14-day period without use of drugs. Comparisons with control groups using laxatives and/or suppositories alone showed that none showed a significant improvement. Occasional relapses were treated with 'booster' conditioning trials. As might be expected, relapses were found to occur with changes of environment.

Suppositories together with the use of operant conditioning techniques were used by Lal and Lindsley (1968) and Wright and Walker (1978). After clearing out the colon with an enema, Lal and Lindsley's (1968) programme involved prompting the child to toilet upon rising and to evacuate without use of medication. Failure to evacuate resulted in the use of a glycerine suppository, and failure to evacuate in response to this resulted in the use of an enema before leaving for school. A graded system of rewards was used with greater rewards for spontaneous evacuation and no reward for evacuation using an enema. Rewards were also given for clean pants, together with a mild unspecified punishment for soiling. Fourteen subjects, from three to nine years of age, successfully completed the programme in a mean of 16.93 weeks, and a range of 10 to 38 weeks. Only one subject had begun soiling again at six-month follow-up. Lal and Lindsley found only one suppository was needed to result in successful training of a three-year-old child who had suffered from constipation and encopresis virtually from birth.

Ferrell-Wright and Bunch (1977) used mineral oil, along with rewards for bowel movements passed into the toilet, in the treatment of a three-year-old girl with severe long-term constipation. Training was successfully carried out over a period of 15 weeks, and follow-up at 93 weeks indicated no recurrence of the problem.

Young (1973) used Senokot with rewards for bowel movements into the toilet to help retrain perception of the gastrocolic reflex in twenty-four children ranging from 4 to 10 years. Twenty-two of these were successfully treated. Treatment time ranged from 2 to 25 months, with a mean of 7 months. Follow-up ranged from 6 to 72 months and four out of the 22 relapsed.

However, Berg *et al.* (1983) studied 40 severe and persistent soilers, mean age seven to nine years, in a controlled trial of the use of Senokot, placebo and no medication along with behavioural techniques. They found no significant difference in improvement across the three groups or in the number of children completely free from soiling. Nine out of the total of 40 children were not relieved of the symptoms at one year. Specific relapse rates are not given due to the difficulty in identification of clear-cut relapses.

Most studies using cathartics combined with behavioural techniques emphasise the need to fade out the use of the former rather than stop them abruptly (e.g. Ferrell-Wright and Bunch 1977; Wright and Walker 1978; Rovetto 1979).

HOSPITAL OR HOME TREATMENT

The vast majority of behavioural treatment programmes described with normal children are carried out in the home/school environment with parents as therapists. Hospital treatment programmes are described by Neale (1963), Gelber and Meyer (1965) and Webster and Gore (1980). In some cases the children were most often admitted to hospital for reasons other than encopresis (Neale 1963), whereas in others the children were admitted specifically because of encopresis (Webster and Gore 1980; Gelber and Meyer 1965). It is not possible to tell whether those children specifically admitted to hospital for encopresis were more severe encopretics than the majority of those cases described using home treatment, although they did appear to be older (mean age 13 years). However, in the case of Webster and Gore (1980), the speed with which success was achieved in all six cases, using time out, punishment and correction procedures for soiling and rewards for clean days, would at least raise doubts about the necessity of hospital admission. One case relapsed and subsequently withdrew. Follow-up ranged from six to twelve months.

Gelber and Meyer (1965) successfully treated one eleven-year-old boy over a period of 62 days in hospital, using rewards for bowel movements in the toilet and clean pants, and punishments for soiling. Follow-up at six months indicated two soilings and occasional stainings due to improper wiping. Neale (1963) used sweets and comics on the toilet as a method of reducing toilet-related anxiety in four children, three of whom displayed marked behaviour disorders along with encopresis, resulting in hospital admission. Rewards were given for bowel movements on the toilet, but no rewards were used for clean pants and no punishments for soiling. Three out of the four were successfully treated in eight to fourteen weeks and one failed, although at first follow-up one to two months after achieving continence, none of the three had an empty rectum.

Gabel (1981), whilst admitting to the high success rate and short duration of treatment using behavioural techniques in combination with the use of cathartics, expresses misgivings about this approach. These seem to relate to the use of parents as therapists administering punishment techniques and suppositories and enemas. He does, however, recommend the behavioural approach in the treatment of encopretics when retention and impaction, poor home situations, mental handicap, emotional problems, etc., are not factors in the aetiology. As he pointed out, results from behavioural studies have not supported his misgivings.

Training of bowel control has been carried out on other hospital populations, such as the elderly and mentally handicapped. For example, Sanavio (1981) successfully retrained bowel control in a 77-year-old hospitalised man suffering from senile dementia, by using rewards for bowel movements in the toilet and overcorrection and positive practice for soiling accidents. An ABAB reversal design showed operant contingencies to effectively control behaviour. Follow-up at eight weeks indicated successful maintenance. Chopra (1973) used rewards for bowel movements on the toilet to successfully retrain an eleven-year-old mildly mentally handicapped boy with Down's syndrome. No data are presented, but improvement was said to occur after six weeks. Matson (1977) reports virtually immediate success using correction procedures for soiling and rewards for cleanliness in treating encopresis in a 16-year-old institutionalised autistic boy who soiled himself several times a day. Matson initially makes the point that 'few effective methods for treating encopresis have been demonstrated to be rapid and enduring'. Although results demonstrate the rapidity of the approach in this case, the reported follow-up period of three months is insufficient to demonstrate whether or not it was enduring.

TREATMENT IN MENTAL HANDICAP

An excellent review of the problems of definition and treatment of encopresis in mentally handicapped people is provided by Groves (1982).

According to Groves, problems of defining encopresis in mental handicap are even greater than those encountered in the 'normal' population, since the difference between an untrained child and an encopretic child is even less clear in developmentally delayed and mentally handicapped individuals. No epidemiological studies exist of encopresis in mentally handicapped populations, partly because of the problem of definition and partly because of a lack of recognition that a problem exists in the first place — it seems to be assumed quite simply that encopresis is quite straightforwardly a 'normal' feature of severe mental handicap, or as Groves puts it, there is an implicit assumption that mental retardation is the major aetiology of encopresis in the mentally handicapped.

Since it is assumed that general developmental delay is the cause of encopresis in mentally handicapped or developmentally delayed individuals, little consideration is usually given to other aetiological factors, including developmental neuromuscular immaturity, constitutional predisposition, attentional problems, constipation, noncompliance, emotional problems, a lack of the other prerequisite skills required for independence at toilet (such as signalling the need to go or being able to go independently) or even straightforward inadequate exposure to adequate toilet training methods, undressing and dressing skills, etc. With regard to inadequate toilet training, for example, Morris (1957) found that improved living conditions and the use of group nursing procedures resulted in a dramatic decrease

197

within six weeks in wetting and soiling in severely doubly incontinent institutionalised adults with severe or profound mental handicap. At this time, it was believed that severely and profoundly
mentally handicapped people were unresponsive to basic 'habit
training'.

Groves (1982) is also critical of the lack of 'substantive treatment
guidelines' in mental handicap. Effective treatment strategies cannot
be developed for the mentally handicapped until serious consideration is given to the above problems.

PARADOXICAL INSTRUCTION

Paradoxical instruction is a technique used when anxiety is believed
to be a substantial factor. Although it seems not quite clear exactly
how it has its beneficial effects (Strong 1984), it has been used in
the treatment of such conditions as agoraphobia, depression, insomnia and procrastination, where it has been found to be more effective
than no treatment or placebo.

Bornstein *et al.* (1981) report its use in a case of chronic constipation and secondary encopresis in a nine-year-old boy in whom
toileting and related activities seemed to be causing considerable
anxiety. The trainee was sent to the toilet every hour for five minutes
and instructed to 'act as if you have to make a bowel movement but
do not allow that to occur'. An ABAB reversal design demonstrated
a clear reduction in soiling and increase in bowel movements on the
toilet during the experimental phases. Treatment was carried out
within a 16-week period. One week of follow-up after one year
indicated successful maintenance.

COGNITIVE THERAPY

Peterson and London (1965) used cognitive behavioural contingencies along with reward for bowel movements on the potty in a
three-year-old suffering from retention and pain on evacuating his
bowels. They propose that although cognition may not be essential,
it can have a significantly facilitating effect in learning more adap-
tive skills. Behaviour therapy has traditionally placed little emphasis
on the effects of factors such as cognition and insight on behaviour,
probably as a reaction to the over-emphasis in psychotherapy.
Cognitive stimulation consisted of explaining to the child why he

needed treatment and why treatment would be good for him. Hypnosis was used to change his expectancy of pain on evacuation and verbal and non-verbal rewards were used for achieving the target behaviour. Treatment was successfully carried out over eight days and follow-up at one year indicated successful maintenance. In fact, this particular study does not seem to differ much from most reported behavioural studies. Mitchell (1978) taught an adult suffering from spastic colitis to use five cognitive control techniques for the control of worry and management of fear and anxiety, along with progressive muscle relaxation and insight training to identify antecedents of tension and worry. Insight training resulted in little change in the frequency of colitis attacks. Muscle relaxation was found to reduce tension and colitis attacks substantially, but not worry. Cognitive control techniques were found to reduce worry substantially and further reduce colitis attacks.

PSYCHOTHERAPY IN THE TREATMENT OF ENCOPRESIS

Doleys *et al.* (1981) regard the psychotherapeutic approach to have been so non-productive and of such little use in the treatment of encopresis that they do not even present a review of reports on its use for this problem. Compared with the number of reports he reviews on successful use of behavioural techniques, Schaeffer (1979), for example, reviews only six successful psychoanalytical studies, no doubt reflecting both on the relative scarcity of published reports and the inadequacy of detail and data provided.

Many of the successful behavioural case studies presented state previous unsuccessful treatments to have included psychotherapy. Some of these report psychotherapy to have improved other, more general aspects of behaviour, leaving the specific problem of encopresis unimproved.

Protinsky and Kersey (1983) report success rates of less than 50 per cent for psychoanalytical treatment. A 50 per cent spontaneous remission rate over two years has been reported. Total absence of support for the notion of symptom substitution in the successful treatment of encopresis by behavioural techniques would seem to negate the basis for lengthy and expensive treatment of the supposed underlying conflict. As with nocturnal enuresis, it is thus hard to justify psychotherapeutic techniques as the treatment of choice in the problem of encopresis.

Psychotherapy, however, is sometimes recommended for use in

conjunction with a behavioural approach, where there are more serious behaviour problems or evidence of maladjustment.

FAMILY THERAPY IN THE TREATMENT OF ENCOPRESIS

The family therapy approach shifts the focus of therapy from the encopretic individual to the whole family, in the belief that the basis of the problem lies in abnormal patterns of interaction between family members. Schaeffer (1979) reports on a variety of maladaptive parental behaviours and attitudes that have been found to be associated with childhood encopresis, and states that the correction of the dysfunctional family patterns should therefore be the first step in the child's treatment.

This approach is very reminiscent of the psychoanalytical approach, the belief being that one cannot treat the symptom without first treating the deeper-rooted family pathology. But an association between encopresis and maladaptive patterns of family and parental behaviour does not necessarily imply a causal relationship, though clearly family pathology must be considered as a factor of possible aetiological significance. Protinsky and Kersey (1983) propose that failure of the behavioural approach in some cases of encopresis might be due to pathological family interactions, a factor largely ignored by the behavioural approach. They report on the use of family therapy in the treatment of seven encopretic boys aged six to ten years, five of whom had previously been treated unsuccessfully with behavioural or psychodynamic therapy. Six of the seven reached the succcess criterion of bowel movements on the toilet and no soiling for one month in a mean therapy time of twelve sessions. Follow-up at six months indicated five of the six to have maintained their success. Margolies and Gilstein (1983) believe dysfunctional family interactions to be a substantial causal factor in encopresis extending beyond childhood and report on the successful treatment of a 14-year-old boy suffering from continuous encopresis.

Family therapy has, as yet, made little impact on the problem of encopresis.

11

Psychological Treatments of Continence-related Problems in Adults

Of Dr. Thomas Goodwin, when ffelow of
Catherine Hall — He was somewhat whimsycall,
in a frolic pist once in old Mr. Lothian's
pocket (this I suppose was before his trouble
of conscience and conversion made him serious).[1]

Thomas Woodcock (1695)

Non-physical methods of treatment of incontinence can be applied not only where there is evidence that the disorder is functional in nature, but can also contribute to the achievement of continence following its loss due to organic causes. First of all, in this chapter, we shall look at the evidence that some toileting problems of a functional nature may have their origins in personality development or personality traits.

TOILET TRAINING AND PERSONALITY

The highly original idea of a possible link between toilet training and later personality was based on clinical observations and reported by Freud in his paper 'Character and anal eroticism' in 1908. He observed that three of his patients were characterised by the traits of orderliness, parsimony and obstinacy and that they had all been subjected to particularly strict forms of toileting training. Freud explained the apparent relationship in terms of the concept of reaction formation, whereby an unconscious mechanism manifests a violent action in the opposite direction to an impulse or desire that is being repressed. Thus, the infant who previously derived a great deal of pleasure from his toileting activities and who has had this pleasure inhibited by severe bowel training, becomes mean,

---

[1]Source: Muir (1976).

meticulous, punctual and self-restrained. The experience generalises so that anything that is free, uncontrolled and spontaneous comes to be regarded as dangerous.

It is hard to appreciate the diffuse, all-pervading influence of Freud's ingenious views on the way in which human behaviour is widely and popularly viewed. So many of his concepts have slipped into everyday language. Benjamin Spock, in his 'Bible' of child rearing (*Baby and Child Care*, 1971), advises that 'a long drawn out toilet training struggle between mother and child in the period between one and three years can bring up a lot of antagonism into a child's impressionable character . . . (and) this results in an outwardly aggressive . . . (person)'. Even psychologists such as Kagan (1969) seem to accept without question the following five consequences of severe toilet training:

1. Hostility and fear towards mother.
2. Anxiety over sexual thoughts.
3. Anxiety over dirt and disarray.
4. Concept of self as dirty or bad.
5. Inhibition of spontaneity and novel anxiety.

There is not room here, nor would it be appropriate, to review all of the evidence arising out of the discussion and the studies that Freud stimulated. Gripping accounts of the disputes between neo-Freudians and more empirically based psychologists who seek and test refutable hypotheses from Freud's theories have appeared almost perennially (see for example Lee and Herbert 1970). One relevant early study, that performed by Beloff (1957), will be mentioned here simply as an example. Beloff (1957) factor analysed ratings on various personality traits of a population of students. She also collected information from their mothers on whether their toilet training could be considered early, coercive and severe, or whether it was late and permissive. The results indicated that first, there was indeed a personality factor corresponding to the 'anal character', but that second, there was no relationship whatever between subjects' anality scores and coercive/permissive toilet training. There was, however, quite a high correlation between the student's ratings and their mother's ratings on anal characteristics, a result indicating that these are related more to mother's personality and not to the toilet training experience *per se*. If this association is to be explained in broad learning terms, then it is more likely that anal characteristics are instilled through the mother's personality in all spheres of activity and not just through toilet training.

Although there is no clear evidence suggesting highly specific effects of toilet training experiences on later personality, there is some suggestion that specific long-term psychological effects of the early experience of penile malformations, surgically corrected in childhood, can occur. Berg, Berg and Svenson (1982) compared 34 men who had had surgery between the ages of 18 months and seven years to correct hypospadias, a congenital malformation, with a control group operated on for appendicitis at the same age. They reported that most of the men operated on for hypospadias were psychologically relatively well adjusted and had no serious psychological disorders. However, they were found to be less assertive, more neurotic and depressive and to have fewer social relationships on average than the controls.

TOILET BEHAVIOUR AND PERSONALITY

It is important to remember that there is a lack of clear evidence linking *specific* effects of toilet training experiences to adult personality. However, there is evidence to suggest personality types or clusters featuring obsessional behaviours, anxiety, etc., that may be associated with toileting problems (either through cause or effect) in adults. Fears and phobias associated with toileting are common and there are close links between toileting and sexual behaviours.

SOCIAL FACTORS AND TOILET BEHAVIOUR

That social factors can affect micturition is a phenomenon familiar to medical and nursing staff when requesting urine specimens. Evidence that micturition responses and control can be directly affected by 'personal space invasions' is presented by Middlemist, Knowles and Matter (1976). Sixty men were observed at a three-stall urinal in a public toilet under three conditions of interpersonal distance: alone, adjacent to another toilet-user, or one urinal removed from the subject. A hidden observer recorded times for delay and persistence of micturition. Closer distances led to significant increases in micturition delay and to significantly shorter persistence times for the urine stream. Delay to onset of micturition increased from a mean of 4.9 seconds in the alone condition to 6.2 seconds and 8.4 seconds in the moderate-distance and close-distance conditions respectively. Middlemist, Knowles and Matter suggest that invasions of personal space are stressful, increasing arousal, and that it is this increased arousal that produces the behavioural response.

Paruresis, defined simply as increased urinary hesitancy or latency in public facilities, is very common. Gruber and Shupe (1982) discuss the differences in definition between various surveys that place the rate at between 14 and 50 per cent for men. Malouff and Lanyon (1985) use the term 'avoidant paruresis' for men whose inhibition is so strong that they actively avoid public toilet facilities. In a study of 381 male students they estimated the rate of avoidance paruresis to be 6.8 per cent, according to strictly defined criteria. Whatever the true incidence, it certainly affects a large number of people and is a further illustration of the mismatch between the development of cultural attitudes and behaviour and the design of toilet facilities. Clearly, the number who present with this as a problem requiring treatment is far lower and the majority must find alternative coping strategies or do not have their life style seriously impaired as a result.

PERSONALITY AND THE EFFECT OF SOCIAL FACTORS

Given that toilet behaviour can be affected by such external factors, the question obviously arises as to whether this is an isolated behaviour within an individual or whether it is correlated with other aspects of personality. Gruber and Shupe (1982) undertook a study of paruresis, personality and body shyness in a group of 90 males. They used a general, standardised personality questionnaire (California Personality Inventory), together with a 28-item questionnaire covering urinary hesitancy in public toilets (difficulty in starting urine flow, avoiding using public toilets, presence of others, etc.) and body shyness (undressing, showering, etc., in presence of other males). The results showed both correlations between urinary hesitancy and various aspects of personality and between hesitancy and body shyness. Greater hesitancy was associated with less sociability, more self-doubt, lack of self control and less tolerance. Malouff and Lanyon (1985) compared a group of 22 men defined as displaying avoidance paruresis with a group of controls and found that avoiders displayed higher general anxiety but did not differ with respect to sexual anxieties nor introversion.

At the opposite end of the pole of anxiety related to urination is general attraction to urine. Fetishes, like phobias, can be attached to just about anything under the sun. The fetish of urine is romantically labelled 'undinism' after the female water nymph Undine, and is described by Denson (1982). Lack of anxiety or motivation has also been professed as one explanation of the common problem of messy toileting, particularly in males (Siegel 1977). The other contributing factor may be lack of visual-motor co-ordination when assuming the male stance for urination. Either way Siegel recommends the use of a floating target in the toilet. Stimulus tracking during urination is related to scent marking and is discussed earlier in this book (pp. 33–6, 122).

The psychometric assessment of aspects of personality such as anxiety has only recently been introduced to this area, although the concept of 'anxious bladders' has long been around in urology. Standardised and well-researched instruments such as the EPQ (Eysenck Personality Questionnaire) have much to add to more objective approaches to study in this area. As incontinence and other toileting problems are such distressing complaints, it is reasonable to ask if a higher-than-average degree of anxiety is present, whether this is simply not secondary to the problem, rather than present beforehand. To investigate this, Crisp and Sutherst (1983) compared a group of fifteen women with urgency and urge incontinence with a group of 42 women presenting with stress incontinence. The former had significantly higher neuroticism (anxiety) scores on the EPQ, but did not differ significantly on the other main factors of extraversion and psychoticism. This finding was not, however, satisfactorily replicated by Morrison *et al.* (1984) using an earlier version of the same questionnaire, although they did find generally high neuroticism scores in a general group of 226 incontinent women.

A small study by Barnes, Harrison and Murray (1983) of male urological patients also found higher neuroticism scores in the three with 'anxious bladders', i.e. with non-organic problems, out of 40 who were urologically screened and assessed using personality questionnaires.

NON-PHYSICAL APPROACHES TO TREATMENT OF BLADDER PROBLEMS

We will now consider psychological methods of treatment or training that have been applied to bladder problems, by reviewing studies according to method treatment. The main alternative approach to structuring the remainder of this chapter would be to consider treatments appropriate to diagnostic categories of bladder disorders such as functional bladder disorder, unstable bladder, stress incontinence, etc. One problem with this latter approach is that frequently, particularly in the literature published by psychologists, insufficient urodynamic information is given about patients to permit a classification according to the recent International Continence Society's (1984) Standardisation of Terminology of Lower Urinary Tract Function. Other threads will be drawn together in the discussion towards the end of this chapter.

Relaxation and systematic desensitisation

If anxiety can be associated with bladder problems, either of frequency or retention, then there is a range of psychological techniques available for coping with this anxiety. One of the best-known approaches is systematic desensitisation. There are two main features involved in systematic desensitisation. The first concerns the construction of an individualised fear hierarchy and the second concerns the systematic deconditioning of those fears, often through the use of deep muscular relaxation or other techniques of anxiety management. A fear hierarchy is a series of situations, ranked in order from safe or least feared situations (such as being at home by oneself with access to a toilet close by), through moderately feared situations (such as having reasonable access to a toilet but being in company or going to the local shops), through to most feared situations (such as being in a concert hall or cinema or travelling long distances on public transport). There may be as many as twenty steps in the hierarchy. Starting with the least-feared situations, each step is then dealt with systematically through, for example, relaxation and cognitive restructuring to reduce anxiety and to change attitudes and perceptions using both imagination and through *in vivo* practice exercises.

Hallam (1976) describes in detail the treatment of a young woman who suffered from panic attacks that included the urgent need to void urine. Her first panic attack had occurred on a tube train on the London Underground and ultimately any situation without easy access to a toilet, such as a lecture hall, cinema or train, was liable to trigger an attack. Hallam constructed a graded programme of prolonged exposure to the feared situations. Relaxation was not used as an anxiety-coping strategy in this instance, however, as anxiety was rapidly extinguished simply by preventing her from making avoidance responses in the feared situation. A clear example of the use of relaxation and counter-conditioning of a fear hierarchy in imagination is given by Seif (1982), who ironically interprets his results in terms of a dynamic psychotherapeutic framework and the use of hypnosis. In this instance, a 68-year-old man who had suffered urinary retention and a fear of voiding in public toilets for as long as he could remember, refused to be hypnotised. Seif taught him to relax using breathing and muscular relaxation exercises. Thereafter, using relaxation together with a series of both imaginary and real situations, from office to restaurant toilets, this problem of 60 years duration was quickly resolved. Espie (1985) describes a combination of techniques that included desensitisation. The stimulus of a 'full' bladder was treated specifically as a target within a fear hierarchy and the associated anxiety was dealt with successfully by progressive relaxation training in the two relevant cases reported. Meyers, MacKinnon and Corson (1982) also describe a combination of treatment that includes relaxation for excessive urinary frequency in five patients. Meyers *et al.* provide more detail of the urological histories than is present in most other papers in the behavioural literature and report that no organic pathology was present. Their relaxation training was supplemented by the use of galvanic skin response (GSR) feedback. Overall, frequency of voiding urine was reduced from a daily mean of 15.7 to 8.7 following an average of thirteen sessions. Relaxation has been considered here as one approach to general anxiety reduction and applied to a graded fear hierarchy of bladder distention and/or feared toileting situations. Relaxation of specific muscles as part of the co-ordination of various muscle groups during voiding will be considered later when biofeedback techniques are discussed.

From the above studies, a number of points are suggested. First, it appears that relaxation techniques have potential application in some instances both of urinary frequency and retention. Second, although desensitisation and relaxation appear to be useful, their precise role has not been thoroughly evaluated as all of the reports are of small sample studies. In fact, practitioners tend not to use this approach in isolation, but rather in combination with other techniques, such as retention-control training.

Retention control training

A description of retention control training in the treatment of nocturnal enuresis is provided by Kimmel and Kimmel (1970), amongst others, and its application in that area is discussed in Chapter 9. Briefly, the behavioural rationale of retention control training in the treatment of daytime urinary frequency is as follows. Baseline recording of frequency of micturition is undertaken to establish the median (50th percentile) length of time between visits to the toilet. This time period is established as a starting point, as it is known that the patient can already successfully achieve postponement of micturition for this period on half the occasions. A shaping procedure is then used whereby the patient is reinforced with praise or other rewards, and feedback for holding out for this period. When the proportion of successes increases, the time period is reset to the new median period and so on to reach the predetermined target period. Fluids may then be increased to introduce a period of overlearning. In practice, many applications of retention control training are somewhat less rigorous. Typically, the patient may simply be asked to wait until the desire to void urine is first felt and is then asked to postpone micturition for a brief period. The periods of postponement are then progressively increased. Fluid intake may be increased concurrent with retention control training.

Hallam (1976), Meyers *et al.* (1982), Rovetto (1983) and Espie (1985) all describe forms of retention control training in combination with other treatments in the treatment of urinary urgency and frequency problems. Although Meyers *et al.* (1982) provide a detailed description of both their patients and their treatment package, which was implemented in stages, no analysis of the separate components in the package was undertaken. However, both Rovetto (1983) and Espie (1985) use multiple-phase designs in their small sample studies that enable some comment to be made about relative effects of specific components in their particular patients. For example, the 20-year-old man described by Rovetto (1983) urinated twelve to twenty-one times per day before treatment. An initial retention control training period alone produced insigificant change. As it appeared that high anxiety was impeding the progress of retention training, a second phase of desensitisation was introduced to deal with his fears of wetting himself in public. Following this, a further period of retention training alone resulted in a rapid and enduring improvement to an average of five to six voidings of urine per day.

Retention control training is an active process whereby the person concerned operates on his or her ability to retain urine. In contrast, physical bladder distension is a passive process whereby the bladder is distended without the patient's active involvement. Ramsden *et al.* (1976) report such an approach with 51 women and men suffering from urgency and urge incontinence and for whom drug treatments had failed. Distension was effected by catheterising the bladder, following epidural anaesthesia, and raising the pressure in the bladder to equal each patient's systolic blood pressure for four 30-minute periods. Overall, sixteen patients of the 51 were rated as having become symptom-free, with a further twenty-five being rated as substantially improved. A problem recorded in this study was that two patients sustained ruptured bladders, which required treatment. Unfortunately, there has been no comparison of active and passive bladder distension procedures.

Paradoxical intention

If it is hypothesised that performance anxiety is a key factor in the problem of psychogenic urinary retention, then it is reasonable to consider treatments that aim specifically at reducing that performance anxiety. A technique that is particularly appropriate in this instance of performance anxiety is paradoxical intention (or paradoxical instruction). If a person has experienced failure on attempting to urinate, successive attempts merely increase arousal and anxiety and impair performance, resulting in a cycle of anxiety, failure to urinate, increased anxiety, further futile attempts, more anxiety, etc. Paradoxical intention operates by removing the performance goal that is producing the performance anxiety. Thus, following a programme to reduce anxiety related to a hierarchy of cues associated with toileting, the therapist may give instructions to enter a toilet and go through all the steps in the toileting process but to refrain from actually passing urine. For example, Ascher (1979) describes how:

A male client was to enter the men's room walk to the urinal, unzip his fly, perform the appropriate manipulation and stand there as if to urinate. But under no circumstances was he to allow himself to pass urine. After a reasonable period of time he was to . . . leave the bathroom.

Permission to urinate was never given by the therapist. When performance anxiety is sufficiently low, having been reduced by the paradoxical instruction and the need to urinate is high, then this instruction is usually voluntarily ignored. Once this happens, the problem is largely solved. The stimulus of a full bladder can obviously be primed by high fluid intake or a short-acting diuretic. Ascher (1979) reported that other psychological treatments, including systematic desensitisation, were satisfactory in the treatment of the majority of cases of psychogenic urinary retention that he saw. However, he describes five cases for whom such treatment failed, but who subsequently improved rapidly when the treatment was changed to include paradoxical intention. Timms (1985) and Espie (1985) both record single cases in which paradoxical intention was included in the treatment of urinary urge or frequency problems. In this situation, the paradoxical instruction when urge occurs is to 'wet yourself'. For many people it is, in fact, extremely difficult to voluntarily pass urine in their clothing. When the therapist gives permission to do so and this difficulty is experienced, then anxiety is reduced. Again, the treatment can progress through a graded series of feared situations, from standing in the bathroom, standing at the front door, walking down the street and so on.

Psychodynamic treatments

Although less common, psychodynamic approaches to treatment of continence problems do occur (Seif 1982; Bistey 1984; Freeman and Kaxby 1982). Seif (1982) and Bistey (1984) both describe single cases of urinary retention. In the case described by Seif, it is clear that a simple relaxation procedure, used to counteract anxiety in a hierarchy of more progressively feared situations, was sufficient to overcome the problem. The author interpreted the treatment of this fear of urinating in public toilets within a dynamic psychotherapeutic framework, but a simpler explanation of systematic desensitisation is sufficient. Bistey (1984), amongst other things, interpreting his patient's problem in terms of sexual anxieties, also used age-regression hypnosis to relieve traumatic experiences.

The only report of the use of hypnosis that should be taken seriously is the much more impressive study undertaken by Freeman and Kaxby (1982) of 50 women suffering from urinary urge and frequency difficulties. Treatment comprised twelve sessions of hypnosis aimed at symptom removal by direct suggestion and ego strengthening. At the end of treatment, twenty-nine of the women subjectively rated themselves as symptom free, with a further fourteen rated as improved. Only seven women reported no change. Of considerable importance is the objective support for these subjective changes from cystometry before and after treatment.

Bladder drill

Bladder drill is the term most widely used in the medical literature for retraining bladder instability, presenting as urge or frequency difficulties in women in whom organic or other physical causes have been excluded. Its theoretical rationale is not usually elaborated, but the procedure is undoubtedly effective. It is described by Frewen (1978) and Stanton (1986) and is often carried out initially on an in-patient basis. The key feature of bladder drill is a micturition chart for baseline recording of times and volumes of continent and incontinent urine passed. This is then used as a basis for timing expected voidings and encouraging the patient to voluntarily gradually prolong the intervals between voiding. Hence, in behavioural terms, it is a form of retention control training using shaping. Commonly, clinicians use it in conjunction with anticholinergic medication (e.g. Frewen 1978; Stanton 1986) and some include triple voiding or stop-start exercises during micturition (e.g. Klarskow, Gerstenberg and Hald 1984).

A particularly impressive study of bladder drill is reported by Frewen (1978). The design of the study comprised an uncontrolled trial of 40 women with moderate or severe urge incontinence and cystometric evidence of detrusor instability. The criteria of cure were very strict and comprised both an absence of symptoms and normal cystometry within three months. Frewen reported that 32 (82.5 per cent) of these women achieved a cure according to these criteria. The seven women who did not achieve complete cure showed some improvement in symptoms but less in cystometry and most had significant sources of additional emotional stress, such as chronically ill husbands. Jarvis (1981a) replicated Frewen's study on a group of 33 women with urge incontinence. In this case, however, the incontinence was not associated with an unstable bladder, as the detrusor remained stable during cystometry. Also, no medication was used. Following treatment, twenty women (60.6 per cent) no longer reported urgency or incontinence and cystometric indices improved significantly as well.

Jarvis (1981b) has provided a rare account of a comparison of bladder drill and drugs that diminish detrusor activity. A group of 50 women with incontinence associated with bladder instability were allocated either to treatment with bladder drill or treatment with a combination of an anticholinergic agent (imipramine) and a musculotrophic agent (flavoxate hydrochloride). There was a significant difference in outcome in favour of bladder drill. Twenty-one (84 per cent) of the twenty-five patients in the bladder drill group achieved continence and nineteen (76 per cent) were symptom-free, compared with fourteen (56 per cent) and twelve (48 per cent), respectively, in the drug group. Additionally, Jarvis noted drug side-effects in fourteen patients, whereas no adverse effcts were reported for the bladder drill group.

Biofeedback

The application of biofeedback to continence problems is also considered elsewhere in this book in chapters concerning encopresis and the elderly.

There has been considerable growth in the scope of biofeedback in behavioural medicine in recent years (Yates 1980, 1985). Biofeedback has been used to treat a number of unconditioned responses previously thought to be outwith voluntary control, such as heart rate and blood pressure. Biofeedback applications to gastrointestinal disorders such as irritable bowel syndrome are reviewed by Latimer (1981). Two good outlines of its relevance to continence are provided by Engel (1981) and Ehrman (1983).

Engel (1981) distinguishes three classes of behavioural responses to which behavioural techniques are applied:

1. Elicited responses such as anxiety or phobic reactions to specific situations, as in paruresis discussed earlier in this chapter. Here, counter-conditioning strategies are appropriately included in treatment.
2. Emitted or operant behaviour that operates on the environment and can be manipulated by environmental contingencies. Examples of this include the behaviour modification toilet-training programmes developed in mental handicap and discussed earlier in this book.
3. Unconditioned responses, such as fluctuations in sphincter muscle tone, that were previously thought to be outside voluntary control, but which are now subject to biofeedback approaches.

Engel also differentiates two ways in which biofeedback has been clinically applied. The first is through feedback of generalised measures, such as EMG and GSR in relaxation training. In the second, patients are taught to control highly specific responses such as high blood pressure, cardiac arrhythmias and sphincter control. Such training is highly specific and does not tend to generalise: for example, control of external and internal and sphincters may have to be taught separately. At first glance, it may seem strange that behavioural techniques be applied to such obviously pathological processes but, as Engel points out, it is important to distinguish between the medical model of disease and the behavioural model of process:

It has been proposed that the medical model of disease, which states that every pathophysiological state is caused by an under-lying organic process, is inappropriate for conceptualising behavioural dysfunction. Rather, behavioural dysfunction is normal function which is inappropriate as seen from the social context in which it occurs. Furthermore, modification of behavioural dysfunction need not . . . depend on an understanding of how the behaviour was acquired. It seems reasonable to characterise acquired behaviour in the language of behaviour rather than in the language of medicine, since many years of behavioural research have shown that behavioural concepts are valid and lead to powerful clinical applications.

There is no necessarily direct incompatibility, however, between medical and behavioural models, as Engel further points out:

Because the nervous system exercises a significant degree of control over the remaining healthy tissue, it is possible either to train such tissue to behave normally, or to suppress the pathological effects which the diseased tissue exerts over the healthy tissue.

The application of biofeedback in the area of bladder problems has encompassed both frequency micturition and stress incon-tinence. An early example of the former is given by Jones (1956), who established a conditioned response between the desire to void urine and a critical bladder pressure recorded through cystometry. Following this, Jones then gradually falsified the pressure readings so that the patient tolerated progressively increasing bladder pressures. Current approaches do not rely on deception and can be divided along two main paths, specific feedback of detrusor pressure through cystometry and more generalised feedback through GSR or EMG of relaxation during bladder filling.

A good example of the first is provided by Cardozo and her colleagues (Cardozo *et al*. 1978a and b), who report on groups of female patients with frequency, urgency or urge incontinence associated with detrusor instability. Detrusor pressure was converted into auditory and visual stimuli and fed back to the patients over four to eight one-hour sessions. The findings of Cardozo *et al*. are encouraging, with 80 per cent of the patients showing improvement. The authors record their impressions that biofeedback requires a high degree of motivation, a reasonable degree of intelligence and that it may not be suitable for cases of severe detrusor instability. Cardozo *et al*. are refreshingly realistic and cautious in their conclusions, but it may be that some of these particular problems can be dealt with by using different approaches or applications of biofeedback, some of which are outlined below.

Meyers *et al*. (1982) and Libo *et al*. (1983) used a different approach. This has been described by Meyers *et al*. as 'biobehavioural' and utilises more generalised feedback for relaxation during bladder filling and emptying. They used GSR with five adults described simply as complaining of frequency micturition and pain. Treatment comprised initially teaching biofeedback-assisted relaxation and subsequently applying the relaxation strategies to gradually increase the time between the urge to urinate and actual voiding. The time periods were generally 10, 15, 30, 45 and 60 minutes over a period of 4 to 12 weeks. Meyers *et al*. hypothesise that the pain complained of was partly due to increased attention paid to the discomfort of a partially filled bladder and partly to an unconscious tensing of the muscles of the body in general as well as those muscle groups associated with the bladder. Both frequency and pain were improved in all patients, but one had relapsed at follow-up. For the four successful individuals, the problem was a relatively isolated one, whereas the woman who relapsed had a set of relatively complex psychological problems.

The use of EMG biofeedback is described by Libo *et al*. (1983), Wear, Wear and Cleeland (1979) and Maizels, King and Firlit (1979) for bladder problems including frequency and incomplete emptying and for children and adults. In the study of an eight-year-old girl reported by Libo *et al*. (1983), for example, treatment utilised intensive EMG feedback separately from the perianal and perivaginal muscles and instruction in alternately tensing and relaxing the pelvic floor muscles and in relaxing during urination. General relaxation training involving other major body muscle groups was also given. The perineal muscle exercises were carried on at home after the initial in-patient biofeedback training and between out-patient biofeedback sessions. Early improvement was evident in muscle control and in frequency, but relaxation during voiding was not acquired until late in the period of seventeen training sessions. It is important to note that the treatment period for this eight-year-old girl is lengthy and that social and other more concrete forms of reinforcement were used in conjunction with the programme to help with motivation. Thus, intelligence and motivation are not necessarily limiting factors. This is even more apparent in a case described later where a thirteen-year-old boy was treated for faecal incontinence by using biofeedback (Kohlenberg 1973).

The only recorded instance of the apparent lack of effect of biofeedback in urinary continence is provided by Castleden, Duffin and Mitchell (1983) on stress incontinence. Castleden and her colleagues used a perineometer in conjunction with pelvic floor exercises in a group of nineteen women suffering specifically from stress incontinence. The perineometer, which was first devised almost 40 years ago, consists of a rubber air chamber that rests in the vagina against the perineum and is connected to a manometer which gives a visual reading of the squeeze exerted by the pelvic floor muscles (Mandelstam 1986b). Patients were randomly allocated to two groups of pelvic floor muscle exercises plus use of perineometer first then exercises alone, and exercises alone first then exercises plus perineometer. Castleden et al. found an overall improvement with treatment, but no significant effect of the perineometer, although both patients and physiotherapists preferred using it.

These negative findings contrast markedly with other recently reported outcomes, including those described by Shepherd, Montgomery and Anderson (1983), Burgio, Whitehead and Engel (1985), Burgio, Robinson and Engel (1986), Mandelstam (1986b) and Shepherd (1986). It is important to look at some of the probable reasons for this difference. Shepherd et al. (1983) treated twenty-two women with stress incontinence in two different ways. Half of this group were instructed in pelvic floor exercises while using a perineometer throughout and were then given the device to use with their exercises at home. The other half of the group were taught pelvic floor exercises entirely without the benefit of the perineometer. In this way the perineometer substantially enhanced treatment effects. The study presented by Burgio *et al.* (1986) provides a more detailed and sophisticated report on the role of biofeedback in pelvic floor exercises for stress incontinence. Again patients were divided into two groups. In the experimental group, thirteen patients received visual biofeedback of bladder, sphincter and abdominal pressures, together with verbal instructions and reinforcement, during training sessions comprising 25 sets of contraction and relaxation exercises. In the control group, eleven patients had similar training sessions without the biofeedback, but with verbal instruction and reinforcement from a therapist, mainly rating vaginal squeeze on two gloved fingers. Each group were given the same exercises to practise at home in between clinic sessions. The results indicated that the biofeedback group improved sphincter contractions, whereas the control group did not. Incontinence improved in both groups, with a 76 per cent reduction in accidents for the biofeedback group compared to a 51 per cent reduction for the control group. Thus, likely reasons for the earlier unsuccessful use of biofeedback become clearer. Firstly, feedback should be given intensively over a series of exercises, and not just at the beginning and end of a session. Secondly, pressure readings on the perineometer can also be affected by abdominal pressure, which is a likely source of unreliability in the perineometer-only study, as opposed to more complex studies using biofeedback.

REFLECTIONS

In the last part of this chapter we will return to some of the issues that generally arise from these different approaches to treatments. Although many different non-physical treatments for continence-related problems have been touched on here, it is clear that training in one form or another has a large role to play in the promotion of continence in cases earlier and more traditionally treated by physical methods or surgery. The reported success rates across a range of procedures is high and many of these bladder problems should be regarded as eminently treatable.

As mentioned earlier, treatments could not be considered under different diagnostic headings, due to the lack of urodynamic information in many of the studies reported by psychologists. Although it is usually clear whether the problem studied was a frequency or retention one, more than that is often difficult to tell. If the problem is one of frequency, it can be assumed in most cases that it is not leakage of urine associated with stress incontinence but, for example, whether there is evidence from cystometry of detrusor instability is often unknown. However, as frequency and urge incontinence in association with both stable and unstable bladder respond in a similar manner to bladder drill (Jarvis 1981a and b), then from this point of view the distinction may not be a particularly valid one. Thus, it is not certain whether the presence or absence of detrusor instability is related to prognosis.

Similarly, the distinction between organic and functional bladder disorders is not necessarily closely linked to whether a problem can be treated by physical or non-physical methods, or not at all. Specific difficulties in, or fears of, toileting in certain situations can easily be regarded as functional. Other cases are less clear. Detrusor instability in the absence of demonstrable pathology is appropriately treated by training methods, but this does not prove conclusively that the problem has a functional basis. Many organic disorders can be treated by training methods and this does not deny their organic cause: for example, the loss of urine in conjunction with walking or jumping that occurs in stress incontinence is often treated with physiotherapy exercises or biofeedback. On the other hand, detrusor spasms and instability could plausibly have arisen for some reason as a learned inco-ordination, or they may have had some original organic cause the effects of which are later maintained by environmental factors.

The specific and general roles of anxiety in bladder disorders is also fraught. The two contrasting problems of frequency and retention, in the apparent absence of organic causes, can both be treated as having a basis in anxiety. The act of micturition requires co-ordinated tensing and relaxing of several groups of muscles, including relaxation of the sphincter(s). It is plausible that anxiety and cortical arousal may inhibit the relaxation of these muscles. Conversely, high states of anxiety and fear in animals often lead to spontaneous evacuation of the contents of bladder or bowel before flight or fight. It is not a paradox that the same techniques of anxiety reduction such as systematic desensitisation and paradoxical intention have been applied to both problems of frequency and retention.

The other issue that arises here is obviously whether or not the treatment of anxiety is a necessary part of successful treatment of any functional bladder disorders. There are successful reports of treatments emphasising the incorporation of anxiety reduction techniques (e.g. Rovetto 1983; Espie 1985), and reports of degrees of success where there is no specific anxiety reduction (e.g. Ramsden *et al*. 1976). Those studies that emphasise anxiety management tend to be carried out by psychologists, whereas the others tend to be carried out by physicians. It is difficult to make direct comparisons, but there are likely to be differences in the populations typically treated by the different disciplines: those referred to psychologists will often have failed to respond to earlier treatments and will often have more complex mental health problems. Urologists and gynaecologists, for obvious reasons, are more likely to treat a broader sample of patients with bladder problems. Frewen (1978), in his study of bladder drill in 40 women with unstable bladders, noted that the seven who failed to achieve complete success had additional sources of stress. It may be that this group is more representative of those reported on by psychologists. This requires further study, however, as many women in the middle years of life currently have, or have suffered, stressful experiences. Frewen does not report the age of the sample in his study and it is not known how many of the successfully treated women had similar sources of stress.

The psychological approaches to treatment reviewed earlier can be very crudely classified in two ways: psychodynamic and behavioural. At the risk of oversimplifying, psychodynamic approaches assume an underlying unconscious conflict, often sexual, that needs to be resolved before the symptom will disappear, whereas behavioural approaches tend to focus more directly on the problem behaviour and its functions. Malouff and Lanyon (1985) found no evidence of increased sexual anxieties in a group presenting with avoidant paruresis compared with controls. There is scant empirical evidence from dynamic psychotherapists on the treatment of bladder problems. Those few reviewed here, in particular Bistey (1984), provide no evidence that resolving underlying unconscious conflicts provides better results than treating the problem directly. It seems that in many cases of bladder disorders, such as frequency, it is not necessary to treat anxiety directly, whereas in others it is likely that this is necessary. Clinically, many of the behavioural reports indicate that they were unable to proceed to retention control training without dealing first of all with the anxiety, as this was impeding attempts to delay voiding for even very short periods. However, the treatment of anxiety in such cases can be dealt with by using behavioural techniques without the need for resolving hypothesised but not objectively verifiable underlying conflicts. The feature that seems common to all of the studies concerning frequency problems is increasing functional bladder capacity.

One additional point is that, in the urological populations with frequency problems, almost any approach has the potential to show a degree of success. Mayhoff, Gerstenberg and Nordling (1981), in a double-blind cross-over trial, found that placebo was significantly better than no treatment, emepronium bromide and flavoxate chloride.

Finally, although the general picture is that training approaches are effective in many cases of different types of bladder problem, the general trend of future studies should be less towards demonstrating the effects of particular treatments on their own and more towards comparing the relative effects of different treatments. Understandably, clinicians tend to use combinations of treatments and this, depending on the methodology, often makes evaluation of specific effects difficult. There is a need for larger studies with random allocation of subjects to treatment groups, with more attention paid in the data analysis to factors associated with treatment failure as well as success.

12

The Loss of Continence Associated with Dementia

But beauty, like the fair Hesparian tree,
Laden with blooming gold, had need the guard
Of dragon-watch with uninchanted eye,
To save her blossoms, and defend her fruit
From the rash hand of bold incontinence.

Milton (1608–1674)

The serried rows of thinly partitioned toilets;
the queue of wheelchairs waiting outside; the
rattling of commodes to the bedside; the
delivery of urinals and bedpans like a milk
round . . .

As the female patients entered, they were
carefully deposited on a pad. Dresses were
folded in front so that their knickerless
backsides were safely on paper. While the
chairs were certainly protected, the obvious
message to patients in that day-room was
'Wet Yourself!

The appalling fate of institutionalised, incontinent, elderly people is vividly described above by Isaacs (1976) and Wells (1975), respectively. The whole size and nature of the problem here is at first glance depressing and it is certainly so for the elderly people concerned together with their carers, whether in community or institutionalised settings. Incontinence is often seen as an inevitable consequence of abnormal or even normal ageing process. It is often viewed as a specific symptom of organic disorders, for example within dementia. It is often viewed as intractable. In this chapter, we will consider whether these views are justified. As elsewhere in this book, the emphasis will largely concern environmental and in particular behavioural determinants of continence and much of the concern here will focus on incontinence and dementia.

220

A glance at the literature indicates clearly that incontinence in the elderly is heavily medicalised, but it is argued here that the evidence warrants a better balance between physical and psychological approaches. In the literature on the elderly in particular, perhaps more than elsewhere, the term 'psychological' tends to have a very psychodynamic, neo-Freudian interpretation (e.g. Sutherland 1976; Wells 1984). Here, we will emphasise rather more objective issues, such as the effects of retraining for continence. A psychological approach does not deny a biological component to a problem and the work described by Ehrman (1983) and Whitehead et al. (1984, 1985) on biofeedback are good examples of this.

Some of the comments made and conclusions reached later in this chapter are critical of the type and quality of studies of incontinence in elderly people. However, it is to the credit of those who have published in this area, and in particular to some authors who have shown a sustained interest over many years, that they have taken this unpopular problem seriously and have recognised it to be of singular importance.

DIAGNOSIS AND AETIOLOGY

Considering the size and nature of the problem there has been scant attention paid to it by most clinicians and researchers. Extensive review and discussion of the predominantly medical literature on incontinence in the elderly has been provided recently by Brocklehurst (1984a), Mandelstam (1986a) and Willington (1976a). These include many descriptions of the known and possible physical causes of, and diagnostic categories for incontinence of the elderly. An algorithm approach to the diagnosis of urinary incontinence, based on research and the utility of which is testable, has recently been provided by Eastwood and Warrell (1985). Cruder, but more memorable mnemonics for classification have been provided by Thompson (1986). He distinguishes reversible and irreversible incontinence. For reversible incontinence he has coined the mnemonic DAMP:

D — diuresis	— renal failure
Osmotic	— hyperglycaemia
	— hypercalcaemia
Drugs	— strong diuretics
	— anticholinergics (retention with overflow)

— ephedrine
— sedatives
A — atrophy   atrophic uretheritis/vaginitis
M — mechanical   — prostate
                  — faecal impaction
                  — pelvic tumour
                  — stone
                  — stress incontinence
P — psychological

For irreversible incontinence he has coined the mnemonic PISS:

P — post-prostectomy symptoms
I — inhibition lost over reflex contractions (from cortical centre in frontal lobe)
S — spinal lesions (motor and sensory loss)
S — sensation loss (peripheral and nerve lesions).

Thompson's ingenious and entertaining classification is chosen here to provide a flavour of the range of possible causes described throughout the relevant literature. His paper is intended as a practical guide to examination and diagnosis and he takes a sympathetic view of the elderly person. It was never proposed seriously as a rigorous model, but it can be taken to critically illustrate two important points: the first is that it is heavily medical with psychological components rating only a brief mention; the second is that the reversible–irreversible distinction is a crucial but neither wholly appropriate nor helpful distinction. It reflects prevailing, rather negative attitudes, whereas positive attitudes towards continence promotion must be regarded as fundamental. In particular, the description of cortical loss of inhibition in dementia as a cause of irreversible incontinence must be regarded as premature. It is true, as we shall see, that there are particular problems in this area, and that retraining in patients with dementia has on average a poorer outcome, but detailed consideration of studies in this area cannot result in the conclusion of complete irreversibility.

EPIDEMIOLOGY

Accurately gauging the size of the problem can be difficult as, with surveys in this area as in other areas, 'the results will vary depending on the questions and the order in which they are asked' (Milne 1976). One of the most recent surveys of incontinence in a sample of over 500 elderly community and institution residents has been conducted by Campbell, Reinken and McCosh (1985). Although their definition of incontinence is not specified precisely, they report a prevalence of urinary incontinence for those over 65 years old to be 11.6 per cent and for those over 80 years old to be 21.7 per cent. The overall estimated faecal incontinence rate for this whole sample was 3.1 per cent. Statistically, frequent urinary incontinence or catheterisation has been found to be associated with death within four years, although as the authors comment, the association is probably not a causal one. Urinary incontinence is usually linked with other factors of poor physical health including poor mobility and dementia.

DEMENTIA

In their large study of prevalence and prognosis of incontinence in the elderly, Campbell *et al.* (1985), apart from finding the expected high rate of incontinence among those with dementia, concluded in general that: 'Urinary incontinence as a predictor of death is probably a marker of conditions such as dementia, poor mobility and poor physical health, rather than a risk factor in its own right.'

Here, it is appropriate for us to consider briefly the controversy and complexity of the specific role of incontinence within dementia. The issues include both whether such incontinence is likely to be organically or functionally determined, and whether it is associated with dementia as a result of a specific organic lesion or general damage. An initial problem in interpreting the results of studies concerns not only the lack of detail often provided about the clients involved, but the apparent over-diagnosis of organic brain syndromes that can occur (Woods and Britton 1985).

Arie, Clarke and Slattery (1976) and Brocklehurst (1984b), for example both include an outline of the arguments for the viewpoint of specific organic effects in their discussions, whereas Whitehead *et al.* (1984) and Holden and Woods (1982) incline much more to a general association. The former, on the one hand, argue that no matter which type of dementia is involved, the lesions occur at cortical and subcortical levels plausibly affecting centres of bladder control; and that as the commonest form of incontinence in dementia is urge incontinence, then this is consistent with this view. The

223

latter, on the other hand, argue that there is a greater need for more careful analysis of which competent toileting skills are actually affected (Holden and Woods 1982). For example, Holden and Woods (1982) describe an observational study of eight incontinent women suffering from senile dementia and established that five of them had difficulty in finding and getting to the toilet at the right time, but were able to use the toilet correctly once there. Whitehead *et al.* (1984) also reason that if incontinence is due to a specific lesion, then one would expect the resulting incontinence to be an all-or-none phenomenon. As they point out, the severity of incontinence correlates highly with the severity of dementia, which tends to weigh more against a specific lesion hypothesis and more in favour of a general association. Furthermore, as some non-cognitively impaired elderly people also suffer from urge incontinence, then it is reasonable to expect that some elderly clients with dementia may also suffer from this without it being directly associated with their dementia.

Viewing incontinence as a general association with dementia, or including a behavioural component in a treatment package, does not necessarily mean that incontinence is necessarily viewed as functional and not as organic in origin. Plausible factors that have been noted (e.g. Whitehead *et al.* 1984) include poor physical health, poor mobility and speed, pain associated with joint movements in going to the toilet and handling clothes, memory and attentional deficits, and for various reasons, reduced effects of social consequences.

BEHAVIOUR MODIFICATION

Behavioural approaches to the re-establishment of continence in elderly people appear, until very recently, to have had, at best, uncertain value in the minds of professionals in this field. Arie *et al.* (1976), for example, express the following view:

> Techniques derived from behaviour therapy such as have had a limited success in the toilet training of normal or mentally handicapped children . . . have not yet been shown to be likely to help incontinent old people, who are much more likely to benefit from measures aimed at preserving and safeguarding individuality and dignity.

A number of important issues are raised here. The key issue is that behavioural techniques have not yet been shown likely to help. Reviewers of a number of relevant 1970s studies have concluded that, with respect to institutionalised elderly people, behavioural methods have had a degree of success with elderly chronic schizophrenic patients, but have had little success with those suffering from dementia (Holden and Woods 1982; Tarrier and Larner 1983; Woods and Britton 1985). The studies reviewed in more detail here, in order to establish whether or not the same conclusion may still be reached, have been largely carried out in the early 1980s. Two other issues from the view of Arie *et al.* (1976), quoted above, are worth commenting on briefly. The first of these concerns the view that there has been *limited* success with behavioural approaches in the field of mental handicap. This is not an accurate reflection of the outcome of a large number of studies discussed in earlier chapters of this book. The second is that elderly incontinent people are more likely to benefit from general environmental measures to enhance dignity. This is an extremely important moral and empirical point. Behavioural approaches should never be used as a substitute for general improvements in the quality of life for elderly or any other clients. More than this though, they should not be viewed as mutually exclusive. If behavioural approaches can be shown to be of some benefit, then it can be argued from a moral standpoint that elderly people have the right to this type of treatment and to have their dignity enhanced through this avenue of continence promotion.

An early and very detailed consideration of the model for retraining continence in elderly people has been provided by Willington (1976b). Although Willington proposes a classical conditioning model, the theoretical basis of the behavioural studies published is actually exclusively that of operant conditioning. Again, the appropriate learning theory models, both for daytime and night-time bladder control, are discussed earlier in this book. Briefly, in considering behaviour in terms of stimuli and responses, operant conditioning focuses heavily, though not exclusively, on response–stimulus links that involve the organism acting on the environment and being affected by environmental consequences.

Turning, therefore, first of all to the issue of environmental determination of behaviour, we may ask whether there is evidence that continence-related behaviours can be affected by obvious factors such as staff attention. Tarrier and Larner (1983) studied the effects of nurses' behaviour on toilet requests from four elderly hospitalised women suffering from dementia. The problem concerned the nursing staff's complaint about the high frequency of requests to defaecate, which were 'false alarms'. This caused a problem, as toileting each person required two nurses and requests tended to come at the busiest times of the ward routines. The intervention procedure was aimed at socially reinforcing appropriate non-attention seeking behaviour and at reducing the social reinforcement consequent upon toilet requests. This was achieved through ensuring that each person received at least two minutes individual attention from, and conversation with, a nurse every hour and through responding to toilet requests in a brisk and neutral manner. The results of this procedure showed a statistically significant reduction in false alarm requests to toilet.

Of considerable interest in this study is Tarrier and Larner's emphasis on staff behaviour and attitudes. As well as recording data about the patients' toileting, they also asked nursing staff to rate their subjective impression of change in patients' behaviour. Reminiscent of the 'clinical vs statistical' debate, they found that despite the outcome reflected in the data, the nurses did not perceive the patients as having improved. Thus, this important aspect of continence-related behaviour in elderly people suffering from dementia is modifiable as a result of environmental contigencies, but staff in a busy ward setting do not necessarily perceive this change as having occurred.

Another continence-related behaviour, that of faecal smearing, was among the range of six disruptive and aggressive behaviours thought to be organically determined, presented by an elderly lady suffering from dementia (Rosberger and MacLean 1983). A differential social reinforcement programme, comprising several phases, was introduced. The first phase largely involved reinforcing appropriate social behaviour or responses and withdrawing social reinforcement for inappropriate, antisocial or aggressive behaviours. Whenever walking by her, staff smiled and greeted her. If she responded appropriately, then the nurse stopped for a short period and gave her some individual attention. If one of the six inappropriate target behaviours appeared, then the nurse abruptly terminated the conversation and walked away. Over a period of weeks, all of the inappropriate behaviours decreased, although faecal smearing was the slowest to respond. Rosberger and MacLean concluded that these apparently organically determined behaviours could be treated behaviourally, but that the staff concerned require considerable training and support to carry out procedures the apparent simplicity of which masks their complex nature.

Moving more directly to the problem of incontinence and retraining of continence, Hussian (1981) briefly reports a bladder-training programme that showed remarkable results. The trainees were described as twelve 'regressed institutionalised geriatric patients' but precise details of age or diagnosis are not given. It is implied that they suffered dementia and showed evidence of organic impairment and chronic deterioration. Following baseline recording, a programme of bladder training involving both toileting at very regular intervals and following accidents, together with social reinforcement for voiding on the toilet, feedback on performance and praise for remaining dry was implemented. Frequency of incontinence reduced steadily and dramatically from an average of about three accidents a day per person to about one every three days at the end of ten days' training. What is particularly interesting about the results is that a reversal to baseline conditions, where no reinforcement and feedback were given, did not result in a deterioration of continence behaviour. This would not be predicted from continence training programmes in mental handicap, where maintenance of gains made in training has to be handled very carefully. Although Hussian reports that staff reverted to baseline behaviour, one wonders if this truly was the case.

Turner (1986), in discussing the possibility of using behavioural approaches to continence training in elderly people, expresses the view that it would be difficult to use an enuresis-type alarm for the treatment of daytime wetting. In fact, such miniature portable enuresis alarms have been extensively used in mental handicap and are discussed in an earlier chapter. A range of discreet, reliable, personal continence alarms, capable of providing auditory, visual or tactile signals, is available commercially (Association of Continence Advisors 1986). Sanavio (1981) describes the use of intensive continence training programmes, based on the work of Foxx and Azrin (1973a) in mental handicap, on two elderly hospitalised men diagnosed as suffering from dementia. This is an important study, as the techniques developed in mental handicap clearly need to be tested in this field. The first patient was incontinent of urine several times a day. Sanavio comments that as Foxx and Azrin's programme is intensive, tiring and has a strong punishment element (see Chapter 6 for discussion of this), he found it necessary to modify the package. Interestingly, despite Turner's (1986) belief, he retained the use of a pants alarm. The programme utilised increased fluid intake, prompts to toilet every hour, substantial reinforcement for successful voiding on the toilet, dry pants checks every 20 minutes with reinforcement for remaining dry, and the use of overcorrection and positive practice training for up to half an hour contingent upon wetting accidents. Despite the caution expressed about the ethics of punishment, Sanavio's programme still seems to have contained quite a strong punishment component. However, in viewing this study simply from the point of view of its effectiveness, the results claimed must be described as impressive. Over a five-day intensive training period, the trainee's frequency of wetting accidents reduced from four or five per day to zero, whereas his frequency of independent self-initiated toiletings rose from zero to three per day. Following this, the programme was discontinued for four days. During this reversal to baseline condition, in contrast to Hussian (1981), continence deteriorated steadily. Training was reintroduced and continence was rapidly established again, to be followed by a period of maintenance training when the programme was gradually rather than suddenly withdrawn. Follow-up after eight weeks showed the improvements to be maintained. The second case that Sanavio recounts specifically concerned bowel training for an elderly man described as suffering from senile dementia and as having been hospitalised many years previously for paranoid schizophrenia. A similar reversal design was used to evaluate a similar continence-training package. The results again showed clear evidence of improvement during the first training period, with deterioration during the return to baseline condition, followed by improvement during the second training and subsequent maintenance and follow-up periods. This is the first study to appear in the literature demonstrating the use of intensive behavioural procedures for continence training applied to an elderly population. Due to small numbers, the results can only be taken as a demonstration of feasibility, and large-scale evaluation is necessary, together with studies to isolate the effects or otherwise of specific factors such as punishment.

A less intensive, but nevertheless highly structured behavioural approach to re-establishing urinary continence has been evaluated using control groups in two nursing homes by Schnelle et al. (1983). In one home, five elderly people were randomly assigned to the experimental group and four to the control, and in the second home, six patients each were assigned to the experimental and control groups. The mean age of the residents was 81 years and all were described as suffering from age-related organic disorders, with 95 per cent of them suffering dementia. During the experimental periods, nursing aides first carried out a dry pants check every hour.

They asked the residents whether they were wet or dry, gave feedback on the accuracy of their reply praise for being dry. Following each check, residents were then asked if they would like to go to the toilet and if they did indicate that they wished to go, they were praised and assisted by the aide. When a wetting accident occurred, the aides expressed disappointment briefly and changed the resident with the minimum possible fuss and interaction. Extensive support for monitoring and recording of the experimental procedure was carried out. Baseline recording procedures for the two experimental groups were the same as for the two control groups: nursing aides simply checked the residents' clothing hourly and responded to their requests for help with toileting. In both homes, continence improved during the three to four week experimental periods, whereas it did not improve in the control groups. Overall, the percentage of occasions that residents were found to be wet on hourly checks fell from 30 per cent to 15 per cent for the experimental groups, but remained stable at about 25 per cent of occasions for the control groups. On the other hand, requests for toileting assistance rose from a baseline average of 0.31 per day per trainee to 2.0 in the experimental group, compared to corresponding rates of 0.30 and 0.23, respectively, for control groups over the same period.

The importance of the study of Schnelle *et al.* (1983) is that, in contrast to the intensive programmes of Sanavio (1981), it was carried out in an institutional setting with largely unqualified staff and with poor staffing levels. Significantly, Schnelle *et al.* place a great deal of emphasis on staff training and support and comment that staff consistency was maintained only with 'strong supervisory pressure'. Indeed, when this project ended in one of the homes, the degree of supervision and support relaxed and the continuation of these training procedures was not consistently maintained.

Practical issues and difficulties also loom large in the interesting account of a behavioural programme in a psychogeriatric setting by Chanfreau-Rona, Bellwood and Wylie (1984), who attempted to isolate and study the effects of the separate factors of behavioural training, baseline recording procedures and specific environmental changes. Three women's hospital wards were chosen for study and, although no specific details of diagnosis are given, the majority of patients appear to be suffering from dementia being described as 'deteriorated'. Following a two-week baseline period, nine incontinent residents were included on the first ward for behavioural training. This comprised toileting at the individual peak times for voiding, together with social and edible reinforcers for appropriate

229

use of toilet. Toileting frequency is not specified, although it may be presumed that it cannot be more frequent than two hourly, as this was the interval between basline checks. The baseline period was extended for the eight incontinent residents on the second ward. This was the only 'intervention' used here in order to control for any possible effects that regular checking might have in terms of making either staff or residents more aware of continence and incontinence cues. For seven incontinent elderly patients in the third ward, there was more emphasis on drawing attention to additional environmental cues, which included painting doors leading to toilet areas bright orange, marking routes to toilet areas with plastic footsteps stuck to the floor and displaying a large picture of a lady using a toilet on the door leading to the toilet area. Briefly, the main findings of Chanfreau-Rona *et al.* were that none of the three groups showed improvement. However, of considerable importance were the similar and marked worsening in frequency of incontinence in the second and third groups. Although the first group did not show a significant improvement within the group, the behavioural training group had not deteriorated with respect to continence.

Thus, the more recent studies of Hussian (1981), Sanavio (1981), Schnelle *et al.* (1983) and Chanfreau-Rona *et al.* (1984) do not offer support for the earlier view that behavioural training methods are unable to promote continence in elderly people suffering from dementia. The earlier reviewers were quite correct in their assessment of several 1970s studies failing to demonstrate effects in those suffering dementia. The question is why this difference should occur? One possible answer is that these results are due to chance. Though this is obviously possible, the emergence of further studies over the next few years will determine this. However, factors weighing against this possibility include four consecutive studies showing experimental effects, and the use of controls in the form of reversal design (Sanavio 1981) and non-treatment controls (Schnelle *et al.* 1983; Chanfreau-Rona *et al.* 1984). The most likely explanation, looking at the progression of studies of psychogeriatric populations, seems to be quite simply that the quality of the behavioural studies is improving. This is reminiscent of the state of the art in mental handicap, in which only the earliest studies, such as that of Blackwood (1962), failed to show treatment effects. The similarity is also enhanced in that both elderly demented people and severely or profoundly mentally handicapped people have traditionally been regarded as extremely difficult populations presenting largely intractable problems. As is apparent in earlier chapters, there have been far more such studies in mental handicap over a longer period of time. This area of work with elderly people is fraught and has its own special difficulties and resource problems, but the level of sophistication of the behavioural training programmes could, in principle, be considerably improved. It is difficult to draw direct comparisons between studies because of different approaches to training, the differing emphases in description of the studies and possible differences between subjects, but the comments made above are further underlined by the probable importance of intensity of training. In crude terms, of the four studies considered above, the two that report the best results (Sanavio 1981; Hussian 1981) also used the most intensive training. Sanavio's approach utilised 20-minute dry pants check and hourly prompts to toilet. Hussian likewise used prompts to toilet at hourly intervals, together with additional toileting following accidents and half-hourly toileting following prolonged periods of no voiding. In contrast, Chanfreau-Rona et al.'s frequency of toileting cannot have been more frequent than two-hourly, and Schnelle et al.'s residents were toileted hourly only if they responded positively to an offer of assistance with toileting.

Habit training

As stated in the introduction, the use of the term habit training has been avoided in this book largely because of the vagueness with which it is used. However, the term is used so widely in continence promotion with elderly people that it is necessary to consider it briefly here. Willington (1976b) has long been aware of this and comments both with feeling and accuracy that:

It is a common action in geriatric wards for the nursing staff to submit the patient to 'routine ward training'. Perusal of the text books of nursing for details of this practice reveals either no reference at all, or very sketchy and inaccurate instructions. The nurse is left on these occasions to carry on as best she may without any systematic plan based on scientific fact, and without knowing when to desist . . ... In short, the nursing training of incontinent patients is performed as a sacred ritual rather than a planned activity.

Thus, although 'habit training' in some form or another is frequently referred to, it is difficult to find examples for discussion that present sufficient detail in terms of the techniques used and sufficient data whereby to evaluate effectiveness. Fortunately, a few notable exceptions occur and will be discussed below, but first it is necessary to outline the difference between behavioural approaches and habit training. This is not straightforward as studies may not give all the relevant details. Also, it is not the case that one is good and the other bad: each is capable of being applied well or badly.

One of the key features of a behavioural approach based on operant conditioning is that following a behavioural analysis of the problem, reinforcement is used to increase the frequency of the operant behaviour, i.e. appropriate voiding. If there is no mention of systematic contingent use of reinforcement in a study, then that study is deemed here not to be based on an operant approach. One obvious difficulty is that some staff may use social reinforcement naturally, so this does not necessarily mean that reinforcement did not occur, simply that it was not systematically applied. A glance at the literature indicates that other features of behavioural reports include an increased emphasis on describing the detail of methods and on objective methods of evaluation.

In a large US survey of the management of urinary incontinence in Veterans Administration nursing homes (Ouslander and Fowler 1985), 45 sets of written guidelines for nursing routines for bladder training were examined. Only two of these emphasised the utilisation of reinforcement procedures in bladder training. These authors agree with Willington that bladder training procedures reported in the literature are 'poorly and inconsistently defined'. Notable exceptions to the overall poor quality of the literature on habit retraining include the work of Clay (1986), Castleden and his colleagues (1985) and Sogbein and Awad (1982).

Sogbein and Awad (1982) carried out a large study involving 58 incontinent elderly hospitalised men. Following exclusion of some patients for continuous catheter drainage and of others for treatment of urinary tract infections, of those patients who remained and for whom consent could be gained from relatives and who could comply with this procedure, a habit-training programme was implemented. An unspecified number dropped out because of terminal disease or severe confusion, the commonest diagnosis in the group being cerebrovascular accident and organic brain syndrome. Twenty men finally managed to complete four weeks of training, which included assisting them to the toilet every two hours. Seventeen of these twenty achieved the criterion of improvement, i.e. being incontinent on less than 20 per cent of the two-hourly checks. Unfortunately, the baseline level of incontinence was only specified as incontinence being more than 20 per cent of occasions, so it is not possible to evaluate in any detail the degree of improvement.

Clay's (1986) description of habit retraining in the elderly is the closest approximation to a habit retraining manual for nurses. She provides more detailed guidelines for procedures than any other author. Her approach is based on baseline recording of continence and incontinence at two-hourly intervals, from which a micturition pattern is determined and used as an individual basis for a training programme. Adjustments in times of toileting then follow to extend the intervals between voiding. Using an undefined rating of outcome, Clay (1986) reports that of 30 elderly incontinent patients, 20 were treated successfully and five with partial success over a thirteen-week period. Ritch and Rooney (1984) have briefly described the use of Clay's approach with 86 elderly people living at home. They reported that 53 per cent became continent and a further 37 per cent substantially improved, although again the data and definition of criteria were not presented in any detail.

Another of the more impressive recent accounts that includes bladder training is the study performed by Castleden *et al.* (1985). In this instance, bladder training comprised initial toileting at half-hour or one-hour intervals, increasing by half-hour periods after dryness was achieved for 48 hours, until four-hourly toileting was reached. This, in conjunction with other procedures that will be described later, resulted in 42 of 95 elderly patients achieving continence, with a further 20 described as improved.

Understandably, most habit-retraining programmes are carried out for clinical rather than research purposes and it is usual that a variety of more general features are also included. These often include emphasising a warm and caring approach with positive staff attitudes, a team approach to assessing and treating incontinence, and general environmental improvements. Whilst all of these are important, at the very least on moral grounds, it does make disentangling variables and evaluating the specific effects of individual procedures such as habit training extremely difficult.

BIOFEEDBACK

Biofeedback is another specifically behavioural form of intervention (see Chapter 11). The use of this method of treatment for elderly patients is described for both urge and stress urinary incontinence by Whitehead *et al.* (1984) and Burgio *et al.* (1985) and for faecal incontinence by Whitehead *et al.* (1985). Features of the bladder biofeedback training used by Whitehead *et al.* (1984) include the provision of auditory or visual feedback of bladder pressure during repeated bladder fillings and intensive hourly sessions at weekly intervals. These authors (1984) briefly report that, having used these procedures with seven elderly patients with unstable bladders, three achieved continence, three others improved by 64 to 83 per cent and the seventh did not respond to training. The baseline incontinence frequencies are not reported, except in so far as the majority of patients referred to them with unstable bladders present only occasional incontinence and still have partial control over their bladders. For stress incontinence, these authors have used biofeedback with twelve elderly women. Here, biofeedback of bladder pressure was used together with feedback of abdominal pressure and external anal sphincter pressure to teach these elderly people to contract the pelvic floor muscles selectively without increasing bladder or abdominal pressure. All of the women are described as having made at least 50 per cent improvement and the authors comment further that, in contrast to earlier recommendations about the benefit of pelvic floor exercises alone without biofeedback, even women with severe stress incontinence improved.

Burgio *et al.* (1985) report even more encouraging results. However Whitehead *et al.* (1984) suggest that the work on bladder biofeedback with elderly people is at a relatively early stage and is characterised by uncontrolled trials. The study reported by these workers on faecal incontinence (Whitehead *et al.* 1985) is characterised by considerably more detail and control. Eighteen elderly faecally incontinent patients were treated by using combinations of habit training, physiotherapy (sphincter exercises) and biofeedback using rectal distension, for comparison of the effectiveness of these various approaches. Before biofeedback training, all patients underwent four weeks habit training. As implied by the term 'habit training', this did not appear to be intensive nor involve the use of reinforcers. Patients attempted to defaecate every day after breakfast. Bulk agents, and also enemas following two days without a bowel movement, were used to prevent faecal impaction.

Also, before the start of biofeedback, half of the patients were instructed to perform physiotherapy (sphincter-tightening exercises), comprising contracting the perianal muscles 50 times a day for 10 seconds. Visual biofeedback of repeated rectal distension was then provided over 45-minute training sessions every two weeks. The number of sessions ranged from two to seven. In addition, the patients were asked to perform 50 sphincter muscle exercises per day throughout the biofeedback treatment period. The relatively weak habit training alone resulted in two of the 18 patients achieving continence and the rest proceeded to biofeedback. Three of these 16 were unable to participate properly in the biofeedback procedure. In two cases this was reported to be because of dementia and basic inability to comply with the instructions, and in the third it was due to total absence of sensation when the rectal balloon was maximally distended. The results for the remaining 13 patients were analysed both with respect to strength of contraction of the anal sphincter and with respect to the frequency of faecal incontinence. Sphincter exercises alone resulted in no decrease in faecal incontinence and in a statistically non-significant increase in strength of sphincter contraction. Biofeedback combined with sphincter exercises resulted in both a significant increase in strength of sphincter contraction. Six of the 13 patients achieved at least 75 per cent reduction in frequency of faecal incontinence.

PHYSIOTHERAPY

Ouslander and Fowler's (1985) survey of bladder-training procedures found that 11 per cent of written nursing guidelines for bladder training provided by hospitals included pelvic floor exercises alone, with no mention of the use of feedback procedures at all.

Again, although this topic in general is touched on in an earlier chapter, it is important to consider the few recent reports in the literature that have attempted to evaluate the use of physiotherapy in the treatment of incontinence in the elderly. The best general description of the rationale and techniques of pelvic-floor muscle training is described in consecutively written articles by Shepherd (1986) and Mandlestam (1986b).

Castleden, Duffin and Mitchell's (1984) study of physiotherapy for stress incontinence included a number of elderly women. The age range of their 19 patients was 23 to 85 years with a mean age of 55 years. Patients were randomly allocated to a different order of consecutive, two-week treatment periods for two different treatments. One treatment involved pelvic-floor exercises alone, and the other included additional use of a perineometer to provide visual feedback. Two main results are of interest here. The first is that although physiotherapy resulted in improvement in incontinence, no additional improvement would be attributed to the use of the perineometer. The second is that there was a suggestion that physiotherapy was less effective with the more elderly patients.

These results contrast with those of Whitehead *et al.* (1985) for faecal incontinence, where feedback produced improvements, but exercises alone did not. Apart from being concerned with different types of incontinence, the studies differ with respect to the intensity of the treatment components of feedback and exercises. Whitehead *et al.* (1985) utilised both intensive use of exercises and intensive use of feedback. Castleden *et al.*'s (1984) procedures involved fairly intensive pelvic floor exercises during which the patients were asked to produce four or five contractions every hour of the day over a four-week period. The use of feedback to measure squeeze was only requested at least once a day for a two-week period. Whitehead *et al.* (1984) note briefly that they have used a combination of biofeedback and exercises in an uncontrolled manner to successfully treat elderly women with severe urinary stress incontinence. They also comment that following an initial popularity in the 1950s, the use of exercises together with a perineometer has waned, so that exercises alone tend to be prescribed with a consequently lower rate of effectiveness. It may well be that the important point is not the use of the perineometer *per se,* but its systematic and intensive use in conjunction with exercises.

FACTORS ASSOCIATED WITH OUTCOME OF TRAINING

There are many studies in the literature over a number of years of factors associated with incontinence alone in the elderly. More recent examples include Campbell *et al.* (1985) and Vehkalahti and Kivela (1985). It is only recently that it has been possible to begin to comment on factors associated with outcome of training programmes for continence in this population. This has been helped to some degree by the relatively more detailed descriptions given in the behavioural studies, together with their greater emphasis on data recording. Also, important studies concerned with the outcome of general treatments of incontinence, including training, have begun to appear, particularly those of Castleden *et al.* (1985) and Eastwood and Warrell (1984). Here, with respect to outcome, we will continue to focus largely on training.

Dementia as a factor in outcome

First of all, there is no avoiding a return to the issue of whether or not incontinence associated with dementia can be appropriately treated at least in part by a training approach. Although, once again, it may risk oversimplifying matters, the evidence for and against this view can be summarised.

The evidence against this proposition includes, first, the conclusions of thoughtful reviews of the earlier behavioural literature by Holden and Woods (1982) and Tarrier and Larner (1983). Also against this is the study reported by Castleden *et al.* (1985) on outcome using a treatment package that included a form of 'habit training'. Although reporting a good overall outcome within a large elderly sample, the major predictor of successful outcome was a high score on a general rating of mental ability. Thirdly, there are the results found by Whitehead *et al.* (1984, 1985) indicating poor outcome using biofeedback where the process of dementia is involved. They considered that two of their patients referred for treatment of faecal incontinence had such severe dementia that they were unable to follow simple instructions and so were '*a priori* judged not trainable with biofeedback'. Similarly, for urinary incontinence they consider that 'patients with significant cognitive impairment (IQ below 70) will have difficulty concentrating on the task', although no clear data appear to be available on this as yet. As the work of Whitehead and his colleagues is particularly important, their comments do seem to carry extra weight.

On the other hand, the results of the more recent behavioural studies discussed in this chapter support the proposition that those suffering from dementia can be retrained. Two of these concerned the continence-related behaviours of requests to go to toilet and faecal smearing (Tarrier and Larner 1983; Rosberger and MacLean 1983, respectively). The remaining four studies (Hussian 1981; Sanavio 1981; Schnelle *et al.* 1983; Chanfreau-Rona *et al.* 1984) concerned continence and incontinence directly. In different ways, all of these showed some evidence of effect.

Thus, with haunting familiarity we are presented with an issue where evidence can be selectivity presented to apparently support opposing views. In the absence of definitive studies, all that we can do is to consider some of the possible and obvious reasons for this that are capable of being reformulated into testable hypotheses for further study. Beforehand, though, it has to be acknowledged that dementia is a difficult problem and that negative findings are no great surprise. At least six main issues leading to possible differences in outcome can be isolated:

1. It is possible that the principles involved in the approach to treatment are valid, but that the actual techniques may need to be different when cognitive impairment is involved. For example, where Whitehead and colleagues experience difficulty in biofeedback procedures with attention to task or comprehension of instructions, ways may need to be devised of overcoming this. Kohlenberg (1973) described an early and relatively less refined approach to the treatment of faecal soiling in a 13-year-old boy using biofeedback. In this instance there was more emphasis placed on social and other reinforcements such as money. Voluntary control over bowel contractions was shaped partly by including coins dropped in a jar contingent upon gradually increasing pressures. Also, it may be that treatment sessions need to be more frequent or shorter in duration or both.

2. Generally, it may well be that the systematic and consistent use of individually tailored reinforcers contingent upon the desired behaviour is more important in dementia than has been widely realised. One of the features of the behaviourally based programmes is that they place more emphasis than the routine 'habit training' programmes on consistent reinforcement. On average they appear more effective and this may be one of the reasons why results differ.

3. The intensity of the training programme may be crucial when with cognitive impairment, learning may not be mediated so easily through the normal adult cognitive mechanisms of comprehension and imitation. As suggested earlier, the impression is gained that the more intensive the programme, the greater the likelihood of an effect. In a small study in mental handicap, Smith (1979a) concluded that when more- and less-intensive toilet training techniques were compared, the improved effectiveness of the intensive techniques outweighed the extra investment of staff time. Similar studies are required with elderly subjects.

4. Linked to some of these issues is the consistency and reliability

with which the training procedures are actually carried out by busy staff in difficult working situations. Staff support and monitoring are important here and the issue of supervision and control of training procedures is highlighted by Schnelle *et al.* (1983). Of interest here is the finding that 'habit training' implemented initially in hospital, was no more effective than that initiated at home (Castleden *et al.* 1985). It is true that the elderly people concerned were not randomly allocated to groups, but if hospital staff do not achieve better results than patients themselves, this is sufficient to make one question the efficiency of the performance of the programme. Suitable methods of observation, recording and support have received attention in the mental handicap literature (e.g. Foxx and Azrin 1973; Bettison *et al.* 1976; Bettison 1983; Tierney 1973).

5. The initial level or degree of incontinence may be important (Chanfreau-Rona *et al.* 1984), so either early intervention to at least prevent further deterioriation appears to be indicated, or there may be higher success with less severe incontinence. However, different studies report data on incontinence in different ways, so it is impossible to make direct comparisons; some record total frequency of mean frequency of incontinence (e.g. Chanfreau-Rona *et al.* 1984; Whitehead *et al.* 1985); some record percentage continent/incontinent eliminations (e.g. Schnelle *et al.* 1983); and many utilise ratings or categories of incontinence as opposed to hard data in their reports (e.g. Eastwood and Warrell 1984; Castleden *et al.* 1985; Sogbein and Awad 1982).

6. Finally, there is typically little information about the nature of the incontinence in those patients suffering dementia. It is possible that a proportion of elderly people with dementia may also suffer specific forms of incontinence in the same manner as the rest of the elderly population. Also, it has been argued earlier that the proposal that the causal link between dementia and incontinence is that of a specific lesion, is suspect. Incontinence is more probably a generalised consequence of a general deterioration, including confusion as to space and time, short-term memory and attentional problems, reduction of the effects of social reinforcement, mobility problems, pain and so on. In the general elderly incontinent population, some attention has already been focused on the urodynamic status of patients and its predictive validity (Castleden *et al.* 1985; Eastwood and Warrell 1984). Within the specific sub-population of elderly incontinent people suffering

from dementia, direct observational studies (e.g. Woods and Britton 1985, p. 42) of continence-related skills would be merited to establish which sequences of toileting behaviour chains are still intact. If there are individual differences, as seems likely, then this would have implications both for remediation and for making comparisons between different studies.

Other factors in outcome

We should now move on from the specific issue of dementia to the predictive value of other factors in the general elderly population, which may also be relevant to those with dementia. Some interest by researchers in urodynamic measures has been mentioned above. Whitehead *et al.* (1984), in discussing the role of behaviour modification and the relevance of mental handicap studies in this area, comment that 'behaviour modification has worked best where there is minimal or no physiological abnormality on urodynamic testing'. Although this sounds plausible, there have, in fact, to our knowledge, been no thorough urodynamic studies published of incontinent mentally handicapped people and the mental handicap literature must be considered weak in this respect. In the elderly population, Eastwood and Warrell (1984) reported on a group of 65 incontinent women. Poorer outcome tended to be associated with a lower cystometric 'score', following a 'standard' treatment that comprised a combination of an unspecified toilet training together with antispasmodic medication. The association was not a very high one, but Eastwood and Warrell argue that one additional value of the cystometry was that without it a small number of women suffering from stress incontinence may have been clinically misdiagnosed. Castleden *et al.* (1985) studied a broader range of factors in order to predict outcome in a group of 95 elderly incontinent patients with unstable bladders, referred to a continence clinic. They give rather more detail about their treatment packages, placing considerable emphasis on supporting, counselling and practical advice as well as 'habit training' and antispasmodic medication. Overall, it must be ranked as one of the more impressive studies in the elderly literature. As well as a range of cystometric measures, their factors also included age, mental state and mobility. As noted earlier, the biggest single prognostic factor was a positive relationship between mental state and outcome, but of considerable interest also was that outcome was independent of age alone. Mobility was also an important factor. Whilst it was also the case that prognosis did correlate with initial cystometric measures, the association was of less importance than mental state and mobility, a result confirming the impression gained from Eastwood and Warrell's study. One obvious difference between the two populations studied here is that Castleden *et al.* focused solely on data relating to those patients diagnosed as suffering from detrusor instability, whereas Eastwood and Warrell's population included patients with urge incontinence, stress incontinence and a mixture of the two. However, as Castelden *et al.* note, unstable bladder is the most common complaint in elderly incontinent patients.

Among the urodynamic data, one of the factors that Castleden *et al.* found to contribute to the association between outcome and cystometry was the volume of post-incontinence residual urine. The role that residual urine plays in the maintenance of incontinence and in interfering with the acquisition of continence may well repay closer study. Earlier chapters have noted, with respect to both daytime bladder training in mental handicap and the achievement of nocturnal dryness in normal children, the suspicion that the presence of residual urine is a sinister factor (Fielding 1982). More attention may need to be paid to treatment or training factors associated with maintaining the urine stream. Among the remaining possible prognostic factors, one commonly raised practical issue concerns urinary tract infections. Sogbein and Awad (1982) found that 27 of 48 incontinent psychogeriatric patients in an institutional setting had a significant urinary tract infection. Although this may be important for general health reasons, Sogbein and Awad were unable to establish that it played an important role in incontinence, reporting that 'bladder control was still poor while urine cultures were negative but improved . . . even when cultures had again become positive'. The evidence from studies of urinary tract infection and nocturnal enuresis would tend to support the view that the enuresis causes the infection rather than the reverse.

General environmental effects

This is, in a way, related to the issue of incontinence as a general versus a specific effect of dementia: if it is a general effect then environmental improvements may have generalised effects and improve continence or at least prevent further deterioriation in continence. The plight and general living condition of many elderly incontinent people are vividly illustrated by the anecdotal evidence quoted at the beginning of this chapter (Isaacs 1976; Wells 1975). Two main themes in this area emerge from the literature on continence promotion and these concern first positive attitudes and dignity, and second the negative effects of avoidable environmental restrictions. The former are particularly emphasised in the literature by Clay (1986), Calder (1976) and Castleden et al. (1975), and the latter by Gray (1986) and Wells (1975), among many others. Of the 46 sets of written nursing home guidelines surveyed by Ouslander and Fowler (1985), 50 per cent emphasised positive attitudes but only 11 per cent emphasised other environmental aspects.

Morally, the case for ensuring the adequacy or improvement of general attitudes and environmental conditions is absolutely undeniable. Empirically, the evidence linking environment and continence or incontinence is scant and largely anecdotal. In simple terms, it is obvious that if access to the toilet is restricted due to poor mobility, mental confusion, poor motor skills for managing doors, clothes, sitting on toilet, etc., then in the absence of toilet aids or environmental changes, incontinence may result. Again, it may be recalled that Holden and Woods (1982) briefly describe an observational study of eight incontinent women suffering from senile dementia, five of whom had difficulty in finding the toilet at the right time, but who could use it appropriately once there. Chanfreau-Rona et al. (1984) attempted to assess the effects of simple environmental changes to improve sensory cues on a female psychogeriatric ward. These changes comprised painting the toilet doors and the doors leading to the toilets bright orange, displaying a large picture of a lady using a toilet on the door leading to the toilet area and providing a trail of plastic footsteps on the floors forming a line leading to the toilets. Two weeks of such changes alone failed to demonstrate any measurable improvements in incontinence, compared with other combined behavioural approaches to treatment.

Holden and Woods (1982), in their comprehensive review of Reality Orientation therapy with confused elderly people, found only a few brief references in uncontrolled studies to claims of some reduction in incontinence as a generalised effective of Reality Orientation. Improvement as a result of Reality Orientation would be evidence for the 'general' view of incontinence and dementia, but clearer evidence is required. The widely experienced phenomenon in psychogeriatric settings of higher incontinence rates being associated with the poorer, more crowded wards may not necessarily demonstrate a causal link between poor environmental conditions and incontinence. It is quite probable in these settings that allocation by staff of patients to wards is not random and that those who are incontinent on admission are placed on the poorer wards. In this instance, it may be argued that while the environment may contribute to the maintenance of incontinence and operate against its effective treatment, it may not be the actual original cause of the incontinence.

Such views may seem somewhat unacceptable and they are certainly not in accordance with those of such as Calder (1976). As already stressed, the moral case for ensuring positive attitudes, dignity and an appropriate environment is undeniable. The point being raised here is that, given that workers in the field of continence promotion believe these to be of practical as well as moral importance, then researchers should address themselves to disentangling the relative effects and possible interactions of these factors. Treatments including drugs and behaviour modification are no substitute for the basic human rights of dignity and decent living conditions. At the same time, elderly incontinent people have the right to appropriate treatment.

It is important to establish what percentage of the variance in incontinence can be accounted for by general environmental and attitudinal factors before implementing other treatments. Chanfreau-Rona et al.'s (1984) environmental changes were carried out only briefly and with very severely demented patients. Shrubsole and Smith (1984) studied the effects of a much broader range of environmental improvements on incontinence in a group of profoundly mentally handicapped adults, consequent upon 'upgrading' a hospital ward. General living conditions were much improved, overcrowding was reduced and staff morale was increased. Following this, and in the absence of additional continence training programmes, a 30 per cent reduction in incontinence occurred. Similar studies in elderly service settings would be welcome.

DRUGS

Drug effects in urinary incontinence in the elderly are most recently reviewed by Brocklehurst (1984c). He states clearly that drug treatments of incontinence in the elderly are aimed largely at the specific problem of the unstable bladder, and much less commonly at other types of incontinence such as stress incontinence, where other forms of treatment including physiotherapy or surgery are usually considered to be appropriate. Our concern here is more with incontinence associated with dementia and, as has already been said, it is likely that most incontinence will be a general association with dementia; however, as other forms of incontinence exist commonly in the rest of the elderly population, they are possibly present in this group too. In cases of dementia in which there is a clearly diagnosed type of incontinence, such as uninhibited bladder, then in principle the same form of treatment normally used should apply. Extending the use of drugs for non-specific forms of incontinence associated with dementia is understandable and attractive, given the likely difficulties in running training or teaching programmes for continence promotion. Firstly, the use of medication is likely to be much simpler. Second, it is plausible that by increasing bladder capacity one may increase the probability of keeping patients dry on a regular toileting schedule. Brocklehurst describes how earlier work has demonstrated that anticholinergic drugs such as emepronium bromide can produce both increased bladder capacity and reduced frequency of micturition. In practice, however, the situation is much less clear. Williams, Prematalake and Palmer (1981) have carried out one of the few double-blind, cross-over drug trials on incontinence and dementia. Of 28 psychogeriatric hospital patients completing their trial of emepronium bromide, 15 were diagnosed as suffering dementia and 13 were diagnosed as presenting with functional disorders. No significant improvement in incontinence was found for the group as a whole, nor within either diagnostic category. Additionally, among other patients who were initially included but unable to complete the trial, ten were withdrawn because of inability to swallow these tablets. Thus, the use of medication is not as simple as it may seem at first sight.

While it is possible to gain a flavour of work that has been carried out in the whole area of drug studies on incontinence in elderly people from Brocklehurst's (1984c) overview, it is impossible not to gain an impression of contrast between the fields of drug studies in the elderly and those in other related fields: Blackwell and Currah (1973), for example, provide a similar review of drug studies on nocturnal enuresis, and by that date 45 double-blind trials of tricyclic antidepressants alone had been published. Many studies of elderly populations also combine drugs with other treatments such as 'habit training' (Castleden *et al.* 1985; Eastwood and Warrell 1984; Sogbein and Awad 1982). Once again, there is a need for some studies separating out variables of drugs and training and in the interaction effects of these. Many workers in this field also refer to the complicating effects on continence of drugs prescribed for other purposes. Green (1986) lists the issues involved very clearly. These include the problems associated with polypharmacy (as older people take more drugs on average thus increasing the possibilities of toxicity), adverse side reactions and complex drug interactions. Such effects can include mental confusion. A further possible contributing factor is poor metabolic and clearance mechanisms in the elderly. Also, apart from the specific difficulty in swallowing tablets referred to above, general compliance with medication may be poorer, leading to either increased chances of toxicity or ineffective treatment.

CATHETERISATION

Catheters are commonly resorted to in the physical management of incontinence if drugs and other treatments have failed. Ouslander and Fowler (1985) found that, in over 3000 elderly incontinent men in Veterans Adminstration nursing homes, 59 per cent were managed with either an indwelling catheter or a continuously worn external catheter. Castleden and Duffin (1981) consider, along with many other authors, that catheterisation is frequently unnecessary, and Ouslander and Fowler report a contrasting very low incidence of catheter use in one of their nursing homes in particular, which home was described as being 'academically oriented'. Kristiansen and Pompeius (1981) studied the long-term effects of catheterisation on 450 hospitalised elderly patients and reported a decrease in bladder capacity by one-third during the first year, with the loss of a further third over the next eight years.

TIMING VERSUS REGULAR TOILETING

One of the basic distinctions made in earlier chapters between different continence training techniques, that of timing versus regular toileting, can again be readily discerned in the elderly literature. Timing involves prompting to toilet at or approaching the predicted time of voiding, and regular toileting involves prompting at regular set intervals of time, regardless of times of accidents. Both approaches may be used together. Each makes different assumptions about the nature of bladder function, although many may not be aware of this. Timing is advocated in Willington's (1976b) classical conditioning analysis, and has been used within an operant learning framework by Chanfreau-Rona *et al.* (1984), by Clay (1986) and by those who have based their training on her methods (e.g. Castleden *et al.* 1985; Ritch and Rooney 1984). Meanwhile, those who have followed a largely regular schedule for bladder training have included Hussian (1981), Sanavio (1981), Schnelle *et al.* (1983) and Sogbein and Awad (1982). Direct comparison between these studies is impossible, because of the different populations studied, other differences in the treatment methods and different methods of data recording and analysis, but in their different ways both timing and regular toileting appear to have had their successes. As a timing approach is more complicated, the burden of proving it better lies with its exponents. In mental handicap, it was concluded earlier in this book that accurate timing in continence training is both extremely difficult and unnecessary in practice.

FLUID INTAKE

The contrasting approaches to general treatment or management of incontinence through fluid restriction versus fluid augmentation are considered in more detail earlier in this book (Chapter 7). As it is such an important area for the general well-being of elderly people, it will again be touched upon briefly here. There is an impression that fluid restriction is a more common practice than the literature would suggest. Ouslander and Fowler (1985) noted that only 15 per cent of the bladder-training guidelines provided by nursing homes for their survey formally recommended fluid restriction at night. Thirty-five per cent specifically recommend their staff to ensure that elderly incontinent patients are encouraged to drink to an adequate level. Where fluid restriction is mentioned, it is noticeable that it usually refers to a reduction in fluids in the early evening alone. Even some sympathetically written and humane reports concerning elderly incontinent people recommend some form of fluid restriction (e.g. Castleden and Duffin 1981; Thompson 1986). In direct opposition to this, a number of authors in this field recommend or have used either no restrictions of any kind or indeed increases in fluid intake (e.g. Calder 1976; Chambers 1976; Isaacs 1976; Sanavio 1981; Volpe and Kastenbaum 1967; Wells 1975).

Empirically, Smith and Wong (1981) found no relation between fluid intake and frequency of daytime incontinence in mental handicap, and many authors in the field of nocturnal enuresis now believe that fluid restriction not only has no beneficial effects on nocturnal enuresis in children, but may be harmful in the longer term by reducing functional bladder capacity (e.g. Morgan 1981). Smith and Wong (1981) found positive associations with increase in fluids, such as increase in bladder capacity. The only relevant study in an elderly population is that of Spangler *et al.* (1984), who successfully used increased fluids as part of the continent-promotion projected aimed at reducing incontinence and increasing hydration in a group of 16 non-ambulant elderly nursing home residents.

Fluid restriction should be regarded as a drastic method of treatment of elderly people. The nights may seem even longer for thirsty elderly people. Bladder capacity may be reduced, thus helping to maintain incontinence. Dryness of the mouth may occur as a common side-effect of drugs, and the extra drugs that elderly people often receive should be flushed through the body with adequate or increased fluids, as quickly as possible. It really is incumbent on anyone proposing fluid restriction in any form to clearly demonstrate its benefits. Such evidence is at present absent.

It is tempting to simply conclude that as far as possible psychological treatments are concerned, behaviour modification is best applied to problems of incontinence associated with dementia, and biofeedback to other forms of incontinence. Such a conclusion would, however, be premature as, relatively speaking, the number of studies in this area is small as yet, compared with both the size of the problem and the number of studies conducted in related areas in mental handicap and in nocturnal enuresis. It is clear though that there is a lack of a detailed training manual for continence-training programmes with elderly people. The emergence of such a manual, despite the problems inherent in 'cookbook' approaches, would do much to stimulate both the quantity and quality of behavioural work in this field, both from clinical and research standpoints.

He knew what to say; he also knew when to leave off, a continence which is practised by few writers.

John Dryden (1631–1700)

References and Further Reading

Abramovici I. & Assael M. (1981) 'Psychogenic retention of urine', *Psychiatrica Clinica*, 14, 196–204

Aegineta Paulus (1864), *The Seven Books of Paulus Aegineta*, Translated with Commentary by Francis Adams, Sydenham Society, London

Allyon T., Simon S.J. & Wildman R.W. (1975), 'Instructions and reinforcement in the elimination of encopresis: A case study', *Journal of Behavior Therapy and Experimental Psychiatry*, 6, 235–8

American Psychiatric Association (1980), *Diagnostic and Statistical Manual of Mental Disorders*, 3rd edition, American Psychiatric Association, Washington DC

Ando H. (1977), 'Training autistic children to urinate in the toilet through operant conditioning techniques', *Journal of Autism and Child Schizophrenia*, 7, 151–63

Arie, T., Clarke, M. & Slattery Z. (1976), 'Incontinence in geriatric psychiatry' in F.L. Willington (ed.) *Incontinence in the Elderly*, Academic Press, New York

Arnaud G. (1763), *Plain and Easy Instructions on the Diseases of the Bladder and Urethra*, Heberhorn, London

Ascher L.M. (1979) 'Paradoxical intention in the treatment of urinary retention', *Behaviour Research & Therapy*, 17, 267–70

Association of Continence Advisors (1986), *Directory of Aids*, 346 Kensington High Street, London

Axelrod S., Brantner J.P. & Meddock T.D. (1978), 'Overcorrection: A review and critical analysis', *Journal of Special Education*, 12, 367–91

Azrin N.H. & Foxx R.M. (1971), 'A rapid method of toilet training the institutionalised retarded', *Journal of Applied Behavior Analysis*, 4, 89–99

Azrin N.H. & Foxx R.M. (1974), *Toilet Training in Less than a Day*, Simon & Schuster, New York

Azrin N.H. & Theines P.M. (1978), 'Rapid elimination of enuresis by intensive learning without a conditioning apparatus', *Behaviour Research and Therapy*, 9, 342–54

Azrin N.H., Bugle C. & O'Brien F. (1971), 'Behavioural engineering: two apparatuses for toilet training retarded children', *Journal of Applied Behavior Analysis*, 4, 249–53

Azrin N.H., Sneed T.J. & Foxx R.M. (1973), 'Dry Bed: A rapid method of eliminating bed wetting (enuresis) of the retarded', *Behaviour Research and Therapy*, 11, 427–34

Azrin N.H., Sneed T.J. & Foxx R.M. (1974), 'Dry Bed training: Rapid elimination of childhood enuresis', *Behaviour Research and Therapy*, 12, 147–56

Azrin N.H., Thienes-Hontos P.T. & Besalel-Azrin V. (1979), 'Elimination of enuresis without a conditioning apparatus: an extension by office instruction of the child and parents', *Behavior Therapy*, 18, 14–19

B.A.R.D. (British Database on Research into Aids for the Disabled) Newcastle upon Tyne Polytechnic, Coach Lane Campus, Newcastle upon Tyne

Bach R. & Moylan J.J. (1975), 'Parents administer behaviour therapy for inappropriate urination and encopresis: a case study', *Journal of Behavior Therapy and Experimental Psychiatry*, 6, 239–41

Baker B.L. (1969), 'Symptom treatment and symptom substitution in enuresis', *Journal of Abnormal Psychology*, 74, 42–9

Bakwin H. (1973), 'The genetics of enuresis' in I. Kolvin, R.C. McKeith and S.R. Meadow (eds.) *Bladder Control and Enuresis*, Spastics International Medical Publications, Heinemann, London

Ball T.S., Seric K. & Payne I.E. (1971), 'Longterm retention of self help skill training in the profoundly retarded', *American Journal of Mental Deficiency*, 76, 378–82

Balson J., Gartley C.B. & Humpal J.J. (1985), 'Personal experiences — people managing incontinence' in C.B. Gartley (ed.) *Managing Incontinence — A Guide to Living with Loss of Bladder Control*, Jameson Books, Ottowa, Illinois

Barker P. (1979), 'Nocturnal enuresis: a behavioural study involving two behavioural approaches', *International Journal of Nursing Studies*, 16, 319–27

Barnes J., Harrison G. & Murray K. (1983), 'The anxious bladder — fact or fiction', Proceedings of the 2nd Joint Meeting of the International Continence Society and the Urodynamics Society, Aachen 1983

Baroff G.S. (1974), *Mental Retardation: Nature, Cause and Management*, Wiley, New York

Barton E.S. (1975), 'Behaviour modification in the hospital school for the severely subnormal' in C.C. Kiernan and F.P. Woodford (eds.) *Behaviour Modification with the Severely Retarded*, IRMMH Study Group No. 8. Assoc. Scientific Publishers, Amsterdam

Baumeister A. & Klosowski R. (1965), 'An attempt to group toilet train severely retarded patients', *Mental Retardation*, 3 (December), 24–6

Bell C. (1820), *A Treatise on the Diseases of the Urethra, Vesica, Urinaria, Prostate and Rectum*, New Edition, Longman, London

Beloff H. (1957) 'The structure and origin of the anal character', *Genetic Psychology Monographs*, 55, 141–72

Benjamin L.S., Serdahely W. & Geppert T.V. (1971), 'Night training through parents implicit use of operant conditioning', *Child Development*, 42, 963–6

Benjamin L.S., Stover D.O., Geppert T.V., Pizer E.F. & Burdy J. (1971), 'The relative importance of psychopathology, training procedure and urological pathology in nocturnal enuresis', *Child Psychiatry and Human Development*, 1, 215–32

Berg I.A. (1944), 'Development of behaviour: the micturition pattern of the dog', *Journal of Experimental Psychology*, 34, 343–68

Berg I., Fielding D. & Meadow R. (1977), 'Psychiatric disturbance, urgency and bacteriuria in children with day and night wetting', *Archives of Disease in Childhood*, 52, 651–7

Berg R., Berg G. & Svenson J. (1982), 'Penile malformation and mental health', *Acta Psychiatrica Scandinavica*, 66, 398–416

Berg I., Forsythe I., Holt P. & Watts J. (1983), 'A controlled trial of "Senokot" in faecal soiling treated by behavioural method', *Journal of Child Psychology and Psychiatry*, 24, 543–9

Besalel V.A., Azrin N.H., Thienes-Hontos P. & McMorrow M. (1980), 'Evaluation of a parents' manual for training enuretic children', *Behaviour Research and Therapy*, 18, 358–60

Bettison S. (1978), 'Toilet training the retarded: analysis of the stages of development and procedures for designing programmes', *Australian Journal of Mental Retardation*, 5, 95–100

Bettison S. (1979), 'Toilet training' in M. Griffin and A. Hudson (eds.) *Childrens Problems*, Circus Books, Melbourne

Bettison S. (1980), 'Daytime wetting and soiling' in A. Hudson and M. Griffin (eds.) *Behaviour Analysis and Childhood Problems*, PIT Publishing, Bundoora, Victoria

Bettison S. (1982), *Toilet Training to Independence for the Handicapped*, Charles C. Thomas, Springfield, Illinois

Bettison S., Davison D., Taylor P. & Fox B. (1976), 'Longterm effects of a toilet training programme for the retarded: a pilot study', *Australian Journal of Mental Retardation*, 4, 28–35

Bistey G.J. (1984), 'The case of the bashful bladder', *Medical Hypno-Analysis*, January 1984, 42–6

Blackwell B. & Currah J. (1973), 'The psychopharmacology of nocturnal enuresis' in I. Kolvin, R.C. McKeith and S.R. Meadow (eds.) *Bladder Control and Enuresis*, Spastics International Medical Publications, Heinemann, London

Blackwood R.O. (1962), 'Operant conditioning as a method of training the mentally retarded', Unpublished Ph.D. thesis, Ohio State University

Blum A. & Friedland G.W. (1983), 'Urinary tract abnormalities due to chronic psychogenic polydipsia', *American Journal of Psychiatry*, 140, 915–16

Bollard J. (1982), 'A two year follow up of bed wetters treated by Dry Bed training and standard conditioning', *Behaviour Research & Therapy*, 20, 571–80

Bollard R.J. & Woodroffe P. (1977), 'The effect of parent administered dry bed training on nocturnal enuresis in children', *Behaviour Research & Therapy*, 15, 159–65

Bollard J. & Nettlebeck T. (1981), 'A comparison of Dry Bed training and standard urine alarm conditioning treatment of childhood bed wetting', *Behaviour Research & Therapy*, 19, 215–26

Bollard J. & Nettlebeck T. (1982), 'A component analysis of Dry Bed for treatment of bed wetting', *Behaviour Research & Therapy*, 20, 383–90

Bollard J., Nettlebeck T. & Roxbee L. (1982), 'Dry Bed training for childhood bed wetting: A comparison of groups with individually administered instruction', *Behaviour Research & Therapy*, 20, 209–17

Bornstein P.H., Sturm C.A., Retzlaff P.O.L., Kirby K.L. & Chong H.Z. (1981), 'Paradoxical instruction in the treatment of encopresis and chronic constipation: an experimental analysis', *Journal of Behavior Therapy & Experimental Psychiatry*, 12, 167–70

REFERENCES

Bornstein P.H., Balleweg B.J., McLellan R.W., Wilson G.L., Sturm C.A., Andre J.C. & Van Den Pol R.A. (1983), 'The "Bathroom Game": A systematic program for the elimination of encopretic behaviour', *Journal of Behavior Therapy & Experimental Psychiatry*, 14, no. 1, 67–71

Borthwick J. (1985), 'Incontinence. Speaking from experience', *Nursing Times*, 3 April 1985

Boswell D.M. & Wingrove J.M. (eds.) (1974), *The Handicapped Person in the Community*, Open University Press, London

Bott E.A., Blatz W.E., Chant N. & Bott H. (1928), 'Observation and training of fundamental habits in your children', *Generic Psychology Monographs*, 4, 1–150

Bradshaw J. (1978), *Incontinence — A Burden for Families with Handicapped Children*, Disabled Living Foundation, London

Brazelton T.B. (1962), 'A child oriented approach to toilet training', *Paediatrics*, 29, 121–8

Brazelton T.B. (1973), 'Is enuresis preventable?' in I. Kolvin, R.C. McKeith, S.R. Meadow (eds.) *Bladder Control and Enuresis*, Spastics International Medical Publications, Heinemann, London

Brocklehurst J.C. (1984a) *Urology in the Elderly*, Churchill Livingstone, Edinburgh

Brocklehurst J.C. (1984b) 'Ageing, bladder function and incontinence' in J.C. Brocklehurst (ed.) *Urology in the Elderly*, Churchill Livingstone, Edinburgh

Brocklehurst J.C. (1984c) 'Drug effects in urinary incontinence' in J.C. Brocklehurst (ed.) *Urology in the Elderly*, Churchill Livingstone, Edinburgh

Brodie B.C. (1842), *Lectures on the Diseases of the Urinary Organs*, 3rd edition, Longman, London

Broughton R.G. (1968), 'Sleep disorders: disorders of arousal?', *Science*, 159, 1070

Brown R.M. & Brown N.L. (1974), 'The increase and control of verbal signals in bladder training of a 17 month old child: a case study', *Journal of Behavior Therapy & Experimental Psychiatry*, 15, 105–9

Bryant V.M. & Williams-Dean G. (1975), 'The coprolites of man', *Scientific American*, 232, 100–9

Burgio K.L., Whitehead W.E. & Engel B.T. (1985), 'Bladder-sphincter biofeedback and toileting skills training', *Annals of Internal Medicine*, 104, 507–15

Burgio K.L., Robinson J.C. & Engel B.T. (1986), 'The role of biofeedback in Kegel exercise training for stress urinary incontinence', *American Journal of Obstetrics & Gynecology*, 154(1), 58–64

Burkitt D.P. (1976), 'Two blind spots in medical knowledge', *Nursing Times*, Jan 1/8, 24–7

Burkitt D.P. (1979), *Don't Forget Fibre in your Diet*, Martin Dunitz, London

Butler J.F. (1976a) 'The toilet training success of parents after reading "Toilet training in less than a day" ', *Behaviour Therapy*, 7, 185–91

Butler J.F. (1976b) 'Toilet training a child with spina bifida', *Journal of Behavior Therapy & Experimental Psychiatry*, 7, 63–5

Butler R.J., Brewin C.R. & Forsythe W.I. (1986), 'Material attributions and tolerance for nocturnal enuresis', *Behaviour Research & Therapy*, 24(3), 307–12

Calder J. (1977), *The Victorian Home*, Batsford, London

Calder M. (1976), 'The nursing of incontinence' in F.L. Willington (ed.) *Incontinence in the Elderly*, Academic Press, New York

Campbell J.A., Reinken J. & McCosh C. (1985), 'Incontinence in the elderly: prevalence and prognosis', *Age and Ageing*, 14, 65–70

Campbell M.S. (1970), 'Neuromuscular uropathy' in M.S. Campbell and J.H. Harrison (eds.) *Urology*, Vol. 2, Saunders, Philadelphia

Cardozo L.D., Abrams P.D., Stanton S.L. & Feneley R.C.L. (1978a), 'Idiopathic bladder instability treated by bio-feedback', *British Journal of Urology*, 50, 521–3

Cardozo L.D., Stanton S.L., Hafner J. & Allan V. (1978b), 'Biofeedback in the treatment of detrusor instability', *British Journal of Urology*, 250–4

Castleden C.M. & Duffin H.M. (1981), 'Guidelines for controlling urinary incontinence without drugs or catheters', *Age and Ageing*, 10, 186–90

Castleden C.M., Duffin H.M. & Mitchell E. (1983), 'The affect of physiotherapy alone and in combination with a perineomotor for stress incontinence', Proceedings of the 2nd Joint Meeting of the International Continence Society and the Urodynamics Society, Aachen

Castleden C.M., Duffin H.M. & Mitchell E.P. (1984), 'The effect of physiotherapy on stress incontinence', *Age & Ageing*, 13, 235–7

Castleden C.M., Duffin H.M., Asher M.J. & Yeomanson C.W. (1985), 'Factors influencing outcome in elderly patients with urinary incontinence and detrusor instability', *Age & Ageing*, 14, 303–7

Cerulli M.A., Nikoomanesh P. & Schuster M.M. (1979), 'Progress in biofeedback conditioning for faecal incontinence', *Gastro-enterology*, 76, 742–6

Chadwick E. (1842), *An Enquiry into the Sanitary Condition of the Labouring Population of Great Britain*, HMSO, London

Chambers R. (1846), 'On incontinence of urine in children', *Provincial Medical & Surgical Journal*, 52, December 30, 617–18

Chambers R.M. (1976), 'Catheters and their management' in F.L. Willington (ed.) *Incontinence in the Elderly*, Academic Press, New York

Chanfreau-Rona D., Bellwood S. & Wylie B. (1984), 'Assessment of a behavioural programme to treat incontinent patients in psychogeriatric wards', *British Journal of Clinical Psychology*, 23, 273–9

Chatfield C. (1975), *The Analysis of Time Series: Theory and Practice*, Chapman & Hall, London

Chopra H.D. (1973), 'Treatment of encopresis in a mongol with operant conditioning', *Indian Journal of Mental Retardation*, 6, 43–6

Christmanson L. & Lisper H. (1982), 'Parent behaviours relating to bedwetting and toilet training and as etiological factors in primary enuresis', *Scandinavian Journal of Behaviour Therapy*, 11, 29–37

Clarke A.M. & Clarke A.D.B. (1976), *Early Experience: Myth and Evidence*, Open Books, London

Clay E.C. (1986), 'Rehabilitative nursing' in D. Mandelstam (ed.) *Incontinence and its Management*, 2nd edition, Croom Helm, London

Cochrane G.M. & Leacock A.F. (1984), *The Management of Urinary and Faecal Incontinence and Stomata — a Guide for Health Professionals*, Equipment for the Disabled, Mary Marlborough Lodge, Nuffield Orthopaedic Centre, Headington, Oxford

Collins R.W. (1973), 'The importance of the bladder cue buzzer contingency in the conditioning treatment for enuresis', *Journal of Abnormal Psychology*, 82, 299–308

Colwell C.N., Richards E., McCarver R.B. & Ellis N.R. (1973), 'Evaluation of self-help habit training of the profoundly retarded', *Mental Retardation*, 11 (3), 14–18

Connolly J.A. & McGoldrick M. (1976), 'Behaviour modification: toilet training procedures in a special care unit', *Child Care, Health and Development*, 2, 267–72

Couchells S.M., Bennett-Johnston S., Carter R. & Walker D. (1981), 'Behavioural and environmental characteristics of treated and untreated enuretic children and matched non-enuretic controls', *Journal of Paediatrics*, 99, 812–16

Crisp A. & Sutherst J. (1983), 'Psychological factors in women with urinary incontinence', Proceedings of the 2nd Joint Meeting of the International Continence Society and the Urodynamic Society, Aachen

Daniels M. (1971), 'Enuresis, body language and the positive aspects of the enuretic act', *American Journal of Psychotherapy*, 25, 564–78

Davis H.M., Mitchell W.S. & Marks F. (1976), 'A behavioural programme for the modification of encopresis', *Child Care, Health & Development*, 2, 273–82

Davis H.M., Mitchell W.S. & Marks F.M. (1977), 'A pilot study of encopretic children treated by behaviour modification', *The Practitioner*, 219, 229–30

Davis K. (1947), 'Final note on a case of extreme isolation', *American Journal of Sociology*, 45, 554–65

Dayan M. (1964), 'Toilet training retarded children in a state residential institution', *Mental Retardation*, 2, 116–17

De Jonge D.A. (1973), 'Epidemiology of enuresis: a survey of the literature' in I. Kolvin, R.C. McKeith and S.R. Meadow (eds.) *Bladder Control and Enuresis*, Spastics International Medical Publications, Heinemann, London

De Leon G. & Mandell W. (1966), 'A comparison of conditioning and psychotherapy in the treatment of functional enuresis', *Journal of Clinical Psychology*, 22, 326–30

Deacon J.R. (1939), 'The conditioned habit treatment of nocturnal enuretics', *Proceedings of the American Association of Mental Deficiency*, 44, 133–38

Denson R. (1982), 'Undinism: the fetishisation of urine', *Canadian Journal of Psychiatry*, 27, 336–8

Dickens C. (1865), 'Everymans poison', *All the Year Round*, 14, 372–6

Disabled Living Foundation (1985), *Incontinence Aids, Notes on Incontinence*, Information Service, 380–384 Harrow Road, London

Dische S., Yule W., Corbett J. & Hand, D. (1983), 'Childhood nocturnal enuresis: factors associated with outcome of treatment with an enuresis alarm', *Developmental Medicine & Child Neurology*, 25, 67–80

Dische S. (1973), 'Treatment of enuresis with an enuresis alarm' in I. Kolvin, R.C. McKeith and S.R. Meadow (eds.) *Bladder Control and Enuresis*, Heinemann, London

Dixon J. & Smith P.S. (1976), 'The use of a pants alarm in daytime toilet training', *British Journal of Mental Subnormality*, 22(2), 20–5

Doleys D.M. (1977), 'Behavioural treatments for nocturnal enuresis in children: a review of the recent literature', *Psychology Bulletin*, 84, 30–54

Doleys D.M., Schwartz M.S. & Ciminero A.R. (1981), 'Elimination problems: enuresis and encopresis' in E.J. Mash and L.G. Terdahl (eds.) *Behavioural Assessment of Childhood Disorders*, Guildford Press, New York

Duche D.J. (1973), 'Patterns of micturition in infancy: an introduction to the study of enuresis' in I. Kolvin, R.C. McKeith and S.R. Meadow (eds.) *Bladder Control and Enuresis*, Spastics International Medical Publications, Heinemann, London

Duker P.C. (1983), 'Determinants of diurnal bladder control with institutionalised mentally retarded individuals', *American Journal of Mental Deficiency*, 87, 606–10

Dunlap G., Koegel R.L. & Koegel L.K. (1985), 'Continuity of treatment: toilet training in multiple community settings', *Journal of the Association for Persons with Severe Handicaps*, 9, 134–41

Eastwood H.D.H. & Warrell R. (1985), 'Urinary incontinence in the elderly female: prediction in diagnosis and outcome management', *Age & Ageing*, 13, 230–4

Eastwood M.A., Kirkpatrick J.R., Mitchell W.O., Bone A. & Hamilton T. (1973), 'Effects of dietary supplements of wheat bran and cellulose on faeces and bowel function', *British Medical Journal*, 17 November, 392–4

Edelstein B.A., Keaton-Brasted K. & Burg M. (1984), ''Effects of caffeine withdrawal on nocturnal enuresis, insomnia and behaviour restraints', *Journal of Consulting & Clinical Psychology*, 52, 857–62

Edgar C.L., Kohler H.F. & Hardman S. (1975), 'A new method for toilet training developmentally disabled children', *Perceptual Motor Skills*, 41, 63–9

Ehrman J.S. (1983), 'Use of biofeedback to treat incontinence', *Journal of the American Geriatrics Society*, 31, 182–4

Eisenberg J.F. & Kleiman D.G. (1972), 'Olfactory communication in mammals', *American Review of Ecology & Systematics*, 3, 1–32

Ellis N.R. (1963), 'Toilet training the severely defective patient: an S-R reinforcement analysis', *American Journal of Mental Deficiency*, 68, 98–103

Engel B.T. (1981), 'Clinical biofeedback: a behavioural analysis', *Neuroscience & Behaviour Reviews*, 5, 397–400

Engel B.T., Nikoomanesh P. & Schuster M.M. (1974), 'Operant conditioning of rectosphincteric responses in the treatment of faecal incontinence', *New England Journal of Medicine*, 290, 646–9

Espie C.A. (1985), 'Treatment of excessive urinary urgency and frequency by retention control training and de-sensitisation. Three case studies', *Behaviour Research & Therapy*, 23, 205–10

Essen J. & Peckham K. (1976), 'Nocturnal enuresis in childhood', *Developmental Medicine & Child Neurology*, 18, 577–89

Esser A.H. (1973), 'Cottage fourteen: dominance and territoriality in a group of institutionalised boys', *Small Group Behaviour*, 4, 131–46

Eyman R.K., Silverstein A.B. & McLain R. (1975), 'The effect of treatment programmes on the acquisition of basic skills', *Journal of Mental Deficiency*, 69, 573–82

Eyman R.K., Tarjan G. & Cassidy M. (1979), 'Natural history of acquisition of basic skills by hospitalised retarded patient', *American Journal of Mental Deficiency*, 75, 120–9

Eysenck H.J. (1975), 'A note on backward conditioning', *Behaviour Research & Therapy*, 13, 201

Favell J.E., Favell J.E. & McGrinsey J.F. (1978), 'Relative effectiveness and efficiency of groups vs individual training of severely retarded persons', *American Journal of Mental Deficiency*, 83, 104–9

Feacham R. & Cairncross S. (1978), *Small Excreta Disposal Systems*, Bulletin No. 8, Ross Institute of Tropical Hygiene, London School of Hygiene and Tropical Medicine

Feneley R.C.L. & Blannin J.P. (1984), *Incontinence*, Churchill Livingstone, Edinburgh

Feneley R. (1986), 'Normal micturition and its control' in D. Mandelstam (ed.) *Incontinence and its Management*, Croom Helm, London

Ferrell-Wright D. & Bunch A. (1977), 'Parental intervention in the treatment of chronic constipation', *Journal of Behavior Therapy and Experimental Psychiatry*, 8, 93–5

Fewtrell W.D. (1973), 'A way of toilet training retarded children', *Apex*, 1(2), 26–7

Fielding D. (1980), 'The response of day and night wetting children and children who wet only at night to retention control training and the enuresis alarm', *Behaviour Research & Therapy*, 18, 305–17

Fielding D. (1982), 'An analysis of the behaviour of day and night wetting children: towards a model of micturition control', *Behaviour Research & Therapy*, 20, 49–60

Fielding D. (1985), 'Factors associated with drop-out, relapse, and failure in the conditioning treatment of nocturnal enuresis', *Behavioral Psychopathology*, 13, 177–85

Fielding D., Berg I. & Bell S. (1978), 'An observational study of postures and limb movements of children who wet by day and at night', *Developmental Medicine & Child Neurology*, 20, 453–61

Fincham F.D. & Spettle C. (1984), 'The acceptability of Dry Bed training and urine alarm training as treatments of nocturnal enuresis', *Behavior Therapy*, 15, 388–94

Finkenstaedt T., Leisi E. & Wolff D. (1970) *A Chronological English Dictionary listing 80,000 words in order of their Earliest Known Occurrence*, Carl Winter, Heidelberg

Finley W.W., Besserman R.L., Bennett L.F., Clapp R.K. & Finley P.M. (1973), 'The effect of continuous, intermittent and placebo reinforcement on the effectiveness of the conditioning treatment for enuresis nocturna', *Behaviour Research & Therapy*, 11, 289–97

Finley W.W. & Wansley R.A. (1977), 'Auditory intensity as a variable in the conditioning treatment of enuresis nocturna', *Behaviour Research & Therapy*, 15, 181–5

Finley W.W., Rainwater A.J. & Johnson G. (1982), 'Effect of varying alarm schedules on acquisition and relapse parameters in the conditioning treatment of enuresis', *Behaviour Research & Therapy*, 20, 69–80

Fitzsimmons J.T. (1971), 'The physiology of thirst: A review of the extraneural aspects of the mechanisms of drinking' in E. Stellar and J.M. Sprague (eds.) *Progress in Physiological Psychology*, Vol. 4, 119–201, Academic Press, London

Foxx R.M. (1977), 'Attention training: the use of overcorrection avoidance to increase the eye contact of autistic and retarded children', *Journal of Applied Behavior Analysis*, 10, 489–99

Foxx R.M. (1982), *Decreasing Behaviours of Severely Retarded and Autistic Persons*, Research Press, Champaign, Illinois

Foxx R.M. & Azrin N.H. (1973a), *Toilet Training the Retarded: A Rapid Program for Day and Night-time Independent Toileting*, Research Press, Champaign, Illinois

Foxx R.M. & Azrin N.H. (1973b) 'Dry pants: a rapid method of toilet training children', *Behaviour Research & Therapy*, 11, 435–42

Foxx R.M. and Azrin N.H. (1973c) 'The elimination of self-stimulatory behaviour by over correction', *Journal of Applied Behavior Analysis*, 6, 1–14

Foxx R.M. & Martin E.D. (1975) 'Treatment of scavenging behaviour (coprophagy and pica) by overcorrection', *Behaviour Research & Therapy*, 13, 153–62

Freeman R.M. & Kaxby K. (1982), 'Hypnotherapy for incontinence caused by unstable detrusor', *British Medical Journal*, 284, 1831–4

Freud S. (1908), 'Character and anal eroticism' in *The Complete Psychological Works of Sigmund Freud*, Standard Edition, Volume I, Hogarth Press, London

Frewen W.K. (1978), 'An objective assessment of the unstable bladder of psychometric origin', *British Journal of Urology*, 50, 246–7

Fried K. (1974), 'A device for enuresis control', *Behavior Therapy*, 5, 682–4

Friedin B.D., Borakove L.S. & Fox K.T. (1982), 'Treatment of an abnormal avoidance of fluid consumption', *Journal of Behaviour Therapy & Experimental Psychiatry*, 13, 85–7

Fritz G.K. & Armbrust J. (1982), 'Enuresis and encopresis', *Psychiatric Clinics of North America*, 5, 283–96

Fry G.F. (1985), 'Analysis of faecal material' in R.I. Gilbert and J.H. Mielke (eds.) *The Analysis of Prehistoric Diets*, Academic Press, New York

Gabel S. (1981), 'Faecal soiling, chronic constipation and encopresis' in S. Gabel (ed.) *Behavioural Problems in Childhood: A Primary Care Approach*, Grune & Stratton, New York

Gartley C.B. & Humpal J.J. (1984), 'Individual socio-psychological coping mechanisms of the incontinent', Proceedings of the 14th Annual Meeting of the International Continence Society, Innsbruck, September 1984, 355–6

Gartley C.B. (1985), *Managing Incontinence — A Guide to Living with Loss of Bladder Control*, Jameson Books, Ottowa, Illinois

Gelber H. & Meyer V. (1965), 'Behaviour therapy and encopresis: the complexities involved in treatment', *Behaviour Research & Therapy*, 2, 227–31

Gesell A. & Armatruda C.S. (1941), *Developmental Diagnosis: Normal and Abnormal Child Development*, Harper, New York

Gideon S. (1948), *Mechanisation Takes Command*, Norton, New York

Giles D.K. & Wolff M.M. (1966), 'Toilet training institutionalised severe retardees: an application of operant behaviour modification techniques', *American Journal of Mental Deficiency*, 70, 766–80

Gillin J.C., Rapoport J.L., Mikkelsen E.J., Langer D., Vanskiver C. & Mendelsson W. (1982), 'EEG sleep patterns in enuresis: a further analysis and comparison with normal controls', *Biological Psychiatry*, 17, 947–53

Girourd M. (1978), *Life in the English Country House*, Yale University Press

Glen E.S. & Rowan D. (1974), 'Enuretic alarm trainers for night and day', *Lancet*, 11, 987–8

Glicklich L.B. (1951), 'An historical account of enuresis', *Pediatrics*, 8, 859–76

Goldberg S. (1971), *Teaching Self Toileting Skills to the Retarded Child*, Division of Social Services, Dept. of Public Welfare, St. Paul, Minnesota 55155

Graham F. (1977), *The Geordie Nettie*, Frank Graham, Newcastle upon Tyne

Graham P. (1973), 'Depth of sleep and enuresis: a critical review' in I. Kolvin, R.C. McKeith and S.R. Meadow (eds.) *Bladder Control and Enuresis*, Spastics International Medical Publications, Heinemann, London

Gray J.A.M. (1986), 'Incontinence in the community' in D. Mandelstam (ed.) *Incontinence and its Management*, 2nd edition, Croom Helm, London

Green M. (1986), 'Old people and disorders of continence' in D. Mandelstam (ed.) *Incontinence and its Management*, 2nd edition, Croom Helm, London

Griffiths P. *A Training Method for the Prevention of Bedwetting in Childhood: Parents Manual*, University of Stirling, Stirling, Scotland

Griffiths P., Meldrum C. & McWilliam R. (1982), 'Dry Bed training in the treatment of nocturnal enuresis in childhood: a research report', *Journal of Child Psychology & Psychiatry*, 23, 485–95

Groves J.A. (1982), 'Encopresis' in J.H. Hollis and C.E. Meyers (eds.) *Life Threatening Behaviour: Analysis and Intervention*, American Association of Mental Deficiency, Monograph 5, Washington DC

Gruber D.L. & Shupe D.R. (1982), 'Personality correlates of urinary hesitancy (paruresis) and body shyness in male college students', *Journal of College Student Personnel*, July, 308–13

Hagglund T.B. (1965), 'Enuretic children treated with fluid restriction or forced drinking', *Annales Paediatriae Fenniae*, 11, 84–90

Hallam R.S. (1976), 'A complex view of simple phobias' in H.J. Eysenck (ed.) *Case Studies of Behaviour Therapy*, Routledge and Kegan Paul, London

Hansen G.D. (1979), 'Enuresis control through fading, escape and avoidance training', *Journal of Applied Behavior Analysis*, 21, 303–7

Harington J. (1596), *A New Discourse of a Stale Subject called the Metamorphosis of Ajax*, Reprinted with notes by E.S. Donno 1966, Routledge and Kegan Paul, London

Harris L.S. & Purohit A.P. (1977), 'Bladder training and enuresis: a controlled trial', *Behaviour Research & Therapy*, 15, 485–90

Harris W. (1980), 'Bran or aperients?', *Nursing Times*, May 8, 811–13

Harrison S.M. (1983), 'Stress incontinence and the physiotherapist', *Physiotherapy*, 69, 144–7

Hattersley J. (1978), 'A behavioural analysis of the toileting skills of a mentally handicapped child', *Behaviour Analysis*, July, 14–22

Hereford S.M., Clelland S.C. & Fellner M. (1973), 'Territoriality and scent marking', *American Journal of Mental Deficiency*, 77, 426–30

Herreschoff J.K. (1973), 'Two electronic devices for toilet training', *Mental Retardation*, December, 54–5

Hindley C.B. (1965), 'Some differences in infant feeding and elimination training in five European longitudinal samples', *Journal of Child Psychology and Psychiatry*, 6, 179–201

Hjalmos K. (1976), 'Micturition in infants and children with normal lower urinary tract', *Scandinavian Journal of Urology and Nephrology*, Supplementum 37

Hobbs S.A. & Forehand R. (1977), 'Important parameters in the use of time-out with children: a re-examination', *Journal of Behavior Therapy & Experimental Psychiatry*, 8, 365–70

Holden U.P. & Woods R.T. (1982), *Reality Orientation: Psychological Approaches to the Confused Elderly*, Churchill Livingstone, Edinburgh

Hull C.L. & Hull B.I. (1919), 'Parallel curves of an infant in vocabulary and in voluntary control of the bladder', *Pedagogic Seminary*, 26, 272–83

Hundziak M., Maurer R.A. & Watson L.S. (1965), 'Operant conditioning in toilet training of severely mentally retarded boys', *American Journal of Mental Deficiency*, 70, 120–4

Hussian R.A. (1981), *Geriatric Psychology: A Behavioural Perspective*, Van Nostrand Reinhold Company, New York

International Continence Society (1984), *The Standardisation of Terminology of Lower Urinary Tract Function*

Isaacs B. (1976), 'The preservation of continence' in F.L. Willington (ed.) *Incontinence in the Elderly*, Academic Press, New York

Isaacs B. (1981), *Incontinence*, Smith and Nephew Medical Ltd.

James L.E. & Foreman M.E. (1973), 'A-B status of behaviour therapy technicians as related to success of Mowrer's conditioning treatment for enuresis', *Journal of Consulting & Clinical Psychology*, 41, 224–9

Jarvis G.J. (1981a) 'The management of urinary incontinence due to vesical sensory urgency by bladder drill'. Proceedings of the International Continence Society 11th Annual Meeting, Lund 1981

Jarvis G.J. (1981b) 'A controlled trial of bladder drill and drug therapy in the management of detrusor instability', Proceedings of the International Continence Society 11th Annual Meeting, Lund 1981

Jehu D., Morgan R.T.T., Turner R.K. & Jones A. (1977), 'A controlled trial of the treatment of nocturnal enuresis in residential homes for children', *Behaviour Research & Therapy*, 15, 1–16

Johnson S. (1755), *A Dictionary of the English Language*, Reprinted by Times books, London 1979

Jones H.G. (1956), 'The application of conditioning and learning techniques to the treatment of a psychiatric patient', *Journal of Abnormal & Social Psychology*, 52, 414–20

Jose C.J. & Perez-Cruet J. (1979), 'Incidence and morbidity of self-induced water intoxication in State mental hospital patients', *American Journal of Psychiatry*, 136, 221–2

Joseph A. (1979), *Water balance in severely retarded adult males*, B.A. Dissertation, Psychology Department, University of Durham

Judkins J.D. (1976), 'Overcorrection procedures with the institutionalised retarded: an evaluative review', *Mental Retardation Bulletin*, 4, 98–110

Kagan J. (1969), *Personality Development*, Harcourt Brace Jovanovich, New York

Kashinsky W. (1974), 'Two low cost micturition alarms', *Behaviour Therapy*, 5, 689–700

Keating J.C., Butz R.A., Burke E. & Heimberg R. (1983), 'Dry Bed training without a urine alarm: lack of effect of setting and therapist contact with child', *Journal of Behavior Therapy & Experimental Psychiatry*, 14, 109–15

Keehn J.P. (1965), 'Brief case report: reinforcement therapy of incontinence', *Behaviour Research & Therapy*, 2, 239

Kennedy W.A. & Sloop E.W. (1968), 'Methadine as an adjunct to conditioning treatment for nocturnal enuresis in normal and institutionalised retarded subjects', *Psychological Reports*, 22, 997–1000

Kiernan P., Murray A., Sutherst J. & Brown M. (1983), 'Measurement of urine loss — evaluation of the urilos nappy in conventional use and by a weighing method', 2nd Joint Meeting of the International Continence Society and the Urodynamics Society, 509–11, Aachen, August/September 1983

Kimbrell D.L., Luckey R.E., Barbuto P.F.P. & Love J.G. (1967), 'Operant dry pants: an intensive habit training programme for severely and profoundly retardation', *Mental Retardation*, 5, 32–6

Kimmel H.D. & Kimmel E. (1970), 'An instrumental conditioning method for the treatment of enuresis', *Journal of Behavior Therapy & Experimental Psychiatry*, 1, 121–3

Kings Fund (1983), *Action on Incontinence*, Report of a Working Group, Project paper 43, King Edwards Hospital Fund, London

Kira A. (1976), *The Bathroom*, 2nd edition, Penguin Books, Harmondsworth

Klarskow B. & Hald T. (1983), 'Reproduceability and reliability of urinary incontinence assessment with a sixty-minutes test', 2nd Joint Meeting of the International Continence Society and Urodynamics Society, 512–14, Aachen, August/September 1983

Klarskow P., Gerstenberg T. & Hald T. (1984), 'Bladder training and terodoline on urge incontinence in females with stable detrusor function', Proceedings of the 14th Annual Meeting of the International Continence Society, Innsbruck 1984

Klonoff E.A. & Moore D.J. (1984), 'Compulsive polydipsia presenting as diabetes insipidus: a behavioural approach', *Journal of Behavioral Therapy & Experimental Psychiatry*, 15, 353–8

Kohlenberg R.J. (1973), 'Operant conditioning of human anal sphincter pressure', *Journal of Applied Behavior Analysis*, 6, 201–8

Koluchova J. (1972), 'Severe deprivation in twins: a case study', *Journal of Child Psychology & Psychiatry*, 13, 107–114

Kolvin I. (1975), 'Enuresis in childhood', *The Practitioner*, 214, 33–45

Kolvin I. & Taunch J. (1973), 'A dual theory of nocturnal enuresis' in I. Kolvin, R.C. McKeith and S.R. Meadow (eds.) *Bladder Control and Enuresis*, Spastics International Medical Publications, Heinemann, London

Kolvin I., McKeith R.C. & Meadow S.S.R. (1973), *Bladder Control and Enuresis*, Heinemann, London

Kolvin I., Garside R.F., Taunch J., Currah J. & McNay R.A. (1973), 'Feature clustering and prediction of improvement in nocturnal enuresis' in I. Kolvin, R.C. McKeith and S.R. Meadow (eds.) *Bladder Control and Enuresis*, Spastics International Medical Publications, Heinemann, London

Kristiansen P. & Pompeius R. (1981), 'The effect of long term catheter treatment on bladder capacity', Proceedings of the International Continence Society 11th Annual Meeting, Lund

Kuru M. (1965), 'Nervous control of micturition', *Physiological Review*, 45, 425–94

Lal H. & Lindsley O.R. (1968), 'Therapy of chronic constipation in a young child by re-arranging social contingencies', *Behaviour Research & Therapy*, 6, 484–5

Lambton L. (1978), *Temples of Convenience*, Gordon Fraser, London

Largo R.H. & Stutzle W. (1977a), 'Longitudinal study of bowel and bladder control by day and at night in the first 6 years of life. I: epidemiology and Inter-relations between bowel & bladder control', *Developmental Child Neurology*, 19, 598–606

Largo R.H. & Stutzle W. (1977b) 'Longitudinal study of bowel and bladder control by day and night in the first 6 years of life. II: the role of potty training and child's initiative', *Developmental Child Neurology*, 19, 607–13

Latham B. (1908), *Sewage*, Chambers Encyclopaedia, W.R. Chambers, Edinburgh

Latimer P.R. (1981), 'Bio-feedback and behavioural disorders of the gastro-intestinal tract', *Psychotherapy & Psychosomatics*, 36, 200–12

Leacock A.F. (1984), *Incontinence and Stoma Care*, Equipment for the Disabled, Mary Marlborough Lodge, Nuffield Orthopaedic Centre,

Headington, Oxford

Leakey R.E. & Levin R. (1977), *Origins*, Rainbird Publishing Group, London

Leath J.R. & Flournoy R.C. (1979), 'Three year follow-up of intensive habit training programme', *Mental Retardation*, 8(3), 32–4

Lee S.G.M. & Herbert M. (eds.) (1970), *Freud and Psychology: Selected Readings*, Penguin Books, Harmondsworth

Levine M.N. & Elliott C.B. (1970), 'Toilet training for profoundly retarded with a limited staff', *Mental Retardation*, 8, 48–50

Libo L.M., Arnold G.E., Woodside J.R. & Borden T.A. (1983), 'EMG bio-feedback for functional bladder sphincter dyssynergia: a case study', *Bio-feedback & Self Regulation*, 8, 243–53

Lieberman L. (1972), 'The changing ideology of socialisation: toilet training, mass media and society', *International Journal of Contemporary Sociology*, 9, 189–99

Litrownik A.J. (1974), 'A method of home training an incontinent child', *Journal of Behavior Therapy & Experimental Psychiatry*, 5, 77–80

Lohman W., Eyman R. & Lask E. (1967), 'Toilet training', *American Journal of Mental Deficiency*, 71, 551–57

Lovibond S.H. (1963), 'The mechanism of condition treatment of enuresis', *Behaviour Research & Therapy*, 1, 17–21

Lovibond S.H. (1964) *Conditioning and Enuresis*, Pergamon Press, Oxford

Lovibond S.H. (1972), 'Critique of Turner, Young & Rachmann's conditioning treatment of enuresis', *Behaviour Research & Therapy*, 10, 287–9

Lovibond S.H. & Coote M.A. (1970), 'Enuresis' in C.G. Costello (ed.) *Symptoms of Psychopathology*, Wiley, New York

Luisselli J.K. (1977), 'An attendant-administered contingency management programme for the treatment of a toileting phobia', *Journal of Mental Deficiency Research*, 21, 283–8

Lumsden L. & Hyner G.C. (1983), 'Effects of an educational intervention on the rate of recurrent urinary tract infections in selected female out-patients', *Women & Health*, 10, 79–86

Lupson S. & Walton D. (1981), 'A trial of bran to relieve and prevent constipation in your mentally and physically handicapped patients', *Apex: Journal of the British Institute for Mental Handicap*, 9(2), 64–6

Madsen C.H. (1965), 'Positive reinforcement in the toilet training of a normal child: a case report' in C. Ullman and C. Krasner (eds.) *Case Studies in Behaviour Modification*, Holt Reinhart & Winston, Philadelphia

Madsen C.H., Hoffman M., Thomas D.R., Koropsak E. & Madsen C.K. (1969), 'Comparisons of toilet training techniques' in D.M. Gelfand (ed.) *Social Learning in Childhood*, Brooks/Cole, California

Mahoney K. (1973), 'Frequency and quantity of nocturnal emission after diurnal toilet training and after training to restrain reflex voiding in children', *Dissertation Abstracts International*, 34 1705A

Mahoney K., Van Wagenen R.K. & Meyerson L. (1971), 'Toilet training of normal and retarded children', *Journal of Applied Behavior Analysis*, 4, 173–81

Maizels M., King L.R. & Firlit C.F. (1979), 'Urodynamic biofeedback: a new approach to treat vesical sphincter dyssynergia', *Journal of Urology*, 122, 205–9

Malouff J.N. & Lanyon R.I. (1985), 'Avoidant paruresis — an exploratory study', *Behavior Modification*, 9, 225–34

Mandelstam D. (1986a) *Incontinence and its Management*, 2nd Edition, Croom Helm, London

Mandelstam D. (1986b) 'A programme for re-education' in D. Mandelstam (ed.) *Incontinence and its Management*, 2nd edition, Croom Helm, London

Mandelstam D. & Lane P. (1981) *Incontinence Bibliography*, Disabled Living Foundation, London

Margolies R. & Gilstein K.W. (1983), 'A systems approach to the treatment of chronic encopresis', *International Journal of Psychiatry in Medicine*, 13, 141–52

Martins T. & Valle J.R. (1948), 'Hormonal regulation of the micturition pattern of the dog', *Journal of Comparative and Physiological Psychology*, 44, 301–11

Masham Baroness (1971), 'Continence — speaking from experience — keeping to routine', *Nursing Times*, 3 April 1971

Matson J.L. (1975), 'Some practical considerations for using the Foxx and Azrin rapid method of toilet training', *Psychological Reports*, 37, 350

Matson J.L. (1977), 'Simple correction for treating an autistic boy's encopresis', *Psychological Reports*, 41, 802

Matson J.L. & Ollendick T.H. (1977), 'Issues in toilet training normal children', *Behavior Therapy*, 8, 549–53

Mayhoff H.H., Gerstenberg T.C. & Nordling J. (1981), 'Placebo — the drug of choice in female motor urge incontinence', Proceedings of the International Continence Society 11th Annual Meeting, Lund, 1981

McCartney J.R. & Holden J.C. (1981), 'Toilet training for the mentally retarded' in J.L. Matson and J.R. McCartney (eds.) *Handbook of Behaviour Modification with the Mentally Retarded*, Plenum Press, New York

MacDonald M. (1980), *No More Nappies*, Dinosaur Publications, Cambridge

McGraw M.B. (1940), 'Neural maturation as examplified in achievement of bladder control', *Journal of Paediatrics*, 17, 580–90

McKeith R.C. (1973), 'The causes of nocturnal enuresis' in I. Kolvin, R.C. McKeith and S.R. Meadow (eds.) *Bladder Control and Enuresis*, Spastics International Medical Publications, Heinemann, London

McKeith R.C., Meadow R. & Turner R.K. (1973), 'How children become dry' in I. Kolvin, R.C. McKeith and S.R. Meadow (eds.) *Bladder Control and Enuresis*, Spastics International Medical Publications, Heinemann, London

McKeith R.C. (1964), 'Sensitive periods: a new concept in development', *Developmental Medicine & Child Neurology*, 4, 111–12

McKendry J. & Stewart D. (1974), 'Enuresis', *Paediatric Clinics of North America*, 21, 1019–28

McMillan M.B. (1961), 'Pavlovian principles in the treatment of an unresponsive, seemingly retarded pre-school child', *American Journal of Mental Deficiency*, 65, 440–7

McNamara E. (1972), 'Dora: or how they met their Waterloo', *Special Education*, 61(3), 9–11

Mercer C. (1894), *Lunatic Asylums — their Organisation and Management*, Griffin, London

Meyers H.K., MacKinnon K.J. & Corson J.A. (1982), 'Biobehavioural treatment of excessive micturition', *Biofeedback and Self Regulation*, 7, 467–77

Middlemist R.D., Knowles E.S. & Matter C.F. (1976), 'Personal space invasions in the lavatory: suggestive evidence for arousal', *Journal of Personality & Social Psychology*, 33, 541–6

Mikkelsen E.J., Brown G.L., Minichiello M.D., Millican F.K. & Rapoport J. (1982), 'Neurologic status in hyperactive, enuretic, encopretic and normal boys', *Journal of the American Academy of Child Psychiatry*, 21, 75–81

Millard P.H. (1979), 'The promotion of continence', *Health Trends*, 11, 27–8

Miller F.J.W. (1973), 'Children who wet the bed' in I. Kolvin, R.C. McKeith and S.R. Meadow (eds.) *Bladder Control and Enuresis*, Spastic International Medical Publications, Heinemann, London

Miller F.J.W., Court S.D.M., Walton W.S. & Knox E.G. (1960), *Growing up in Newcastle upon Tyne*, Oxford University Press, London

Miller N.E. & Di Cara L. (1967), 'Instrumental learning of heart rate change in curarized rats', *Journal of Comparative & Physiological Psychology*, 63, 12–19

Miller P.M. (1973), 'An experimental analysis of retention control training in the treatment of nocturnal enuresis in two institutionalised adolescents', *Behavior Therapy*, 4, 288–94

Milne J.A. (1976), 'Urinary tract' in R. Passmore (ed.) *Companion to Medical Studies*, Vol. 1, 2nd edition, Blackwell Scientific Publications, Oxford

Milne J.S. (1976), 'Prevalence of incontinence in the elderly age groups' in F.L. Willington (ed.) *Incontinence in the Elderly*, Academic Press, London

Minge M.R. & Ball T.S. (1967), 'Teaching of self help skills to profoundly retarded patients', *American Journal of Mental Deficiency*, 71, 864–8

Ministry of Health (1968), *Enuresis alarms: a performance specification*, R/E 1004/03

Miron N. (1966), 'Behaviour shaping and group nursing with severely retarded patients' in Fisher and Harris (eds.) *Reinforcement Theory in Psychological Treatment*, Monograph Research 8, Dept of Health Hygiene, California

Mitchell K.R. (1978), 'Self management of spastic colitis', *Journal of Behaviour Therapy & Experimental Psychiatry*, 9(1), 269–72

Montgomery E. (1983), *Regaining Bladder Control*, John Wright & Sons, Bristol

Morgan R. (1981), *Childhood Incontinence*, Heinemann Medical Books, London

Morgan R.T.T. (1978), 'Relapse and therapeutic response in the conditioning treatment of enuresis: a review of recent findings on intermittent reinforcement, overlearning and stimulus intensity', *Behaviour Research & Therapy*, 16, 273–9

Morgan R.T.T. & Young C.C. (1975), 'Parental attitudes on the conditioning treatment of childhood enuresis', *Behaviour Research & Therapy*, 30, 197–9

Morris J.V. (1957), 'The habit training of severely retarded defectives', *American Journal of Mental Deficiency*, 61, 474–7

Morrison L.M., Eadle A.S., McAllister A., Glenn E.S. & Taylor J. (1984), 'High neuroticism in 226 incontinent women', Proceedings of the 14th Annual Meeting of the International Continence Society, Innsbruck

Mowrer O.H. & Mowrer W.M. (1938), 'Enuresis — a method for its study and treatment', *American Journal of Orthopsychiatry*, 8, 436–59

Muellner S.R. (1960), 'Development of urinary control in children: a new concept in cause, prevention and treatment of primary enuresis', *Journal of Urology*, 84, 714–16

Muir F. (1976) *The Frank Muir Book — An Irreverent Campaign to Social History*, Heinemann, London

Multiple Sclerosis Society (1984), *Incontinence Information Sheet*, Multiple Sclerosis Society, 286 Munster Road, Fulham, London

Murphy G. (1978), 'Overcorrection: a critique', *Journal of Mental Deficiency Research*, 22, 161–73

Myers H.K. (1982), 'Bio-behavioural treatment of excessive micturition', *Bio-feedback and Self Regulation*, 7, 467–77

National Association for Maternal and Child Welfare (1975), *Enuresis*, Smith and Watts Ltd

Neale D.H. (1963), 'Behaviour therapy and encopresis in children', *Behaviour Research & Therapy*, 1, 139–49

Nettlebeck T. & Langeluddecke P. (1979), 'Dry Bed training without an enuresis machine', *Behaviour Research & Therapy*, 17, 403–4

Newson J. & Newson E. (1968), *Four-years-old in an Urban Community*, George Allen & Unwin, reprinted by Pelican

Newson J. & Newson E. (1963), *Infant Care in an Urban Community*, George Allen and Unwin, reprinted by Pelican

Niblett J.E.D. (1984), 'Incontinence — a study of the frequency, quantity and other characteristics of urine losses', Proceedings of the 14th Annual Meeting of the International Continence Society, Innsbruck, 136–8

Nohain J. & Caradec F. (1967), *Le Petomane*, Souvenir Press, London

Norgaard J.P., Knudsen N., Hansen J.H., Nielsen J.B. & Djurhuus J.C. (1984), 'Overnight monitoring of children with nocturnal enuresis', International Continence Society Proceedings 14th Annual Meeting, Innsbruck, 105–6

Norton C. (1986), *Nursing for Continence*, Beaconsfield Publishing Co., Beaconsfield, Buckinghamshire

Norton C. (1982), 'The effects of urinary incontinence in women', *International Rehabilitative Medicine*, 4, 409–14

Norton C. (1981), 'The effects of incontinence in women', Proceedings of the International Continence Society 11th Annual Meeting, Lund, 175–6

Olness K. (1975), 'The use of self-hypnosis in the treatment of childhood nocturnal enuresis', *Clinical Paediatrics*, 14, 272–9

Oppel W.C., Harper P.A. & Ryder R.V. (1968a), 'The age of attaining bladder control', *Paediatrics*, 42, 614

Oppel W.C., Harper P.A. & Ryder R.V. (1968b) 'Social psychological and neurological factors associated with nocturnal enuresis', *Paediatrics*, 42, 627–41

Ouslander J.G. & Fowler E. (1985), 'Management of urinary incontinence in Veterans Administration nursing homes', *Journal of the American Geriatrics Society*, 33, 33–40

Pacey A. (1980), *Rural Sanitation: Planning and Appraisal*, Oxfam and Intermediate Technology Publications Ltd, London

Palluck R.J. & Esser A.H. (1971), 'Territorial behavior as an indicator of clinical condition of severely retarded boys', *American Journal of Mental Deficiency*, 76, 284–90

Parker G. (1983), *Helping Incontinent Disabled Children — The Study of Provision in Four Areas*, University of York, Department of Social Administration and Social Work, Social Policy Research Unit Working Paper, DHSS 136.3/83/GP

Parker G. (1984), 'Training for continence amongst children with severe disabilities', *British Journal of Mental Subnormality*, 30(1), 38–43

Passman R.H. (1975), 'An automated device for toilet training', *Behaviour Research & Therapy*, 13, 215–20

Peterson D.R. & London D.R. (1965), 'A role for cognition in the behavioural treatment of a child's eliminative disturbance' in C. Ullman and C. Krasner (eds.) *Case Studies in Behaviour Modification*, Holt Rinehart & Winston, Philadelphia

Peterson R.A., Wright R.L.D. & Hanlon C. (1969), 'The effects of extending the CS-UCS interval on the effectiveness of the conditioning treatment for nocturnal enuresis', *Behaviour Research & Therapy*, 7, 351–7

Pfadt A. & Sternlicht M. (1980), 'Clinical and administrative issues in the large scale implementation of the Azrin–Foxx self initiation training program', Paper presented at the AAMD Annual Meeting, San Francisco

Pfadt A. & Sullivan K. (1980), 'Application and data based modification of overcorrection training in an institutional toilet training program', Paper presented at the Association for the Advancement of Behaviour Therapy, 14th Annual Convention, New York, November

Pfadt A. & Sullivan K. (1981), 'Issues in the generalisation and long term maintenance of the treatment gains achieved by the Foxx–Azrin self initiation training procedures', Paper presented at the Eastern Psychological Association Annual meeting, New York, April

Phaire T. (1553), *The Boke of Chyldren*, Reprinted 1955 by Livingstone, Edinburgh

Phibbs J. & Wells M. (1982), 'The treatment of nocturnal enuresis in institutionalised retarded adults', *Journal of Behavior Therapy & Experimental Psychiatry*, 13, 245–9

Plachetta K.E. (1976), 'Encopresis: a case study utilising contracting, scheduling and self-charting', *Journal of Behavior Therapy & Experimental Psychiatry*, 1, 195–6

Protinsky H. & Kersey B. (1983), 'Psychogenic encopresis: a family therapy approach', *Journal of Clinical & Child Psychology*, 12, 192–7

Protinsky H.Y. & Dillard C. (1983), 'Enuresis: a family therapy model', *Psychotherapy: Theory Research & Practice*, 20, 81–9

Pumroy D.K. & Pumroy S.S. (1965), 'Systematic observation and reinforcement techniques in toilet training', *Psychological Reports*, 16, 467–71

Ralls K. (1971), 'Mammalian scent marking', *Science*, 171, 443–9

Ramsden P.D., Smith J.C., Dunn M. & Ardram G.M. (1976), 'Distension therapy for the unstable bladder: later results including an assessment of repeat distensions', *British Journal of Urology*, 48, 623–9

Record R. (1651), *The Urinal of Physick*, Dawson, London

Reynolds R. (1943), *Cleanliness and Godliness*, George Allen & Unwin, London

Richmond G. (1983), 'Shaping bladder and bowel continence in developmentally retarded children', *Journal of Autism & Developmental Disorders*, 13, 197–204

Rister E.S. (1983), 'Understanding enuresis as a deficit in mental imagery: the case of Larry', *Individual Psychology*, 39, 83–91

Ritch R. & Rooney V. (1984), 'Habit training of the elderly incontinent at home by a nursing rehabilitation team' in proceedings of the 14th Annual Meeting of the International Continence Society, Innsbruck

Rolider A. & Van Houten R. (1985), 'Treatment of constipation — caused encopresis by a negative reinforcement procedure', *Journal of Behavior Therapy & Experimental Psychiatry*, 16, 67–70

Rolider A., Van Houten R. & Chlebowski I. (1984), 'Effects of a stringent versus lenient wakening procedure on the efficacy of the Dry Bed procedure', *Child & Family Behaviour Therapy*, 6, 1–17

Rollings J.P., Baumeister A.A. & Baumeister A.A. (1977), 'The use of overcorrection procedures to eliminate the stereotyped behaviours of retarded individuals: an analysis of collateral behaviours and generalisation of suppressive effects', *Behaviour Modification*, 1, 29–46

Rosberger Z. & MacLean J. (1983), 'Behavioural assessment and treatment of "organic" behaviours in an institutionalised geriatric patient', *International Journal of Behavioural Geriatrics*, 1, 33–46

Rovetto F. (1979), 'Treatment of chronic constipation by classical conditioning techniques', *Journal of Behavior Therapy & Experimental Psychiatry*, 10, 143–6

Rovetto F.M. (1983), 'Treatment of excessive urinary frequency and urgency by de-sensitisation and progressive retention training', *Journal of Behavior Therapy & Experimental Psychiatry*, 14, 155–9

Rowell T. (1972), *The Social Behaviour of Monkeys*, Penguin Books, Harmondsworth

Rutter M. (1973), 'Indications for research III' in I. Kolvin, R.C. McKeith and S.R. Meadow (eds.) *Bladder Control and Enuresis*, Spastic International Medical Publications, Heinemann, London

Rutter M., Tizard J. & Whitmore K. (1970), *Education Health and Behaviour*, Longmans, London

Rutter M., Yule W. & Graham P. (1973), 'Enuresis and behavioural deviance: some epidemiological conditions' in I. Kolvin, R.C. McKeith and S.R. Meadow (eds.) *Bladder Control and Enuresis*, Spastics International Medical Publications, Heinemann, London

Sacks S. & De Leon G. (1973), 'Conditioning two types of enuretics', *Behaviour Research & Therapy*, 11, 653–4

Sacks S. & De Leon G. (1978), 'Training the disturbed enuretic', *Behaviour Research & Therapy*, 16, 269–99

Sacks S. & De Leon G. (1983), 'Conditioning functional enuresis: follow-up after retraining', *Behaviour Research & Therapy*, 21, 693–4

Sadler O.W. & Merkert F. (1977), 'Evaluating Foxx and Azrin toilet training procedure for retarded children in a day training centre', *Behaviour Therapy*, 8, 499–500

Salmon M.A., Taylor D.C. & Lee D. (1973), 'On the EEG in enuresis' in I. Kolvin, R.C. McKeith and S.R. Meadow (eds.) *Bladder Control and Enuresis*, Spastics International Medical Publications, Heinemann, London

Sanavio E. (1981), 'Toilet retraining psychogeriatric residents', *Behavior Modification*, 5, 417–27

Savage D.S. (1975), *The Cottagers Companion*, Peter Davies, London

Schabel J.A. (1984), 'Positive reinforcement and logical consequences in the treatment of classroom encopresis', *School Psychology Review*, 13(2), 238–43

Schaeffer C.E. (1979), *Childhood Encopresis and Enuresis: Causes and Therapy*, Van Nostrand Reinhold Company, New York

Schnelle J.F., Traughber B., Morgan D.B., Embry J.E., Binion A.F. & Coleman A. (1983), 'Management of geriatric incontinence in nursing homes', *Journal of Applied Behaviour Analysis*, 16, 235–41

Scott J.E.S. (1973), 'A surgeon's view of enuresis' in I. Kolvin, R.C. McKeith and S.R. Meadow (eds.) *Bladder Control and Enuresis*, Spastics International Medical Publications, Heinemann, London

Seif B. (1982), 'Hypnosis in a man with fear of voiding in public facilities', *American Journal of Clinical Hypnosis*, 24, 288–9

Selig L. (1982), 'Treating nocturnal enuresis in one session of family therapy: a case study', *Journal of Clinical Child Psychology*, 11, 234–7

Seligman M.E.P. (1970), 'On the generality of the laws of learning', *Psychological Review*, 77, 406–18

Selzer J.G. (1971), *No More Diapers*, Boston Childrens Medical Centre Publications for Parents, Delacorte Press

Shaeffer D., Gardner A. & Hedge B. (1984), 'Behavior and bladder disturbance of enuretic children: a rational classification of a common disorder', *Developmental Medicine & Child Neurology*, 26, 781–92

Shepherd A.M. (1986), 'Re-education of the muscles of the pelvic floor' in D. Mandelstam (ed.) *Incontinence and its Management*, 2nd edition, Croom Helm, London

Shepherd A.M., Montgomery E. & Anderson R.S. (1983), 'Treatment of genuine stress incontinence with a new perineometer', *Physiotherapy*, 69(4), 113

Shettleworth S.J. (1972), 'Constraints on learning' in D.S. Lehrman, R.A. Hinde and E. Shaw (eds.) *Advances in the Study of Behavior*, Vol. 4, Academic Press, New York

Shrubsole L. & Smith P.S. (1984), 'The effect of change in environment on incontinence in profoundly mentally handicapped adults', *British Journal of Mental Subnormality*, 30, 44–53

Siegel R.K. (1977), 'Stimulus selection and tracking during urination: auto-shaping directed behaviour with toilet targets', *Journal of Applied Behavior Analysis*, 10, 255–65

Simmonds J.F. & Parraga H. (1982), 'The parasomnias: prevalence and relationships to each other and to positive family histories', *Hillside Journal of Clinical Psychiatry*, 4, 25–38

Singh N.N. (1976), 'Toilet training of a severely retarded non-verbal child', *Australian Journal of Mental Retardation*, 4, 15–18

Sloop E.W. (1970), 'Conditioning treatment of nocturnal enuresis amongst the institutionalised', Doctoral Dissertation, Florida State University, Tallahassee, Florida, University Microfilms — 70-8574

Sloop E.W. & Kennedy W.A. (1973), 'Institutionalised retarded nocturnal enuretics treated by a conditioning technique', *American Journal of Mental Deficiency*, 77, 717–21

Slucki H., Adam G. & Porter R.W. (1965), 'Operant discrimination of an interoceptive stimulus in the rhesus monkey', *Journal of the Experimental Analysis of Behaviour*, 8, 405–14

Slucki H., McCoy F.B. & Porter R.W. (1969), 'Interoceptive S.D. of the large intestine established by mechanical stimulation', *Psychological Reports*, 24, 35–42

Smith L.J. (1981), 'Training severely and profoundly mentally handicapped nocturnal enuretics', *Behaviour Research & Therapy*, 19, 67–74

Smith P.S. (1976), 'The dark incontinent: a general introduction to toilet training', *Apex*, 4(Sept), 20–2

Smith P.S. (1977), 'POTTIE: Products on toilet training incontinents and enuretics', *Apex*, 5(Sept), 20–2

Smith P.S. (1979a) 'A comparison of different methods of toilet training the mentally handicapped', *Behaviour Research & Therapy*, 17, 33–43

Smith P.S. (1979b) 'The development of urinary continence in the mentally handicapped', Ph.D. thesis, University of Newcastle upon Tyne

Smith P.S. & Smith L.J. (1977), 'Chronological age and social age as factors in daytime toilet training of institutionalised mentally retarded individuals', *Journal of Behavior Therapy & Experimental Psychiatry*, 8, 269–73

Smith P.S. & Wong H. (1981), 'Changes in bladder function during toilet training of mentally handicapped children', *Behaviour Research & Severe Developmental Disabilities*, 2, 137–55

Smith P.S., Britton P.G., Johnson M. & Thomas D.A. (1975), 'Problems involving in toilet training profoundly mentally handicapped adults', *Behaviour Research & Therapy*, 15, 301–7

Smith R.E. & Sanderson R.E. (1966), 'Relationship of habit training to measured intelligence in severely retarded patients', *California Mental Health Research Digest*, 4, 154–5

Snooks S.J., Setchell M., Swash M. & Henry M.M. (1984), 'Injury to innervation of pelvic floor sphincter musculature in child birth', *Lancet*, September 8, 546–50

Sogbein S.K. & Awad S.A.L. (1982), 'Behavioural treatment of urinary incontinence in geriatric patients', *Canadian Medical Association Journal*, 127, 863–4

Soldoff S. (1971), 'Operant discrimination of an interoceptive stimulus in the urinary bladder of intact and dorsal root transected female rhesus monkeys', Unpublished Ph.D. thesis, University of Southern California, Los Angeles

Soldoff S. & Slucki H. (1974), 'Operant discrimination of interoceptive urinary bladder stimulations in the monkey', *Physiology & Behaviour*, 12, 583–7

Sorotzkin B. (1984), 'Nocturnal enuresis: current perspectives', *Clinical Psychology Review*, 4, 293–316

Spangler B.F., Risley T.R. & Bilyew D.D. (1984), 'The management of dehydration and incontinence in non-ambulatory geriatric patients', *Journal of Applied Behavior Analysis*, 17, 397–401

Spock B. (1971), *Baby and Child Care*, New English Library, London

Srivastava F., Nigam A. & Singh S.B. (1982), 'The personality characteristics of enuretic children', *Child Psychiatry Quarterly*, 15, 109–12

Stafford Clark D. & Smith A. (1978), *Psychiatry for Students*, 4th edition, George Allen & Unwin, London

Stansfeld J.M. (1973), 'Enuresis and urinary tract infections' in I. Kolvin, R.C. McKeith and S.R. Meadow (eds.) *Bladder Control and Enuresis*, Spastics International Medical Publications, Heinemann, London

Stanton H.E. (1979), 'Short term treatment of enuresis', *American Journal of Clinical Hypnosis*, 2, 103–7

Stanton S. (1986), 'Gynaecological aspects' in D. Mandelstam (ed.) *Incontinence and its Management*, 2nd edition, Croom Helm, London

Stanton S.L. (1977), *Female Urinary Incontinence*, Lloyd-Luke, London

Starfield B. & Mellits E.D. (1968), 'Increase in functional bladder capacity and improvements in enuresis', *Journal of Paediatrics*, 72, 483–7

Stehbens J.A. & Silber D.O. (1971), 'Parental expectations in toilet training', *Paediatrics*, 48, 450–5

Stoddart G.D. (1983), 'Research project into the effect of pelvic floor exercises on genuine stress incontinence', *Physiotherapy*, 69, 148–9

Storm R.H. & Willis J.H. (1978), 'Small group training as an alternative to individual programmes for profoundly retarded persons', *American Journal of Mental Deficiency*, 83, 283–8

Strong S.R. (1984), 'Experimental studies in explicitly paradoxical intervention: results and implications', *Journal of Behavior Therapy & Experimental Psychiatry*, 15(3), 189–94

Sutherland S.S. (1976), 'The psychology of incontinence' in F.C. Willington (ed.) *Incontinence in the Elderly*, Academic Press, New York

Swift J. (1726) *Gulliver's Travels*, Reprinted many times.

Swift J. (1744) *The Benefit of Farting Explained*, Thomas, London

Swift J. (1748) *Human Ordure*, Carpenter, London

Tarrier N. & Larner S. (1983), 'The effects of manipulation of social reinforcement on toilet requests on a geriatric ward', *Age & Ageing*, 12, 234–9

Taylor P.D. & Turner R.T. (1975), 'A clinical trial of continuous, intermittent overlearning bell and pad treatment for nocturnal enuresis',

Behaviour Research & Therapy, 13, 281–93

Thomas T.M. (1986), 'The prevalence and health service implications of incontinence — a study in progress' in D. Mandelstam (ed.) *Incontinence and its Management*, 2nd edition, Croom Helm, London

Thomas T.M., Egan M., Walgrove A. & Meade T.W. (1984), 'The prevalence of faecal and double incontinence', *Community Medicine*, 6, 216–20

Thomas T.M., Karran O.D. & Meade T.W. (1981), 'Management of urinary incontinence in patients with multiple sclerosis', *Journal of the Royal College of General Practitioners*, 31, 296–8

Thomas T.M. & Meade T.W. (1982), *The Incontinent in the Community — Who Are They?*, Proceedings of the International Continence Society, Leiden

Thomas T.M., Plymat K.R., Blannin J. & Meade T.W. (1980), 'Prevalence of urinary incontinence', *British Medical Journal*, 281, 1243–9

Thompson, M.K. (1986), 'Management of the elderly patient in the community' in D. Mandelstam (ed.) *Incontinence and its Management*, 2nd edition, Croom Helm, London

Thompson T. & Grabowski J. (1972), *Behaviour Modification of the Mentally Retarded*, Oxford University Press, London

Thompson T. & Hanson R. (1983), 'Overhydration: precautions when treating urinary incontinence', *Mental Retardation*, 21, 139–45

Thyer B.A. & Curtis G.C. (1984), 'Furosemide as an adjunct to exposure therapy of psychogenic urinary retention', *Perceptual & Motor Skills*, 59, 114

Tidy N. (1952), *Massage and Remedial Exercises in Medical and Surgical Conditions*, 9th edition, Wright, Bristol

Tierney A. (1973), 'Toilet training', *Nursing Times*, December 20/27, 1740–5

Tierney A. (1976), *Behaviour modification in mental deficiency nursing*, Unpublished Ph.D. thesis, University of Edinburgh

Tierney I. (1978), 'The need for a functional analysis of the overcorrectional procedure', *Behaviour Analysis*, July

Timms M.W.H. (1985), 'The treatment of urinary frequency by paradoxical intention', *Behavioural Psychotherapy*, 13, 76–82

Tinbergen N. (1951), *The Study of Instinct*, Oxford University Press, London

Townsend J., Heng L., Thomas T., Egan N. & Mead T.W. (1981), 'Costs of incontinence to families with severely handicapped children', *Community Medicine*, 3, 119–22

Trombini G., Rossi N. & Umilta C. (1982), 'Experimental stress and cystomanometric recordings and patients with primary enuresis, a preliminary report', *Perceptual & Motor Skills*, 54, 771–7

Trott M.C. (1977), 'Application of Foxx and Azrin toilet training for the retarded in a school programme', *Education and Training of the Mentally Retarded*, 12, 336–8

Turner R.K. (1973), 'Indications for research' in I. Kolvin, R.C. McKeith and S.R. Meadow (eds.) *Bladder Control and Enuresis*, Spastics International Medical Publications, Heinemann, London

Turner R.K. (1986), 'A behavioural approach to the management of incontinence in the elderly' in D. Mandelstam (ed.) *Incontinence and its Management*, 2nd edition, Croom Helm, London

Turner R.K. & Taylor P.D. (1974), 'Conditioning treatment of nocturnal enuresis in adults: preliminary findings', *Behaviour Research & Therapy*, 12, 41–52

Turner R.K. & Young G.C. (1966), 'CNS stimulant drugs and conditioning treatment of nocturnal enuresis: a long-term follow up study', *Behaviour Research & Therapy*, 4, 225–8

Turner R.K., Young G.C. & Rachman S. (1970), 'Treatment of nocturnal enuresis by conditioning techniques', *Behaviour Research & Therapy*, 8, 367–81

Van Wagenen R.K. (1974), 'Book review of Azrin and Foxx's "Toilet training the retarded" ', *Behaviour Therapy*, 5, 280–2

Van Wagenen R.K. & Murdoch E.E. (1966), 'A transistorised signal package for toilet training of infants', *Journal of Experimental Child Psychology*, 3, 312–14

Van Wagenen R.K., Meyerson L., Kerr N.J. & Mahoney K.E. (1969a) 'Rapid toilet training: learning principles and prosthesis', Proceedings of the 77th Annual Convention of the American Psychological Association, 781–2

Van Wagenen R.K., Meyerson L., Kerr N.J. & Mahoney K.E. (1969b), 'Field trials of a new procedure in toilet training', *Journal of Experimental Child Psychology*, 8, 147–59

Vehkalahti I. & Kivela S.L. (1985), 'Urinary incontinence and its correlates in very old age', *Gerontology*, 31, 391–6

Vereecken R.L., Jacquemyn E.M. & Cornelissen M. (1983), 'Detection and quantification of female incontinence using the Urilos system — a new approach', 2nd Joint Meeting of the International Continence Society and the Urodynamic Society, 507–8, Aachen August/September 1983

Verhulst F.C., Van Der Lee J.H., Akkerhuis G.W., Sanders-Woudstra J.A.R., Timmer F.C. & Donkhurst .D. (1985), 'The prevalence of nocturnal enuresis: do DSM III criteria need to be changed?', *Journal of Child Psychology and Psychiatry*, 26, 989–93

Vieweg V., Rowe W., David J. & Spradlin W. (1984) 'Hyposthenuria as a marker for self-induced water intoxication and schizophrenic disorders', *American Journal of Psychiatry*, 141, 1258–60

Vincent S.A. (1964), 'Treatment of enuresis with a perineal pressure apparatus: the irritable bladder syndrome', *Developmental Medicine & Child Neurology*, 6, 23

Visser G., Goodman J., Levine D. & Davies G. (1981), 'Micturition and the heart period cycle in the human foetus', *British Journal of Obstetrics & Gynaecology*, 88, 803–5

Volpe A. & Kastenbaum R. (1967), 'Beer and TLC', *American Journal of Nursing*, 67, 100–3

Walsh J.B. & Mills G.L. (1981), 'Measurement of urinary loss in elderly incontinent patients — a simple and accurate method', *Lancet*, 23 May, 1130–1

Watson L.S. (1967), 'Application of operant conditioning techniques to institutionalised severely profoundly retarded children', *Mental Retardation Abstracts*, 4, 1–18

Waye M.F. & Melnyr W.T. (1973), 'Toilet training a blind retarded boy by operant conditioning', *Journal of Behavior Therapy & Psychiatry*, 4, 267–8

Wear J.B., Wear R.B. & Cleeland C. (1979), 'Biofeedback in urology using urodynamics: preliminary observations', *Journal of Urology*, 121, 464–8

Webster A. & Gore E. (1980), 'The treatment of intractable encopresis: a team intervention approach', *Child Care, Health & Development*, 6, 351–60

Weir K. (1982), 'Night and day wetting among a population of three year olds', *Developmental Medicine & Child Neurology*, 24, 479–84

Weir M.R. (1982), 'Things that go damp in the night: a review of childhood enuresis', *Military Medicine*, 147, 568–71

Wells T. (1975), 'Promoting urinary incontinence in the elderly in hospital', *Nursing Times*, November, 29, 1908–9

Wells T.J. (1984), 'Social and psychological implications of incontinence' in J.C. Brocklehurst (ed.) *Urology in the Elderly*, Churchill Livingstone, Edinburgh

Werry J.S. & Cohrssen J. (1965), 'Enuresis: an etiologic and therapeutic study', *Journal of Paediatrics*, 67, 423–31

Whitehead W.E., Burgio K.L. & Engel B.T. (1984), 'Behavioural methods in the assessment and treatment of urinary incontinence' in J.C Brocklehurst (ed.) *Urology in the Elderly*, Churchill Livingstone, Edinburgh

Whitehead W.E., Burgio K.L. & Engel B.T. (1985), 'Biofeedback of faecal incontinence in geriatric patients', *Journal of the American Geriatric Society*, 33, 320–4

Whiting J. & Child I.L. (1953), *Child Training and Personality: A Cross Cultural Study*, Yale University Press, New Haven

Williams A.J., Prematalake J.K.T.G. & Palmer R.L. (1981), 'A trial of emepronium bromide for the treatment of urinary incontinence in the elderly mentally ill', *Pharmatherapeutica*, 2, 539–42

Williams C. & Hattersley J. (eds.) (1975), *Overcoming Delayed Incontinence*, National Society for Mentally Handicapped Children, London

Willington F.L. (1976), *Incontinence in the Elderly*, Academic Press, New York

Willington F.L. (1976b) 'The physiological basis of retraining for continence' in F.L. Willington (ed.) *Incontinence in the Elderly*, Academic Press, New York

Wilshere E.R. (1985), *Personal Care Equipment for the Disabled*, Mary Marlborough Lodge, Nuffield Orthopaedic Centre, Headington, Oxford

Wilson B. (1980), 'Toilet training' in W. Yule and J. Carr (eds.) *Behaviour Modification for the Mentally Handicapped*, Croom Helm, London

Woman & Home (1973), *Bed Wetting*, Health Leaflet SH 12. IPC Magazines Ltd, London

Wood P., Murray A., Brown N. & Sutherst J. (1983), 'Reproduceability of a one-hour urinary loss test', 2nd Joint Meeting of the International

Continence Society and the Urodynamic Society, 515–17, Aachen August/September 1983

Woodmansey A.C. (1972), 'On taking pressure off bowel training', *British Medical Journal*, 3, 161–3

Woods R.T. & Britton P.G.B. (1985), *Clinical Psychology with the Elderly*, Croom Helm, London

Worth H. (1977), *Incontinence*, Family Health, *Woman & Home*, IPC Publications, London

Wright H., Wilkinson J. & Proud A. (1983), 'Success after failure: the re-assignment of responsibility in an integrated approach to a family with an adolescent bed-wetter', *Journal of Family Therapy*, 5, 189–98

Wright L. (1960), *Clean and Decent: the Fascinating History of the Bathroom and Water Closet*, Routledge and Kegan Paul, London

Wright L. & Walker C.E. (1978), 'A simple behavioural treatment program for psychogenic encopresis', *Behaviour Research & Therapy*, 16, 209–12

Yates A.J. (1985), 'The relevance of fundamental research to clinical applications of biofeedback' in S. Reiss and R.R. Bootzin (eds.) *Theoretical Issues in Behaviour Therapy*, Academic Press, New York

Yates A.J. (1975), *Theory and Practice in Behaviour Therapy*, Wiley, New York

Yates A.J. (1980), *Bio-feedback and the Modification of Behaviour*, Plenum Press, New York

Yeates W.K. (1973) 'Bladder function in normal micturition' in I. Kolvin, R.C. McKeith and S. Meadow (eds.) *Bladder Control and Enuresis*, Heinemann, London

Yeates W.K. (1972), 'Disorders of bladder function', *Annals of the Royal College of Surgeons of England*, 50, 335–53

Yeates W.K. (1976), 'Normal and abnormal bladder function in incontinence of urine' in F.L. Willington (ed.) *Incontinence in the Elderly*, Academic Press, New York

Yoder J.W. (1966), 'Toilet training the profoundly defective patient at Greene Valley Hospital and School using an S-R reinforcement analysis', *Mind over Matter*, 11, 28–34

Yonovitz A. & Michaels R. (1977), 'Durable efficient and economic electronic toilet training devices for use with retarded children', *Behavior Research Methods & Instrumentation*, 9, 356

Yonovitz A. & Michaels R. (undated), *The Construction of Durable, Efficient and Economical Electronic Toilet Training Devices*, Manual available from University of Texas, Speech and Hearing Institute, Houston, Texas 77025

Young A.C. (1973), 'The treatment of childhood encopresis by conditioned gastro-ileal reflex training', *Behaviour Research & Therapy*, 11, 499–503

Young G.C. & Morgan R.T.T. (1972) 'Overlearning in the conditioning treatment of enuresis: a long-term follow up study', *Behaviour Research & Therapy*, 10, 419–20

Young G.C. & Morgan R.T.T. (1972a) 'Overlearning in the conditioning treatment of enuresis', *Behaviour Research & Therapy*, 10, 147–51

Young G.C. & Morgan R.T.T. (1972b) 'Childhood enuresis: termination of treatment by patients', *Community Medicine*, December, 72, 247–50

Young G.C. & Morgan R.T.T. (1973a), 'Conditioning treatment of enuresis: auditory intensity', *Behaviour Research & Therapy*, 11, 411–16

Young G.C. & Morgan R.T.T. (1973b), 'Analysis of factors associated with the extinction of a conditioned response', *Behaviour Research & Therapy*, 11, 219–22

Young G.C. & Turner R.K. (1965), 'CNS stimulant drugs and conditioning treatment of nocturnal enuresis', *Behaviour Research & Therapy*, 3, 93–101

Yule W. & Carr J. (1980), *Behaviour Modification for the Mentally Handicapped*, Croom Helm, London

Zaleski A., Gerrard J.W. & Shokeir M.H.K. (1973), 'Nocturnal enuresis: the importance of small bladder capacity' in I. Kolvin, R.C. McKeith and S.R. Meadow (eds.) *Bladder Control and Enuresis*, Spastics International Medical Publications, Heinemann, London

Zaleksi A., Shokeir M.K. & Gerrard J.W. (1972), 'Enuresis: familial incidents and relationships to allergic disorders', *Canadian Medical Association Journal*, 106, 30–1

Zubenko G.S., Alteman R.I., Cassidy J.W. & Barreira P.J. (1984), 'Disturbances of thirst and water in patients with affective illness', *American Journal of Psychiatry*, 141, 436–7

Index